1200 HOURS

Karl Androes

This is a work of fiction. All the characters, organizations, and incidents portrayed in this novel are either products of the author's imagination or used fictitiously.

Foreword

In your hands you hold a novel.

According to the Cambridge Dictionary a novel is a "a long, printed story about imaginary characters and events." In other words, novels are works of fiction. They aren't true. They never happened. They are quite intentionally elaborate and extended lies.

And, yet, the line between reality and fiction, has never been particularly well defined. If an author creates a character based on a real person—with the same tics and flaws, and, perhaps, even lifts quotes from real conversations—is that character imaginary or real?

Readers who have a knack for "suspending disbelief"—the ability to take a novel on its own terms—tend to appreciate and enjoy fiction. But what of genres like historical fiction or science fiction? The authors of those often pride themselves on the authenticity of the "facts" that they include, even when those facts are marshalled in support of falsehood.

What kind of story is this one?

This novel describes a quest: a hero's difficult journey towards a goal. In this case, his odyssey seeks not a "Golden Fleece," but the key to improving children's reading achievement in inner city schools.

In the 21st Century, American schools—particularly those serving the most disadvantaged children—are failing at teaching literacy. The statistics are horrible. According to the most recent National Assessment of Educational Progress (2017) only 37% of fourth-graders are fully proficient at reading. The results are even worse for some demographic groups. From 1992 through 2017, the average reading scores for White 4th-, 8th-, and 12th graders were significantly higher than those of their Black and Hispanic peers; the gaps between economic classes are equally severe.

And, this, at a time, when literacy plays a bigger and bigger role in economic attainment, academic achievement, and civic and social participation. The way to happiness and success in 2018 America is definitely through reading. It wasn't long ago that one could get high paying jobs without reading. Not anymore. These days so much social communication is written, too (e-mails, messaging, social media) and requires reading skills.

Finding effective solutions to our literacy problems really would be a modern day Golden Fleece.

Spoiler alert: Our hero's quest is successful.

How real are the "keys" to literacy that he manages to find?

As a scientist with decades of experience in the field of literacy, who has spent much of his career summarizing the burgeoning literature on teaching reading for the federal government, I can say each one of our hero's three discoveries (the importance of the amount of teaching students receive, the content of the curriculum that students are taught, and of the amount of student participation in interaction and response) really works. There are hundreds and hundreds of studies showing that schools that manage to address these "keys" are more successful than those that do not; markedly more successful.

Like most quests, the hero in this one confronts assorted dragons, witches, and cyclops, and must get over impenetrable mountains and across impassible rivers to reach his goal. Unfortunately, in this novel these barriers are not imaginary. They are the very real obstructers and obstructions that stand in the way of our children's literate success.

Educators, of course, should already know the keys that our hero sets out to find. They should know them and should do everything in their power to use them to unlock the doors to literacy for children. Sadly, too often, this information is not easily accessible to teachers and principals. They would benefit from taking on a quest such as this one.

Happy reading.

Timothy Shanahan

Distinguished Professor Emeritus

University of Illinois at Chicago

How It All Starts

Monday, January 10

I must be in the wrong place again. This is the address I wrote down, but I'm sitting outside what looks like an abandoned building. My four years in music school near Chicago were all about gilded concert halls downtown, not abandoned buildings in dodgy neighborhoods on the city's west side. So, double-wrong place.

Music school wasn't about mornings either, but it's morning now. No class started before ten. We were, after all, training for a career that happens 8 p.m. to midnight.

I got a call late yesterday to play a concert today at 9 a.m., so here I am outside what is supposed to be an elementary school. Money explains why I'm not still in bed, why I'm dressed in my work tux, and why I'm doing anything at a grade school.

I'm only a half-mile from the house my wife and I just bought -- our first house. I didn't figure it would take so long to drive over here. This is west of us, and we've only explored east, so far. Trucks unloading their wares into mom-and-pop storefronts on Central Street didn't help. The neighborhood changed a lot in just the few blocks after Central -- no more businesses, few people visible, fewer cars on the street. Ah, Chicago, city of neighborhoods.

As I sit here trying to figure out what to do, I notice three guys in matching baby blue sweat suits in the parking lot. The lot is full, which must mean something is going on in the building. My eyes keep coming back to those three guys. They've got a big hoist with chains going down into the open engine compartment of a late-model sedan. Two of them are hunched over the vehicle. The third guy is holding a flashlight and pointing it into the dark compartment.

"Those baby blue jackets are gonna get dirty," I say to myself. It's 8:55 in the morning and I already missed the 8:30 meet up. Still, even if it is ten years old, I'd better drive my 2003 Toyota around the block and park on the street, if I ever want to see my engine again.

I drive around the block to the other side of the building, get out and try a door. It's locked. Try another door farther down the building, also locked. I get back in the car, wondering if it's safe to be on the street here.

My phone buzzes in my pocket. I pull it out and see it's my wife, Grace. "Patrick! That school you're at today is where Joey would go." Joey's our five-year-old son.

"I'm in front of the school right now, trying to find a door that's not locked tight. I'm late. Let me call you later."

"Reading scores are all over Facebook this morning. The city just announced scores are down across all the schools."

"This place looks as dead as a doornail. I'll try one more door, then I'm out of here."

"I asked a neighbor about that school when I saw her taking her kids to the car," Grace continues, as I try to zip my jacket to get back out of the car to check another door. "She says that school is no good. Why didn't we check this out before we bought this place?" She sounds upset.

"OK, let me find out more. I can't imagine this is the school for our block. It's kind of scary over here. Let me call you back." I hang up. I shouldn't have said that last bit. What if this really is the school for our new neighborhood?

As I'm thinking about all of that, a loud rap on the passenger-side car window makes me jump in my seat. Turning quickly, I see Eric, leader of our merry quintet of brass musicians. "You're late. Get out of your car and follow me."

Eric is in shirt sleeves and a bow tie, shivering in the brisk winter temps. I get out, grab my trombone and music from the back seat and follow him to a door he has propped open with his music folder.

"Let's go, they're waiting for us in the gym," says Eric as he pulls me inside the building. Warmth. Sounds of children. We move up the ancient stairs. Each step is smoothed from years of little and big shoes trudging up and down. Each stair has a noticeable dip in it from all that use, even though each appears to be made of hard stone. I imagine a million individual trudges, wearing those dips into the ancient stairway.

The sounds of children get louder, joined by what I can only call "school smells" -- pizza cooking, rubber cement, floor disinfectant, and a lot of other smells that can't be pulled out of the mix. A wave of memories swells in my head. Am I in 3rd grade again?

As we move down the huge hallway, lined with a 1930's era trophy case and dusty American and state flags, the sounds get louder. As we turn the corner I see we have arrived at the gym, now filling up with really small students sitting on the floor and already restless. A steady line of youngsters is filing through a different door, all jostling each other, all energy and excitement and happiness.

"Eric, I need to tell you something," I say, remembering Grace's call.

"Not now," says Eric, always the focused, one-thing-at-a-time kind of guy. "We've got a concert to play." He puts on his tuxedo jacket, sits, puts his music on his stand and picks up his trumpet from its case. It looks like the last of the kids have been seated. It's a gym full of tiny humans sitting on their butts on the floor, and a few larger humans sitting at intervals near the children, but on folding chairs. I throw off my overcoat, adjust my tie and pull my trombone from its case. Cold metal mouthpiece touches warm lips. Brr. Time to play.

At the conclusion of our opening fanfare, there is an immediate wave of sound -- tiny hands hitting tiny hands, like 300 small birds' wings flapping all at once, joined by high-pitched squeals.

We stand and bow. For the first time since walking into the gym, I look around as we sit back down and Eric says a few introductory words. Three hundred tiny faces look back at me, seemingly enraptured. They're cute, but they're not at all why I practiced trombone four hours a day starting in high school, went to music school 2,000 miles from home, and never gave up on the dream of playing in an orchestra full-time.

Our whole 40-minute performance goes smoothly. As the kids file out and we pack up, an older man approaches us and introduces himself as the principal. "Thank you for coming this morning. The students have never seen anything like that. They really seemed to enjoy it. We have one of you going into several classrooms to tell some of these same students about your instruments and classical music, or whatever you have to say."

"You have so many kids. How were the classrooms for us chosen?" I ask, wondering how I might best connect with these children. They're too young for me to teach them how to play, or suggest where to go to get lessons, something I do with older kids.

"We chose rooms that need something extra, our lower performing kindergarten and 1st grades," the principal explains. "We told them to behave or they'll never get something like this again."

Reminds me of an old joke: two old ladies sitting in a retirement home. First lady says, "The food here is so terrible!" The other lady responds, "Yeah, and such small portions!" This guy is telling kids, "Enjoy this or we won't give you any more of it."

Anyway, let me go do my classroom thing, make sure some little darlings learn something about music, and then I'll see what I can find out about this place and why our neighbor says bad things about it.

Sleeping Teacher Awakens

This is going well. Thirty two young minds, excitedly focused on me! After a few years of this, I've figured out how to make music basics entertaining for 1st graders. That's not why I went to music school, but a guy's got to eat.

An adult voice suddenly arises from behind me and to my left. "Who said that? Which one of you is causing trouble today?" It's a stern voice, and somewhat disoriented. It sounds like an animal awakened from a deep sleep and not happy about it.

I continue talking as I grab a quick glance around. Out of the corner of my eye I see a large shape moving slowly from its seated position to standing. Oh, it's the teacher, who I had forgotten for the past ten minutes as I engaged the kids. Maybe he was sleeping!

"Who said that? You are being rude to our guest, and I don't like rude." He takes three lumbering steps to his desk. A hush falls over the classroom. "Was it my usual friend over there?" The kids are all looking back and forth between the teacher and one boy in the back row of desks. The teacher takes two steps toward the back of the room. The room gets very quiet. The target of his gaze is that boy who was, truth be told, responding very enthusiastically to my presentation. I just thought he was digging what I was presenting. Maybe he'd never seen anything like it and was thinking, I could do that. Please let me do that.

"Mr. Johnson, can you help me with this next portion, please? The kids seem very excited about music."

Mr. Johnson stops mid-room, pivots slightly, and seems to be sizing me up. Then he turns back toward his desk. "You go ahead then and continue your lesson. Students, pay attention."

For sure, none of this is why I went to music school.

First Meeting With The Principal

"Here we are, minding our own business for 30 years, and suddenly our scores are on the front page," says the principal, whose name I missed. He has called me to his tiny, cluttered office after my classroom sessions. He's leaning back with his hands behind his head, looking as though he sees me as his new best friend. "I've got this year and next, then my pension kicks in and I'm done. I used to be a good guy, just like you and your concerts in schools. I miss that me. But every year Central Office does something to make life harder and less fun. It wears you down. Just wait, you'll see. Next they'll send someone poking around, trying to tell us how to educate children." He looks to be 60 years old, wisps of thin grey hair hanging on for dear life on both sides of his head.

"I can tell you about your teachers, from the morning I just spent with some of them," I say.

"Oh, Mr. Johnson, right?" asks the principal. "He's a piece of work. Really old-school. But we never have any discipline problems come to the office from his room."

"We just moved close to here," I tell him. "Our neighbor says this might be where my son would go. Now my wife wants to know everything about this place."

"We'll take any free help you can provide." He asks for help as if I'm a reporter, and he thinks it will make a good part of the story. Never mind the stories that are already out there, as of today. Never mind that he's got three guys pulling engines out of teachers' cars in his parking lot in broad daylight.

"I don't know what I can do, but let me think about it and get back to you," I say. Really I'm thinking, Oh, shiitake mushrooms! Get me out of here.

"Okay, but don't take too long," he says.

As soon as I'm outside, sitting in my car, I call Grace. "Hi, again. Good concert. Some happy, excited kids in my classroom workshops, too. But some other stuff here is weird."

"I think we should start looking at other schools for Joey, and soon," she says, sounding different from earlier this morning. I know her. She's made a plan since this morning, she's moving forward on that plan. Stand back, she's a train gaining speed.

"Come on, didn't we agree we were going to be all about making the public schools work for everyone's kids?" I ask her. "I'd rather just find a better public school and move to that neighborhood. But we borrowed everything we could from your parents and mine to get the down payment here. Let me see what the real situation is. Fair?"

"Find out whatever you can at that school, but I'm starting to look around," she says.

Geez. I've got plenty of other projects dragging on my time. The roof is leaking at home. The sink in the powder room won't drain. Don't even get me started about hustling up more performances, getting Eric to write more pieces for kiddie concerts. All while I'm trying to get auditions for a "real" music job, preferably playing trombone in an orchestra. That means practicing several hours every day to keep my chops in shape, and perfecting short excerpts from the orchestral repertoire that feature the trombone.

I do not need another problem to research and solve. Still… for Grace…

I call the school principal from the car. "I'm still telling you I don't know how I can help, but can I come out tomorrow to meet with you and learn more?"

"That'd be great," he responds. "Come after school, maybe 3:30 or so. See you then."

Patrick Loves Grace

T he first time I ever saw Grace, she was on a stage, dancing in our university's production of the Nutcracker in December of our sophomore year. From my seat in the orchestra pit, I was immediately smitten. I saw someone physically beautiful and poised, but the most attractive thing for me was her drive for excellence. She was the one pulling the others up to her level as dancers. Once I'd seen her, I wanted a way to see her again and again, convinced she'd recognize that same drive in me.

In January that year, post-Nutcracker, I saw my chance. Our College of Fine and Performing Arts had a requirement that all sophomores do a collaborative project with someone from another discipline in the college -- musicians, dancers, visual artists, actors, video artists. It was, I still think, a great way to get geeky arts majors to broaden their horizons. I asked Grace, this beautiful dancer I'd just met, to meet with me about creating something together, for this class and a grade, I mean. I suggested an off-campus coffee shop I'd spotted.

That first meeting went on for three hours, much longer than either of us expected, and we barely mentioned the project after the first few minutes. Our conversation flowed freely, covering her love for hiking the Appalachian Trail, mine for bike racing and fascination with the Tour de France. I was intrigued that she knew lots about Paris, jazz saxophonist Paul Desmond, bread making technique, and black and white photography. In return, I could tell her some things about choreographer Pina Bausch's Rite of Spring (it's based on music by Igor Stravinsky, after all), delivering newspapers by bicycle, crystal clear lakes in Oregon's mountains, and David Byrne's music. (He once collaborated with choreographer Twyla Tharp to create Catherine Wheel, which we discovered we had both seen the same night's performance of at Chicago's Auditorium Theater several years before). In many ways, we were both anachronisms, interested in things from a previous era. Looking back, I recognize we were also typical name-dropping college arts majors.

At the end of three hours, we agreed to collaborate on a visual art, dance and music project, and I had gained an insight into the future, thinking, I could marry this woman.

Our first "date" wasn't even a date. We were officially just working on that project. It was a trip to the circus -- literally, old-school Ringling Brothers. We were doing research for our project, which was somehow going to combine music and dance and visuals, just like the circus. It was fun: the smells of popcorn and elephants, the sounds of Souza marches and carnival barkers, the sights of tamed tigers and colorful clowns. We tossed around lots of possibilities for our project. She had strong opinions. She was also a great listener. We discovered we both loved ideas and creating new things from them. Riding the city bus home, I turned to her as we approached the stop for campus, and I asked, "Is this the part where we kiss for the first time?" She smiled and it was, her dark hair warm as I reached up to run my fingers through it.

As we spent more time on that project, I found I liked everything about Grace. She was smart, full of knowledge and curiosity about many topics, including politics and visual artists, which had never been part of my consciousness. She was also kind, volunteering her time to cook lunch for the homeless every Friday at a local church, and giving a dollar every day to the first person on the street who asked her, even when she had little money to spare. I experienced her thoughtful heart when she showed up one Thursday evening at my practice room in the music building with a peanut butter and jelly sandwich on homemade bread. I had mentioned that Thursday was my long and uninterrupted day of rehearsals and classes until late at night. "I thought you'd be hungry by now," she said, as she stepped toward me for our second-ever kiss.

After about four months of being together more and more, Grace said, "Let's go hiking." She'd already told me she loved week-long treks in the deep woods of eastern states, "the simplicity of having everything you need to survive right on your back, seeing those blazes on trees to let you know you're still on track, and something unknown around the next turn in the trail. You'll love it." I wasn't sure my first hike with Grace should be for a whole week, so we went for just a long weekend at nearby Kettle Moraine State Forest in southern Wisconsin. It was late April. For a non-arts class, Grace had been reading about the unique geology of this location.

She said its moraines were formed by two huge glaciers that collided, thereby piling up sediment that became lovely hills and ridges. Its "kettles" are ponds and lakes formed by buried glacial ice that calved off a receding glacier and got entirely or partly buried in glacial sediment and then melted. I was, to be honest, mostly intrigued by the idea of being with Grace overnight, under the stars, and didn't give a hoot about kettles or moraines.

Grace was a different person in the woods, in delightful ways. As we headed into the trees from the trailhead, she started singing, "Tis the gift to be simple, tis the gift to be free, tis the gift to come down where we ought to be. And when we find ourselves in the place just right, twill be in the valley of love and delight."

My ears perked up. "That's from Aaron Copland," I said, recognizing the melody.

"It's originally a Shaker song called Simple Gifts," Grace responded, giggling. "Copland copped it as the melody to accompany Martha Graham's ballet Appalachian Spring. So, you're right. I sing it every time I start a hike. It immediately reminds me of how happy I am in the woods."

Hiking with Grace for three days -- the intimacy of shared experiences, long uninterrupted conversations, frequent laughing and even just being silent as we hiked along, hand in hand or steps apart, under the clear spring sky -- altered the course of our blossoming romance. It was like we'd had our Carnegie Hall debut, the reviews had been glowing, and now everyone expected exciting things to come from our established duo.

How To Fix A Broken School?

"How to fix a broken school?" That's my Google search when I finally get to my computer later in the day. I don't want to fix my kid's possible school, but I should at least know what I'm looking at and hearing when I visit again tomorrow. Up pop 120 million results. Literally. No, wait, Google is not done yet -- 121 million results, but who's counting? Going down the list:

Fixing broken schools

How to rescue the American family and fix the broken school system

Fixing Detroit's broken school system

How to fix a broken high schooler, in four easy steps

A high tech fix for broken schools

How can we fix the very broken American education system?

Award-winning teachers dole out advice on fixing public schools

Egypt's Generation Lost (Huh, the schools in Egypt are broken, too?)

Fix our teachers, then fix the rest

How to fix a broken school funding formula

Fixing our broken system of testing and accountability

Where to start? This broken school thing looks like hard work. I've never minded working hard. My family moved us 200 miles from the woods outside Seattle to rural Oregon when I was going into 3rd grade. Rural Oregon was rich farmland as far as you could see in any direction. We moved in early summer. Right away, the neighbor kid who was two years older than me told me about picking strawberries. "You get paid for every crate you pick," he said. My parents said yes, and I was up before sunrise the next morning and for weeks after, out in a dirt field on my hands and knees alongside all the Mexican and Eastern European immigrants, picking strawberries until the midday sun chased us home for the day.

I love learning, too, so I loved school, as early as I can remember all the way through college. I have always loved solving puzzles that others said were hard. When I was visiting my parents during the summer last year, my dad pulled out some old VHS tapes he'd shot when we were kids, and there I was as a three or four year old, working on a wooden puzzle with intense focus for maybe ten minutes straight. At the end, I looked up at the camera, with a big smile, and asked, "More?"

Making a living as a freelance musician has the puzzles and the hard work. It also has low pay, and it's not why I went to music school. So, before I get sucked too far into this, I'm determined to get an orchestra job and leave freelancing to someone else.

I decide to look at the news about today's announcement, instead. I see the reading scores dropped across the district in almost every school. Some are saying it's because of the new state test. Others say the district has cut lots of resources from the classrooms and that's why the scores are dropping. The district is already saying they'll be doing more reading initiatives to fix this. Others are saying so-called 'extras' like music and art will probably be eliminated in order to pay for those reading things.

Maybe the principal I just met this morning will know more. The next question for me to answer is what can Grace and I do about this? And should we do anything? We are not school fixers. We are not in the reading business, either. We are "arts-in-schools-are-good" folks.

"Patrick, the photographer just called." It's Eric on my cellphone. "The school for the photo shoot is all set. She'll meet you there in the morning."

I forgot all about that photo shoot.

I do need more information. Doing concerts in schools, I never have spent much time wondering how the schools actually work. I've always got my hands full just trying to get enough work to pay myself and keep my key musicians busy enough so they hop when I need them for a morning. Of course, there's finding the best musicians and rehearsing new pieces to play. Plenty to keep me busy not thinking deeply about how schools actually work on a day-to-day basis. Or how to get the music performance job that I went to college to get.

"And don't forget dinner tonight, Eric." Like the world's skinniest trumpet player ever forgets a meal.

Patrick And Eric Talk

"Hey, Eric!" I say, waving him toward my booth at Bill's Diner. "Thanks for making time for dinner with me. That was quite a morning at that school today, right?"

"Yes, it was," he responds while sitting across from me. "Did you stay and do workshops in classrooms?"

"Yup, sure did," I say, pushing a menu toward him to order dinner. "I needed the money for the extra work. Turns out that school is where Joey could go next year."

"That dump?" he asks. "Is your house close to there? Is that area safe?"

"I don't know if it's safe or not," I respond honestly. "I saw some stuff at that school that makes me wonder."

"Like what?"

"Just weird stuff," I say, not wanting to go through the whole story with him. "What I really know is this job is not what I went to music school to do, playing kiddie concerts and watching teachers sleep in class while I teach their kids. Why didn't you do the extra stuff today?"

"I definitely need the money," he says. "I'm paying my own way to fly to that orchestra audition in Canada in March. But I needed the time even more, for more practice. I've got a real chance to get this gig."

"Brad and Ian both got orchestra jobs in the past month," I say, feeling the sting of their good news. "Gail and Bobby have been in Singapore playing in that orchestra for the past year. So pretty soon it will be just you and me still looking for a real music job."

"That's not true, and you know it." It sounds like a reprimand. "Some folks from music school got playing jobs and are doing okay. But others chickened out and got teaching jobs right away. Others are living with their parents and not doing anything. Besides, you're so creative, maybe this orchestra thing is just not right for you."

"Right or not, that's the dream we're chasing. It's what everybody calls success for guys like us. At least you're getting on a plane and going to auditions. I'm too busy playing school concerts and doing the extra workshops and working on my fixer-upper house. We've been out of school long enough that it should have happened by now... or it isn't going to happen. I've got a wife and a kid and responsibilities now, too."

The waitress comes to take our order. I sip my water and eat a breadstick while Eric orders, then I give her my choices.

Once the waitress leaves, Eric and I sit in silence for a bit. I've known him since freshman year in college. Our friendship came easily, with so much in common. We both came from small towns, his in Wisconsin and mine in Oregon. We both got up at 3:00 in the morning all of junior high to deliver papers by bike to earn spending money. We both chose off-beat sports in high school: cross country running for him, bicycle racing for me. We were both very good at anything we really set our minds to doing.

By sophomore year of college, we were roommates. We were the complete music jocks, listening to all the latest recordings by favorite orchestras playing favorite pieces, practicing more than anybody else, and winning the school auditions for the principal trumpet and trombone chairs in the orchestra and wind ensemble, which nobody at our music school had ever done before as sophomores.

"You really think you'll get this orchestra job?" I ask. Eric is not cocky. Rather, in all the time I've known him, I have learned he says what he thinks is true. He is just very rational.

"If I play well enough, have a good day, I should get the gig, yes," he responds. "I know everybody else who's auditioning this time, and I can play better than any of them. I just have to do it at the right time."

"Do you think you really want to play in an orchestra the rest of your life?" I ask. This is a question I have been asking myself almost constantly since graduating from college. "You probably heard that Gail and Bobby are coming back at the end of their contracts in

Singapore. I hear they found the actual playing pretty monotonous once they were doing it every day for real."

"I don't know about the rest of my life or not," he says. "But I trained to do this, and it's been my dream since high school. I'm giving it a shot. But somebody's got to give me an orchestra job first."

"I hope you get this one, Eric," I say, genuinely excited by his confidence. "I should be doing orchestra auditions, but I am bored stiff by practicing trombone excerpts for auditions. Eight bars from this Mahler symphony and 12 bars from the Mozart Requiem, blah-blah-blah. It's so non-musical for me, and you have to play it all perfectly in the audition or you have no chance at the job." Eric nods in agreement, then we both take a few more bites of the breadsticks.

"You seem really good at this school thing," Eric says after a minute or two of chewing, being his usual encouraging self.

"I probably am," I say. "But who cares? It's just little kids. What do they care about music?"

"As opposed to blue-haired ladies in the suburbs?" Eric spits back to me. "Look, we're both small town boys. What do we care about orchestra music? I bet changing a bunch of little kids' lives could be plenty fulfilling as a career, if that's what somebody finds interesting. Music can do that. I'm just saying you should pay attention to what I'm seeing, which is you having a very good time with kids in schools and being really good at it."

"I hear you," I say, feeling genuine appreciation for his opinion. "But I want something that uses what I went to college to do -- play music at a world class level. I want to be doing something that uses me creatively, gets my innovation juices flowing, uses my creative brain and my musical brain. I want to be proud at our 25th college reunion when someone asks, 'So, Patrick, what are you doing these days?' It should be something that actually matters, that makes the planet a little better than I found it. That's all."

"You might want to stay away from playing trombone in an orchestra, then," says Eric. "Having some third-rate conductor waving his arms at you in some back-water city for an audience of seniors at a Friday matinee, as they fall asleep in a darkened concert hall after a big lunch at the local hotel. Where's the creativity and innovation and spark in that? How's that making the world any better? Besides, you've never been very good at letting others tell you what to do, you know."

"Hey, you're the one going off to an audition to do pretty much that very thing you just destroyed!" I say, a little confused, and stung by his insight into one of my character flaws.

"Good point," Eric concedes. "But, I'm not you. I'm fine with all that nonsense, because I love the music so much and the routine. And I've secretly got a thing for older women -- way older!"

That gets a laugh out of both of us, then we sit quietly for a moment. It's a comfortable reminder of a thousand previous times when we've talked and laughed and dreamed together of our futures in music. The waitress brings our food. As we each start to eat, my mind snaps back to working in schools.

"But how does working in schools not just become a cop-out," I continue, "like those musicians we know from college who became music education majors in junior year, as 'something to fall back on?' What are they doing now? Falling back on that decision and teaching music in some dump like we played at today, while they count the days until they can collect their pension in 30 more years. I don't want to be one of those guys."

"Don't let anyone else determine what makes you happy, Patrick," says Eric. "Follow wherever your heart and head and your actual experience lead you."

Photo Shoot Day

Tuesday, January 11

It's hard to believe we're doing a new website, since we don't have any money. But Eric got one of his non-musician friends to donate the design and photography, so here we are to shoot photos. This school is one I know, as we have played multiple concerts here during the past several years. We have also done workshops in most of their classrooms from K-8th.

The photographer is sitting in the school office as I walk in, talking quietly with our French horn player, Mary. We decide to go to a kindergarten classroom first. Walking into the classroom, the kindergartners are full of energy and hugs for visitors. One little girl plops down at my feet and declares, "I'm gonna read you a book." How cute. She doesn't get all the words, but she's got the storyline down cold. The teacher walks by and says in a whisper, "She's one of my best readers." The girl gets another book by the same author and illustrator and reads it to me. She uses the same storyline as the first book, even though the words on the page are completely different. Hmm, there's something weird going on there, but what do I know?

The teacher and photographer confer, then Mary runs a short music lesson with the students. The photographer says she's got what she needs – cute kids, full of joy and curiosity, lots of smiles – so we thank the teacher and depart.

Next we go to a 3rd grade room that got three sessions with Mary this fall. The teacher lets us know they are preparing for the high-pressure tests that are given for the first time in 3rd grade. The basic message is to keep our photo session short, even though she seems glad to see Mary again. The kids are cute and energetic, but with a seriousness. They don't seem so interested in visitors, after they all give Mary hugs. As in the kindergarten room, lots of good photos.

Finally, we go to a 6th grade classroom. Mary says she was never in this classroom before. Here the kids slouch at their desks lifelessly. Three in the front are paying close attention, while others are either sleeping in the back or mouthing off and laughing with each other, disrupting what Mary is trying to teach. As we're packing up afterward, the photographer says, "It's like we just watched the hope drain out of these kids. By 6th grade, they've given up."

My cell phone is buzzing -- yesterday's principal. "I can't meet today. A lady from Central Office is here poking around. She's making us assemble a committee, too."

"Wow, news story one day, Central Office inspection the next. Why your school?" I ask, thinking this can't be a good sign for where his school falls on the performance list.

"I don't know. Our students aren't great at reading, but what do they expect?" he says, like he's talking to himself and not to a stranger he just met. "I just need to play the game."

"What game, exactly, are they playing?" I say, thinking out loud. "And what are the rules?"

"Hey," says the principal, like I reminded him of something, "will you be the community rep on this committee? You seem smart and you live here now. We're meeting tomorrow morning at 8:00. Can you be there?"

"Uh, I suppose, but…"

"Great! Thanks, and see you at 8 in the morning."

Did I just volunteer for something?

A Little More Research

Being a musician doesn't come with training in research or terms like validity, rigor, and, my favorite, regression analysis. I didn't learn those in trombone lessons or music theory class. No, that was on the other side of campus, in Joe Pinzarone's research methods class. In junior year, I thought about becoming some kind of researcher or social worker. My interest was based on ideas I was exposed to in sophomore year that opened my eyes to world issues such as how economic systems distribute resources unevenly in the United States and other nations, and what works to alleviate some of poor people's misery. It feels wacky to remember that, for most of a year, I carried a little book about a public health effort that cured diarrhea for millions in Bangladesh. Grace says I slept with that book during junior year.

Ultimately, trombone won. My grandfather on my mother's side was a trombone player. His brother Earl was a trumpet player, too, who made it big playing TV shows in LA. Family reunions always included a jam session with multiple generations playing while everyone danced and sang. That all looked like so much fun to me as a kid, and I wanted to make it big, just as all of them had done. I got my first trombone in fifth grade. Tim Roth was better than me all through junior high, but then I discovered practicing in high school, and I beat him for the first chair trombone spot in the middle of freshman year. That felt good! From there I was first chair ever after, except freshman year in college when a junior named Andre-something hung on to the coveted spot for a year.

Yes, trombone beat research and social work, but not before I picked up some geeky research skills. So now, post photo shoot, what to research? Locally, I need to know what "game they are playing." What might the rules be for winning that game?

Bigger picture, to show up at this first committee meeting without making a fool of myself in front of what might be Joey's teachers, I need to know about schools, what goes wrong with them, and what experts propose can help to make them better. I already know there are 121 million hits about fixing broken schools (or broken families, or high schoolers, or anything broken). Let's try Googling "education" and "reading".

Again, lots of hits. Clicking on one, I skim a study that says turning around a struggling reader at 3rd grade is three times as difficult as turning around a struggling 1st grade reader. Another says math textbooks are 80% words and only 20% numbers. Hmm. So, if you can't read, you can't do math? One link is talking about how many kids are misdiagnosed as special education eligible, when the issue is really poor reading skills due to poor instruction. It's a real hodge-podge.

As Grace announces from downstairs, "We're home!" I find one more study saying kids' reading skills are stable at the end of 1st grade, 88 times out of 100. It says the good readers keep being the good readers, and the bad readers keep being the bad readers, all the way through 11ᵗʰ grade. I bookmark that and the other studies on my computer, to read fully later.

"Hi, Patrick," Grace says as I come down the stairs. "How'd it go today with the photographer?"

"Parts were great and parts were depressing," I say, giving her a big kiss, then leaning down to kiss Joey's forehead and tussle his thick, curly red hair. "It was like I was watching the life drain right out of kids as they got older. So, how was your day?"

"Let me get dinner started before we talk," she says. She goes to the sink and turns on the water to start doing something for dinner. Joey scampers off to the living room to play.

Watching her now, I'm reminded that it almost didn't work out this way. The several months leading up to graduation from college were stressful. Would I go back to Oregon and figure out what came next, or would I stay in Chicago and figure it out with Grace? Would she go to New York and pursue dancing there? After months of discussion and worry, it became clear that staying together was what we both wanted most. Figuring that out brought a huge release of emotion and excitement. Finally, our first big hurdle to adulthood was cleared! If we were going to stay together, why not get married, just as generations of couples before us had done? It all felt simple, freeing. We jumped. In hindsight, we were blissfully overconfident, unaware of the dulling effects on any relationship of, say, making a living.

Joey wasn't part of the plan, but a surprise that made us both very happy. Grace's growing belly, my long foot rubs for her while discussing rearing the perfect little human being, baby showers with all our friends from college -- it was all new and fun! For two people who love to make lists and plans for every part of our lives, those first years as a married couple seem now like a blur of random joy and discovery, no lists in sight.

We've grown up a lot in the few years since, while grasping at that old youthful exuberance. One of us was supposed to get a steady arts job. That hasn't happened yet. We've each kept performing as much as we can, which gives us satisfaction. I've got my freelancing and Grace has her dancer-in-residence work. Neither of us likes drifting. We get cranky with each other. When she gets bossy, I get defensive.

"Our day was fine," Grace says, finishing up washing something in the sink. "While Mr. Destructo here napped, I did some research about what our other school options might be. There are a couple of things we need to do right away. Let me get dinner ready first."

I see a package of fresh fish poking out of the grocery bag she brought in the door. "Let me help. I'll do the fish." My wife with a mission is a force to be reckoned with. Best to lay some "cooperative husband" groundwork. I grab the Worcestershire sauce from one cabinet and some bread crumbs from another. Once some butter is melted in a pan, I dip the fish in the sauce, then in bread crumbs, and then gently place the fish into the pan to simmer.

"Thanks, honey," she says. Grace is a blur, pulling another delicious dinner together, while keeping an eye on Joey, whom she has moved to the sofa with several favorite picture books in hand. I'm used to her doing several things at once. When we first met in college, she wasn't just performing in the student dance company, she was running it and choreographing pieces for the other dancers.

She had a double major -- dance and visual art -- which meant I went to dance performances from sophomore year on and helped hang her friends' art shows. In turn, she came to all of my performances: orchestra, wind ensemble, recitals. Right now she stays very busy, doing artist-in-residence projects in schools, while doing most of the care and driving for Joey.

For the past year or more we've been stumbling through what I'd call a "transitional period" in our relationship. Our lives are full of the stresses that come with a five-year-old kid and a first house and careers that are sputtering to get going, with declining quantities of the joys that originally brought us together. Eric once referred to this as the "seven year itch," when he and I noticed another couple getting less and less happy with each other after about seven years together. He says it's a real thing in psychological research, made popular by a 1950's movie with Marilyn Monroe, apparently. Has it been seven years already for Grace and me? Or eight or nine?

After a few minutes of quiet side-by-side work in the kitchen, little things -- the length of time she rinses the lettuce under the water, the lessening vigor of her chopping of carrots - tell me Grace is ready to talk again.

"I'm eager to hear your research on schools," I start. "I've been doing a little, too. I've been looking at what exactly the school results are all about. And the principal of our neighborhood school called to ask me if I would be on a committee that meets at 8 tomorrow morning."

"I thought you were going there at 3:30 today to meet with him," she says.

"He cancelled our meeting because some lady from Central Office was there. Then he asked me to be the community representative on his committee about how to fix his school."

"That's nutty, Patrick. He just met you yesterday. After one date he wants to get married? Really, you said yes?"

"Well, not exactly. I tried to say maybe and he took it for yes and then hung up."

"We need information, not another bunch of meetings early in the morning," she says, flipping the fish in its pan of hot butter. "You're a musician, not a school expert. Just tell him no."

"Maybe I will," I say, feeling my don't-tell-me-what-to-do side rising. "But first there's a meeting of his committee tomorrow morning and I think I'll go. You and I want to know what's going on there, right?"

"I guess, but I'm also doing research to see how to get Joey into school somewhere else next year. We have options -- magnet schools, charters, private schools, Catholic schools. Even the suburbs, if we have to. Patrick...," she stops and turns, looking at me with those lovely green eyes of hers. "Say we're together in this. This is about Joey's future."

"Grace," I say, my voice softening, "we said education was the great equalizer for all kids, not just ours. We were going to stay with the public schools, and stay in the city and be part of that and be a positive force for our own child and everyone else's kids at the same time. Right?"

"That's all fine in theory," she says, flipping the fish again in the pan. "But in practice, with our neighborhood school struggling, we have to make sure Joey gets a great school."

"So, it's every man, woman and child for themselves?" I ask.

"Patrick, don't take that tone with me," she responds, as she chops the ends off some vegetables. "We need to look at our options, together. Don't get all wrapped up in that one school that we hear is bad. Dinner is ready." She practically flings the food onto plates and thrusts them toward me to carry to the table. We sit, Joey looking quietly at us, and eat in silence.

First School Committee Meeting

Wednesday, January 12

I arrive at the school at 7:45 the next morning. I chose to drive because I need to go to a gig immediately afterward. I'm thinking I've got 60 minutes.

I check in at the office. The clerk, whose name is Dorothy, is a pleasant and efficient woman of 60. "The meeting is in room 203," she says. "It's the library. But for you today, it's 'the war room.' Mr. Bevington says you're going to save our school from closing." So that's the principal's name.

"Who said anything about closing?" I ask.

"Don't worry," she says, retreating, with a smile in her voice. "If you need some ideas, I've been here 35 years. I know where all the bodies are buried."

Dorothy is an oasis in the wilderness.

I head upstairs, looking for Room 203. I find 201, so 203 must be two doors down. But the next room is 215. The third room is 204, then 210.

"You look lost." It's Mr. Bevington, the principal.

"What's with the room numbers?" I ask as we walk.

"What do you mean?"

"You know, room 201, then 215, 204, 210. No pattern?"

"Oh, that. Don't pay attention to the numbers," he says.

"Yeah, but the kids must get confused. Why are the numbers random?"

"I asked the same question when I got here. The first numbers got painted back when the rooms were bigger. Then, the school got more students in the 1970's and someone split rooms into two. The maintenance guys painted random numbers, apparently. The students just follow their teacher long enough to know where they are going and forget about the numbers."

"Isn't that a missed opportunity for teaching kids math or something?" I ask.

He looks at me, quizzically. "In schools, we call the young people students, not kids. Kids are young goats, very disrespectful," he says, then moves on. That didn't feel good.

Nobody else is in room 203, so we turn on the lights. I follow his lead and pull chairs down off tables.

Soon another adult shows up. Mr. Bevington introduces her as Mary, the librarian and asks, "Are you here for the committee meeting."

"No. Are you using my library?"

"Yes, if it's all right with you. Our scores were in the paper."

"I heard," she says with a sigh. "How many chairs do you need?"

"About 20. This is our new community rep," he says, pointing to me.

"I'm Patrick," I say. Mr. Bevington seems to have forgotten my name. Mary doesn't say anything, not "welcome" or "glad to meet you." "My wife and I just moved into the area. Our son would go here," I explain, extending my hand. She ignores it.

"If we stay open," she says. "I guess that's up to you." She sighs again and turns away.

Mr. Bevington taps my shoulder and says, "This is our community rep. Meet Mr. Ferris, our gym teacher, and Ms. Peterson, our upper grades science teacher." He can't remember my name.

"Hi, I'm Patrick." Mr. Ferris is the classic gym teacher: whistle on a braided string, sweat pants, gym shoes, clipboard in hand, 50 years old, but dressing as though he's 20. Ms. Peterson looks a little older than me, maybe 35. She's smiling, and neatly dressed in a grey skirt and black high heels.

"Nice to meet you, Patrick," Ms. Peterson says, smiling. "Thanks for helping on this."

There are four of us. If the librarian joins, we are five. It's a weird collection, considering the main issue we are supposed to be tackling is reading. Where is the upper grades reading teacher? Or the 3rd grade reading teacher?

"Okay, let's get started," says Mr. Bevington. We find seats. It's 8:05. "As you know, our school was in the news two days ago for low reading scores. There was an inspector here yesterday from Central Office. She made it clear we have to do something."

"Or what?" asks Mr. Ferris.

"What's that, Ed?" asks Mr. Bevington.

"The inspector said we have to do something. What if we don't?" Mr. Ferris asks.

"We get in trouble. Maybe we all lose our jobs. I don't know. I didn't push it. I'm almost ready to retire. I'll do whatever. Can we all just play the game, please?"

"What are the rules of this game?" asks Ms. Peterson. "What do we have to do? Some of us have a lot of years left before we can retire."

"If you're any good, you can get another job when this school closes," says Mr. Ferris. "There are always jobs, if you're willing to teach where they send you."

"This school is near where I live. These students are my neighbors," says Ms. Peterson. "If you're ready to retire, Ed, then retire. But don't take me with you." She's not taking any guff.

"Oh, hey, Ms. Zara," says Mr. Bevington, greeting a middle-aged woman. "Have a seat and join our discussion."

"Is there an agenda?" she asks.

"Our agenda is to save these people's jobs," says Mr. Ferris.

"Why are you here this morning?" Ms. Peterson asks Mr. Ferris.

"For the donuts, but somebody forgot them." He glares at Mr. Bevington. "So, I'm outta here." With that, Mr. Ferris gets up and leaves.

"Well, then," says Mr. Bevington, shaking his head. "We have a week to pull something together." Two more people arrive.

"If the parents would do their job, we wouldn't be in this position," says one newcomer, a man of about 60 years, with a huge paunch and fuzz on his ears. "It would sure help me out in 6th grade."

"What is their job, exactly, Mr. Bean?" asks Ms. Peterson.

"To help their children with homework," says Mr. Bean.

"Let's not refight that whole thing," says Mr. Bevington.

"So, what do we need to give them?" asks Ms. Peterson. "I can get test scores across multiple years."

"That's a good idea," says the other newcomer. "I can get parent testimonials from the after-school program. I can ask some parents to come to the meeting, too."

"Thank you, Ms. Grabowski. It's at 4, two Mondays from now," says Mr. Bevington.

"That's lousy timing for parents who work," complains Ms. Grabowski. "Parents are still at work at 4:00." It sounds like she runs the after-school program.

Mr. Bevington shrugs. "Let's keep this nice and simple, folks. What else can we pull? How about attendance data?"

What does that have to do with reading scores, I wonder?

"I'll try to compile something about the high schools our students go on to," says Ms. Peterson, writing the first note anybody has written in this meeting. "Several of our 8th graders last year got into the selective enrollment schools. Maybe that makes us look better. What about drop-out rates?"

Ms. Grabowski adds: "We adopted that new math series, 1st through 8th grades. We have iPads in some of our 3rd grade rooms, too. There's the new computer lab."

Mr. Bevington stops her: "This is just about reading scores, so don't go looking at math and everything else," he says, answering the question in my head.

A bell rings loudly.

"It's time to stop. Grab whatever statistics and information you can," says Mr. Bevington, as everyone gathers his or her stuff and stands to leave. "I will be here to meet Friday this week, and Monday and Wednesday next week. Come keep me company."

"I can't. I've got other meetings," say several people.

"Welcome aboard, Patrick," Ms. Peterson says cheerily as she heads for the door.

Soon everyone is out the door and gone.

Principal Asks For Help

"Patrick," says Mr. Bevington as I put on my coat. He must've heard Ms. Peterson say my name. "What do you think we need, from the community and all, to make our case?"

"I'd have to think about it. Others had pretty good ideas for what to gather."

"Sure, but they have students all day. Can you pull some of that together, in case they don't?"

"Where would I get student test scores and attendance and such?" I ask.

"Here's my log-in name and password for our data tracking system. You can see all of that there, just as though you were the principal," he says, writing on a scrap of paper and handing it to me. "This shouldn't be shared with anyone else. Right?" Right, nobody but a guy he just met.

"Will a bunch of data be enough?" I ask. "Didn't you say the lady wants a plan?"

"You get some data together and let me worry about the plan."

*   *   *

Back at home I log onto the school data site, to see how easy or hard it would be to help. I don't need the headache Mr. Bevington wants me to take on, but he may have given me access to what I need for Grace and me to make some decisions.

There are tabs for math, reading, overall test scores, student mobility, attendance. A quick scan says overall test scores have been flat. Attendance is 90%. Is that good or bad? Looks like 650 students are enrolled, grades K-8th.

Last year's attendance is based on 750 students. That can't be right.

I call the school. "Hi, Dorothy, it's Patrick, the community guy, from the committee? Right! Can you tell me why enrollment went down 100 students this year over last. Did something change in how they count? Oh, really, just lost that many students, huh? Is that normal? Really? Okay, thanks."

She did not seem at all concerned. She said enrollment numbers go up and down every year. "Just depends," she said. She said she'd let Mr. Bevington know I called.

Looking at the data site again, I see math scores have trended slightly up over the past few years, which seems like a good thing. Reading scores, the thing the district is saying is most important, are down slightly the past few years, though some grades went up and others down.

Bottom line, there isn't much bottom line. What makes some numbers go up and others go down? Does the school do something to make that happen, or does it just happen? How does Central Office create a list of so-called bad schools from all this? The news says Central Office is going to launch some new initiatives to make reading better across the whole system. How do they decide which reading initiatives to try?

The Pastor Vs. The Parents

Joey got his first bike for Christmas, from my parents, who must remember how much bike riding and racing meant to me at a younger age. So I've been helping him learn to ride, even though it's usually dark and cold when I get home at this time of year. Teaching a five year old to ride a bike is, shall we say, a "bumpy" process, involving bending over and grabbing the back of the seat, then running along behind as he pedals. My back can only take that for so long. Then I let go, he coasts for four or five feet while I shout, "Pedal, Joey," and he tips over. Somehow I look forward to this, and so does Joey, even as my back complains and his trousers get rips and tears from spilling. He has cried occasionally, after the sidewalk tore skin beneath his jeans. Loud wailing, wrapped in my arms for a minute, then he wipes tears from his cheeks and goes back to his bicycle. "More, Daddy?"

Instead of bike lessons and dinner together tonight, Grace and I decide I should go to a community meeting. It's about crime in our neighborhood. "Is crime a problem here?" I ask. "Go find out!" she urges. So, I go right from a music gig, grabbing a sandwich and eating it in the car.

Crime is a hot topic, apparently, as about 80 people are jammed in a room made for 50 or so. People are standing along the sides and back of the room. A group of city staff, a guy with a police badge on, and the alderman enter from a side door and sit at a table facing the crowd.

The meeting starts with brief presentations from this panel about crime stats, which are basically good news. After a few questions about specific streets and one possible drug house, the audience gladly moves to other topics, including garbage collection and stop signs.

Eventually, a tall, older African-American man stands to address the panel and audience. He is wearing the collar of a religious leader.

36

"Ladies and gentlemen, I am Pastor Albert from Saint Nick's, three blocks down on Western. Some of you I know from church on Sunday. Others of you, there's always room for more on Sunday. Don't be shy." A ripple of polite laughter runs through the crowd.

"In the 20 years I've been in this neighborhood, I have seen some changes. The one I want to address tonight affects the school in this neighborhood. Some of you know I have been interested in this city's schools as a member of the editorial board of the citywide education journal, Education Now." Someone gave me a copy of that publication when it had a story about the arts in schools. It reports on citywide issues affecting education, and has articles on best practice in education nationally. He should have something valuable to say.

"The changes I've seen have not been about the teachers," he continues. "I see some teachers here tonight, whom I know are doing some amazing work. What I've seen change is the parents. They are not making sure homework gets done. They are not turning off the TV and making their kids go to sleep at a decent hour. Parents are not sending their children to school ready to learn. I was in a classroom recently where a child had his head down on the desk, sound asleep. How is a teacher supposed to teach that child?"

Well, good point for that one child. You can't learn when you're asleep in class.

Pastor Albert continues, "This week, schools all saw their test scores in the news. Teachers are in the hot seat now, but there's only so much a teacher can do. Parents aren't talking to their kids. Students living in working class households, let alone children in wealthy households, hear something like 30 million more words spoken by adults than poor children hear. That's by the time they all arrive at kindergarten. Let's not be pointing the finger at our hardworking teachers. Thank you."

Applause arises as Pastor Albert returns to his seat.

"Thank you, Pastor," says the chair of the panel. "We appreciate all that you and your church have done to keep this community together all these years, and what you personally have done to help improve all schools. Thank you for rising to share with us."

More applause for Pastor Albert.

I'm confused. Is it really all about parents? Are teachers just babysitters, keeping children safe all day so parents can work, then teach them at night? That's where my brain goes when he says, "What can we expect from teachers when parents don't do their job."

Other people in the audience are approaching the microphone to speak. "Thank you, Pastor Albert. As a parent and a teacher, I was angered to read those stories in the news. I agree it is parents who need to step up. We have to feed our children good food and make sure they get enough sleep. We have to help with homework. Or at least until we can't do the advanced math anymore with them."

Laughter again in the audience.

After several more comments like this, the meeting breaks up and I head home. Grace and Joey are already in bed and asleep as I come quietly into the house. I find a bite of cold dinner Grace has left out for me, then sit quietly, still thinking about parents' roles in their children's development and skills. I'm feeling inadequate and a bit dazed.

What might Mr. Bevington think of this idea that parents are all that matter? If he believes that, has he put resources into training all parents to teach the early skills at home?

How do our teachers like this idea that they don't matter? Maybe they were thinking, "I love Pastor Albert, so I know he really means we should just leave teachers alone and let them teach."

Do other parents think it's their fault that our school is in trouble? Do other parents think teachers should assign more homework? (Pastor Albert, please ask God to keep that from happening! Joey already gets homework -- in half-day pre-school!)

I am beginning to see how complicated this school thing is. Teachers, parents, students, community members, religious leaders, politicians. So many self-interests, some masquerading as public interest. So many variables to consider.

Maybe Grace is right. Let's just find another school and stay out of this mess. Problem is, Grace and I always said the success of public schools was everyone's responsibility. If the parents with resources take their kids away, where's that leave the remaining kids?

There's another issue in this that's very personal for me. If we can't find a good school in the city, I'll be forced to find a "real" day job, one that pays enough to afford a house in the suburbs. My musical life will be over and I'll be trudging through the next 30 years like all the others I see when I go to lunch downtown with friends who've taken that route already.

Mother And Children At Clover School

Friday, January 14

My latest idea is to see what a higher-performing school looks like, if that's what Grace and I want our local school to become. I did a little research, then I had Dorothy vouch for me with the clerk at Clover Elementary, a school east of my house. Go west, my son's probable school. Go east, a better school. Dorothy is amazingly connected. She got me an appointment for today with the Clover principal.

Traffic was light getting to the school, so I'm early. The clerk is fine with me sitting in the office reception area, since I have an appointment with the principal. No problem, I've got emails to read on my smart phone.

Two young students come in right after I sit, bearing a note from their teacher. They look to be 1st or 2nd graders. The clerk reads the note, looks crossly at the two students, then writes something on the note and hands it back to them. "All right, back to class," she says to them both.

The phone rings occasionally, but otherwise it's rather hushed. A teacher comes in, gets her mail from her teacher mailbox, then leaves right away. A woman and two children enter. The clerk is smiling at them, indicating she knows the woman.

"What are you doing here today? Aren't you here on Tuesdays?" asks the clerk.

"I'm here to transfer my two to another school," says the mom.

"Oh, no! Why?" asks the clerk, stopping what she is doing, but not moving toward the woman and her children. One of the children, a boy, looks to be about seven or eight years old. The other, a girl, is maybe five or six years old, I would guess. The boy looks like he is trying hard not to cry, standing in the main office in front of strangers and the clerk and his sister and mom.

"I just can't get them here anymore in the morning," says the mom, sounding very tired.

"Where are you living now?" asks the clerk.

"About half a mile from here," says the mom. "I just got a new job and I have to be there by 8:30. It takes me 10 extra minutes to drive my kids here in the morning, then my job is the other direction. There's another school a block away from me. My kids can walk themselves there in the morning. I just can't do it all anymore, with working two jobs and all." She's not apologizing. It's more like just explaining reality, direct and matter of fact.

The clerk's face softens. "We will miss you and your mom," she says to the two children. The boy hides his face in his mom's coat. Addressing the mom, the clerk asks, "How's the new school?"

"We went to register," says the mom, pulling some papers from her purse and handing them to the clerk. "They said we had to bring these here for you to sign. It's real nasty in there, the way the clerks treat you when you want anything. Why can't I just sign my kids up and start classes? I had to take another day off work to come over here and get you to sign my papers. I'm not liking the people over there."

The clerk looks at the papers for two seconds, signs each, then eyes the two children again. "We'll really miss you two. But I know you are going to like your new school. You'll make new friends there, and you can still see your friends here. You'll have twice as many friends." The girl seems to be buying it, but the boy definitely is not.

The mom tries to brighten the mood. "You'll like your new school," she says directly to her children, kneeling to unzip her daughter's jacket. Standing again, she turns back to the clerk. "I have to do this. I can't keep driving them every morning. I'm just exhausted. It's too much!"

"Well, good luck. I'm sure it will work out for you all. We really appreciate all your help here. What programs and all do they have?"

asks the clerk, probably hoping for something nice to think about, for herself and the two children.

"I don't know anything they've got over there," says the mom. "My son has been crying for a week since I made the decision." The clerk gives her back the paperwork and wishes her and the children good luck again at the new school. With the papers in-hand, the mother turns, opens the old wood door and pushes through, two children in tow.

Clover School Principal And Classroom

At the exact time of my appointment, a sharply dressed older woman walks into the office. The clerk stands and gestures toward me: "Mrs. A, your appointment is here for you."

The older woman turns slightly to look at me and extends her hand. "Hello, I'm Mrs. Abernathy, the principal here at Clover Elementary. How can I help you?"

"Thank you for seeing me today. My wife and I and our future Kindergartner just moved into the neighborhood, and I think your school is one of our options for our son next year," I say, telling a small lie in the process, as I am pretty sure Clover is not one of our options. "I hear Clover is a great school. I was hoping to be able just to sit in a classroom or two and see what your teachers are doing."

"That would be fine, since Mr. Bevington's clerk sent you. What grade levels are you interested in seeing then?" she asks.

"I'd love to start with kindergarten, if I could."

"We have four kindergarten rooms. Go ahead and start there. My clerk can give you a pass to carry, in case anyone stops you in the hallway. She'll just need to see your driver's license." She is friendly and efficient, making me feel seen and heard, yet not wasting extra minutes with me, a stranger who doesn't have any children here yet. "Down those big stairs over there," she says, pointing behind me and out the door.

I head down to the surprisingly cheery basement and walk quietly into the first room that has children in it.

"I'm here visiting classrooms," I say as the teacher looks up from a table where she is seated with three or four children, and I flash my hall pass.

"That's fine. Just have a seat or feel free to walk around and ask students what they are working on," she says, quickly going back to her students.

Looking around, I see several coats lying messily on the floor by students' desks and chairs. Lots of smiling students are working noisily around the room, chattering and carrying on as they work at a table or draw together on a big paper pad and chatter about what should go in their picture. After ten minutes of looking, I say thank you and make my exit. Much as I might like to spend the whole day in this pleasant classroom, I set myself the goal of seeing several rooms today, to help me analyze what "good" or "great" looks like in classrooms.

In the next room the students are very quiet, like in a library almost. Coats are hung neatly on hooks. After several minutes of work at individual students' desks, I watch the teacher lead part of a lesson with the whole group. I go to a third room. There students all have little book bins in front of them and are looking through them silently while the teacher sits at her desk and grades some papers, clearly keeping an eye on the students all the while.

After three rooms I pause in the hall to write some quick notes about what I have been seeing, with one more room to visit in kindergarten. How to tell a good classroom from a bad one? The school is succeeding, so these might all be good classrooms, right? But rather different things are going on in each – quiet reading by students here, noisy writing and drawing stories there, neatness and order here, and happy, messy noise over there. Maybe the fourth room will consolidate some impressions into a pattern.

I enter the fourth room. The teacher greets me, same as in the other rooms, and I sit in one of the small chairs out of the way to observe for a few more minutes.

The teacher has her students seated cross-legged on the rug at one end of the classroom. They are doing some kind of reading lesson. The teacher asks a question, the students respond. The teacher immediately quells a disturbance between two students on one side of the rug.

I hear a noise behind me. I turn and, coming through the classroom door, I see that same mom and her two children from the office. It's like they are following me, a dark cloud lingering overhead to rain on my day. The two children have shed a layer in the overheated school, and the mom is carrying their coats under her one arm while holding her daughter's hand with her other hand. The teacher sees them about the same time as I do and has a look on her face like something unsettling is about to happen. She gets up and walks to the mom.

"Hello, Ms. Vazquez. We were wondering where Maria was. Is she okay?" she asks.

"We just came to say goodbye," says the mom. "We are transferring to the school closer to where we live now. I need my kids to walk to school. I just can't do it anymore." The girl is whimpering quietly. It looks like maybe the boy is crying, too.

"Oh, we will really miss you," says the teacher to the mom and the daughter. "You were such a big help in our classroom."

"I know. But I got a second job. I just can't do it all," says the mom.

"Where will they be going to school?" asks the teacher.

"Harlow Elementary," says the mom. "The people in the office there are really rude. We're just here to get these papers signed and for Maria to say goodbye to all her friends."

The other students are completely silent, watching from the rug as this scene unfolds.

"We'll really miss you three," says the teacher. "Give me a hug, Maria." She kneels and Maria eagerly hugs her, then pulls back. "Students in Room 103, Maria is transferring to a new school. Let's wave goodbye." The students all wave with limp arms. Maria starts crying, quietly.

The teacher, sensing this needs to conclude, turns back to the mom. "Thank you for all your help this year. I hope it works out really well. I'm sure it will." She gives her a hug.

I played a concert at Harlow, and I looked up its reading scores online yesterday, too, because it is another comparison to my son's local school. Harlow looks, in person and on paper, like a really troubled school. Clover Elementary is a really good school. Middle class parents buy junky houses in this neighborhood, then spend real money to fix them up, so their children can go to Clover and get a good education in the city limits. Parents move away from Harlow's neighborhood if they can, to the suburbs, as soon as their children are old enough to go to school.

I see an amazing paradox, looking at this scene as an outsider. This parent already has what many other parents want: seats for her children at a good school. To keep those seats, all this mom has to do is drive ten extra minutes in the morning. Ten minutes. Not a bus ride. She said she has a car. Not 30 minutes each way to deliver her children to a magnet school across town.

But she's willing to throw that away for the ten minutes.

It's evening and I am telling this story to Grace. "How could she make such a lousy choice that will negatively affect her children's prospects and outcomes, quite possibly for the rest of their lives,? All for ten minutes in the morning!" I ask.

"Maybe that mom really feels she has no choice, that ten minutes every day really does make it impossible for her. Maybe her life really is just that hard," Grace offers.

Meeting Veronique

Monday, January 17

I've had five sleep-deprived nights in a row. After that community meeting, I lay in bed thinking about whether Grace and I are all our son needs in order to succeed. Are we doing all the things we should be with Joey, before it's too late -- reading books with him every night, going to the library and museums and concerts, creating flashcards or something to practice reading and math? I finally must have fallen asleep around 2. The same thing happened the next night.

My visit to Clover Elementary made sure I didn't sleep well on Friday night. I kept thinking about the very different classrooms I had witnessed, and the despair of that woman and her two children.

On Saturday morning, with me feeling groggy, Joey and I had a breakthrough on his bike riding. Eric told me several days ago, as I did some stretches to straighten out my aching back at the gig we were playing, that his dad taught him to ride when he was five by sticking a broom handle in the bike frame, behind the seat. The sweeping part of the broom then sticks up at about eye level for the adult, who can hold onto it and guide the bike without bending over at all. When Eric told me that, I couldn't imagine what he was talking about. Sure enough, this weekend when I found a broom and Joey's bike, it worked. Joey went three times down the alley behind our house this "broom way," as I ran along behind. He suddenly could balance and pedal. It was a miracle!

When I should have been sleeping on Saturday and Sunday night, and despite my success with Joey, I continued thinking about my visit to Clover Elementary. What is a good versus a bad classroom? What is wrong in families that would compel a mother to make those choices?

To combat my sleepiness on Monday morning, I'm at a local coffee place I've noticed several times. Being from the Pacific Northwest, I love a good coffeeshop, even though I avoid caffeine. Given the last few nights I've had, this morning I'll make an exception about caffeine intake. From the street, this place has everything a coffeeshop needs: ambient lighting, lots of woody surfaces, a hippy crowd, and baristas with extravagant facial hair.

The place is really crowded. I order and then wait to pick it up. As I look around, I'm thinking maybe I will just have to take it with me. Finally I spot a seat that's not occupied, along one side of one of those long "co-working" tables that are so fashionable these days. My drink is ready, finally, so I make a beeline to the open seat before someone else grabs it. As I'm putting my cup on the table, I hear a familiar voice from the other end of the table. "Shellfish bisque!"

I would recognize that voice anywhere! It's Veronique Accart, who I had for a class during sophomore year called, "World Music and Community Building." I liked it so much that I took a class of hers in junior year, too. She seemed old then, but she's clearly old now. She insisted we all call her by her first name. In the spring, we were all invited to her legendary "One World Dance Party and BBQ." I heard she'd dropped out of teaching and moved away -- Cape Cod or Mexico or India or somewhere.

Her hair is dyed a bright red, still framing the intense eyes I remember. She had a unique teaching style. She could connect Tupac, Smashing Pumpkins, and Karl Marx into a single narrative. She described Mont St. Michel, Stonehenge and Jim Morrison's grave in such vivid detail that I wanted to rush out and buy a plane ticket.

She claimed to know the anonymous street artist, Banksy. I questioned that one, but was still in awe of her wisdom and spirit of possibility. Her favorite quote was, "Your burden is that you can do anything, but you can't do everything."

She swore like a sailor and invented cover-ups, hence, "shellfish bisque."

I feel nervous seeing Veronique. She is always challenging and often unpredictable. I wait to catch her eye, but can't, so I say,

"Son of a biscuit," another of her euphemisms. Nothing. I say it again, louder, and she finally looks up, miffed by the interruption.

"Hi. Remember me?" I ask, waving. "Patrick Fitz. I took a couple of classes from you back in the day." Veronique blinks behind her glasses, her synapses firing. She is wearing a tie-dyed sweatshirt adorned with a dancing bear, the Grateful Dead symbol.

"Why....yes...Patrick. How are you?"

"I'm well. I'm married and have a kid, Joey. So, what are you up to now?"

"Consulting," she answers. "You played trombone, right? Still playing?"

"Of course," I say. "Still chasing the orchestra dream, I guess." For some reason I pause before my next reveal. "I've also been doing some work in schools, with young students."

"You mean playing music in schools?" she asks. "What's the goal there?" Now I remember she never let us get too comfortable.

"Yes, playing trombone in schools," I continue. "The goal is to expose kids to music, basically. You know, 'music is good, let's give some to students to make the world better.'"

"And is it?" she asks.

"Is it what?"

"Making the world better."

"Well, I guess it's not stopping any wars or keeping any children from getting shot on the streets," I respond. "I also got roped into trying to help save our local neighborhood school. It's on that list that just came out in the news, of low-performing schools."

"Oh. How's that going?" she asks, seeming a little more interested. "Let me guess. They have a teacher committee that blames the parents or the students. Right?"

"Well, some in the community are blaming the parents, and, yes, there is a committee. Some teachers on the committee blame the students. It's a confusing mess of finger-pointing," I say, wondering why she knows anything about schools.

"They asked you to join the committee, and you said yes, without any real expertise. So, you're really just another warm body, with no ability nor authority," she says, "and with no strong leader. Am I close?" It's weird how close she is.

"I don't want to be just another warm body," I say, feeling a bit defensive and a little hurt. "The principal asked me to gather a bunch of data, and he gave me access to the school's site. I don't know what I'm looking at or for, exactly."

"I hear they are going to close twenty schools from that list," she says after a moment.

"Close twenty schools? Where'd you hear that?" Suddenly I'm very interested in what she's saying. I haven't heard anything but rumors, but she has a number. Why does she even think this?

"I can't say. But that's not important for you," she adds. "How does your music background connect to keeping your school open?"

"I'm just getting started with figuring that out," I answer. "I played a concert there, but I'm not sure music has anything to do with fixing these low schools."

"Music, and all the arts, can serve powerful roles in improving schools," she says. "So can pizza making or building robots or outdoor exploration, if they are done well. What's stopping this school from being great?"

"Geez, I wish I knew that answer," I admit. "I visited a school last week that has great reading scores, and each of the classrooms I saw was different. One was messy, another tidy, one loud, another quiet. I don't understand what was good or bad in any of their classrooms."

She glances at her watch, as if it had silently reminded her of something. She starts putting papers into her satchel, then stands and grabs the fake fur jacket from the back of her chair.

"Once you know what's stopping one school, or even one classroom, from being great," she says, "you'll be able to figure out the rest from there, including what music and you can do to help.

That's the one answer you need to get started." With that, she turns and moves toward the door.

"Wait, do you know the answer?" I plead. She turns back toward me and stops.

"You can figure it out, Patrick," she says, "I'm sure of it." With that, she turns again, steps quickly to the door and is gone.

Coffeeshop Questions

My drink, now lukewarm, is right where I put it down. Suddenly the room is full of people again, all talking and carrying on. "What's stopping this school from being great?" So clear, yet I have no answer.

Wait, Veronique was a "world music and community building" professor. Her course got me thinking about a lot of things - including diarrhea in Bangladesh. Did she also teach education? Reading? Now she's sitting around in coffee shops, doling out tough questions to former students?

"What's stopping this school from being great?" The question is piercing my brain. The committee says... who cares, they'll say 200 things are the answer. She said there's just one thing. Why not just tell me? I take a sip of lukewarm coffee and wait for the caffeine to kick in.

Money could be the answer. Schools are always crying for more money. But I've seen the expense budget for my school and it has enough funding to do whatever it chooses to prioritize. Instead, the cash is spread around among nine different grade levels, so no teacher files a grievance with the union or no parent gets worked up enough to raise a ruckus.

What about reading skills? That's certainly what gets schools on or off the list, and might get 20 schools closed. Besides, if students can't read, they can't do other subjects, including math, if math textbooks are 80% words, as the research seems to say.

Then what does "great at reading" look like? The district says it's lots of students scoring at a certain level on the standardized test. "Lots of students at each school" means 3rd- 8th graders, as that is who takes the standardized tests each year. So, that's the goal, right? I take another sip of coffee.

The revised question should be, "What's stopping this school from getting lots more 3rd - 8th graders reading at level?" The research I've found says it's harder to turn around a struggling 3rd grader than a 1st grader, and a student's future reading scores are predictable 88 times out of 100 by the end of 1st grade. So, 8th grade is too late and so is 3rd grade. If a school can't get 1st graders reading at level, you won't have 3rd graders, nor 4th - 8th graders, reading and succeeding.

This reminds me of what my dad taught me one summer. I needed money for college, so he gave me a job building a house with him. He was a skilled carpenter, but I was lucky if my hammer hit nails, not fingers. It took me days to get the forms nailed together for the foundation. He measured them and used instruments to check if they were level and square, then he said, "Tear it out, do it again."

"Dad," I pleaded, "it looks fine. It's close enough." He was a patient man.

"It all starts with the foundation. If it's not right, the walls won't be straight, the roof won't fit, and it'll fall off. Do it again."

So, the question should be about the foundation of a school: "What's stopping this school from having lots of kindergarten and 1st graders reading at level?" It's this level of questions that kept me awake all weekend. Maybe others on the committee will have answers. Not Mr. Bean, but maybe Ms. Peterson. Right now, I really am just "another warm body" on that committee.

More Team Meetings

I've been to three school committee meetings. Most people at each session were new, so we spent the bulk of the time recapping the previous meeting. Mr. Bevington then asked the newcomers what they thought and they gamely proceeded to tell us the reason they came that day, often thinly-veiled defenses of their own or a friend's pet program.

Mr. Bevington is here for number four. The librarian is hovering in the background, just close enough to hear all but far enough away for deniability if anyone later asks. Ms. Peterson is back. She's been doing research, judging by the bunch of papers in front of her.

"So, we have two new people," says Mr. Bevington.

"Ralph, can we dispense with the review and just get down to business?"

"Well, Ms. Peterson, I'm fine with that," responds Mr. Bevington. "You two okay with that?" Two heads nod.

"Thank you, Ralph. I brought the research I've been doing about our school," she says, pointing to the stack of papers. "To summarize, we've got some great programs here: 8th grade algebra club, that thing where 2nd graders read to friendly dogs, family literacy night in May for the whole school. We put iPads in all 3rd grade rooms, too. Our new after-school program has been very popular with students and their parents."

"It's a little bit of everything, but it'll look pretty good when it's on slides," someone says.

"I also looked and we had several students last year who are now at top magnet high schools. The school names are impressive.

Finally, I looked up our dropout rates in high school. Central Office tracks that by elementary school. Anybody want to hazard a guess?"

Nobody moves. Really? If I were a teacher I'd want to know how my students did later.

Ms. Peterson continues, undaunted. "A study from the University of Chicago says students who pass all their classes as high school freshmen are 'on-track' to graduate. Students getting all D's in freshman year are on track, but even one F means you are not on track. Crazy low, right? Furthermore, U of C's preliminary evidence says 8th grade on-track rates predict high school graduation, too. Cool, eh?"

Still just puzzled looks around the table.

"Our students go on to high school and then drop out in larger percentages than the district as a whole. So I looked up several of our students' grades in 8th grade. You all remember that girl four years ago who we all thought just needed to mature some in high school and get her act together? Anybody remember her name?"

"Rebecca," says Mr. Bevington. "A real pistol, always in my office. Yes, I remember."

"That's her," says Ms. Peterson. "She flunked two freshman classes. Then she dropped out of high school. Here, she flunked my science class. What little bit more could I have done to get that F up to a D? It makes me realize how important we are to these students' futures."

"Well, we are not putting Rebecca in our report for Monday, are we?"

"No. But I say we put it in our eventual plans to do something about the other Rebeccas we have here," says Ms. Peterson.

"That will come. We just need to get ready for Monday now. Who else has something?"

"I've got reading and math data for the past four years," I say, "and attendance numbers. This school has 90% attendance. Is that good or bad for us?"

"In our district, that 90% means the number of days that all students are in attendance, compared to the number of days the school is open," says Mr. Bevington. "So, hypothetically, if 1,000 students are registered at our school and there are twenty days of school, that's 20,000 possible days of student attendance. If students show up for just 18,000 of those days, that's a 90% attendance rate."

"Here's why that all matters," says Ms. Peterson. "Research says a student who misses two days per month of school is five times less likely to graduate from high school, even if he or she is just in kindergarten. So, figure it out – 90% attendance means the average student misses one of every ten school days. There are about 20 school days per month, so the average student is missing two of those twenty days per month. That's terrible!"

"In reality, though," Mr. Bevington responds, "many students are attending every day and a few are missing three or more school days per month. Those few are the students we should be paying attention to, if we want our attendance percentage to go up."

"And to keep students from failing," Ms. Peterson responds. "Bottom line, the district says elementary schools should have attendance rates of 95%. So, our 90% is a mark against us."

"People! We're looking for good news!" Mr. Bevington sounds frantic.

"Give me the figures for attendance and for reading and math scores, and I'll make some kind of positive slide or two to use on Monday," Ms. Peterson responds, giving him a look.

The bell rings, and everyone starts to move immediately. "Ms. Peterson is putting everything onto slides. We'll do our best. See you at Central Office at 4 p.m. Monday."

As I'm putting on my coat to leave, Ms. Peterson approaches me. "You seem like a good guy, Patrick. Don't be so quiet. We need your data and your community voice." With that, firm but friendly, she turns and is gone.

The Bad Burger Joint

Sunday, January 23

It's Sunday evening and I've forgotten all about work and the whole school thing. I'm lying here in bed, trying to get to sleep after a full weekend.

Grace and I went to a family wedding on Saturday. We left Joey with the grandparents, and I was looking forward to some time with just Grace. It was a 90-minute drive. We were early, so we went into a burger joint near the church. The wedding was three blocks away. You know how it works with weddings: once the ceremony is over, it takes a while before anybody gets to eat dinner. I just wanted a bite to tide me over, in case no real food showed up until way past my usual "feeding time." Grace said she was hungry, too. Maybe an original chicken sandwich (two for $5 special in the window). Something easy and quick.

At the front counter, people were milling about, watching us as we walked in. "The line is over there," said one woman, helpfully, pointing to our left. Nobody else was over there, just everyone standing to our right, apparently waiting for their food orders to come out. So, we went left and stood in front of the cash register, ready to order.

Behind the counter, the most senior-looking person was giving orders to her teenage charges. She was maybe 40. "Put on the headset and go back to the drive-up window," she said, sounding exasperated. She then looked at the screen overhead to see what was up there in orders. She launched into putting fries into little cardboard containers. Another guy came over, and she handed off the fries task to him. He pulled on the cardboard containers dispenser and four came out together. He put one by the fries and then, one by one, put the other three back into the dispenser to use later, before he set about putting fries into the first container.

I didn't see anybody cooking the actual burgers or assembling sandwiches, but I assumed they were nearby, out of sight. I looked to see if there were any burgers in the rack where typically someone slides them from the other side where the cooking is occurring. Up there I saw one wrapped burger, along with lots of extra brown paper bags to put customer orders into, and a salt shaker for the fries. But those paper bags dominated that space. Where are they going to put the sandwiches we order? I wondered.

After a few minutes of this, I turned to the woman who pointed us left. "Have you been waiting long?" She nodded, but said nothing, her eyes and facial expression signaling, "Yes, isn't this ridiculous?" Nobody was stepping up to the register in response to us standing there. Nobody was asking, "Can I take your order?"

The senior woman behind the counter started barking orders to her younger charges again. "Take the headset and go back to the window. Tell Josey to take her break." Three bodies were moving about aimlessly, and that one woman was barking orders while she did one small task at a time. Eventually, she closed a bag into which she had placed two sandwiches. "Two Big Burgers?" she asked while holding the bag in the direction of a resigned-looking gentleman standing on my side of the counter. He shook his head, indicating that was not his desired order. "What did you order?" she asked.

I finally got to order our two chicken sandwiches, and they came some time later, piping hot. "Should we eat in the car?" asked Grace. Was she worried about time or about the general uncleanliness of the seating area? We decided to avoid a lap full of lettuce and special sauce in the car, and headed to the seats to eat. We asked for and received a cup for water. Standing in front of the soft drink dispenser, we couldn't find any little tab to pull for just plain water. Grace filled the cup halfway with Diet Coke and ice. "We tried," she said. "They don't give us much choice but to steal their Diet Coke."

We started eating in silence. My mouth was quiet, but my brain was noisy. What is it that makes this burger joint so bad? I think I know what bad looked like, in this case, so that's a nice change from my recent experiences with schools.

Eventually, Grace and I begin to chat quietly about how any organization avoids becoming "the bad burger joint." Should organizations be more like an orchestra playing a Beethoven symphony, with the conductor making most of the decisions? Or, instead, like a modern dance company, with everyone collaborating to create something new?

Now it's Sunday night, the wedding's long over, and I'm lying here in bed, realizing all this has been percolating in my head since Saturday night. I'm still thinking about how systems decay: burger joints, schools, music organizations. All systems. Must be a law of nature, like inertia and all that "an object at rest will remain at rest unless acted upon," or whatever I have forgotten from physics class.

I know some of what makes an orchestra great: talented and enthusiastic musicians, experienced conductor with sure ideas about how the music should sound. I know what makes a more intimately scaled brass quintet work: five talented musicians who get along, want to do something exceptional together, and are willing to set aside lots of ego issues. Still, in my experience, one must be willing to step up and be the leader who points the group in a direction.

Can I learn just enough to get Joey into a good school and avoid the bad schools? Veronique says there's one key thing that's keeping any school from being great. I've been thinking the answer might be 1st grade reading skills. Is that enough? Do I even care? I think I might, as I drift off to sleep finally, thinking about this and tomorrow's meeting at Central Office.

The Central Office Lady Meeting

Monday, January 24

Our team went to the Central Office meeting this afternoon. We were loaded with facts and figures we had gathered about our school.

It was a frustrating meeting, all about them telling us the criteria for judging whether our school will stay on the list or not. Our team didn't get to present anything. The only talking was from their staffer, who did not even give us her name.

"You must have a plan for the long-term, not just for now or next year. How are you going to increase your students' skills and scores in reading? Is that sustainable for years to come? You have five months to make your plan and make your case. If we don't like your plan, you will stay on the list and face more onerous sanctions, or you may be closed." Once she said that, our team wasn't hearing anything else, judging from the looks on their faces.

We're out in the parking lot now, before we all pile back into our individual cars and drive solemnly home. "The lady didn't even let us present!" someone says. Some want to quit. Others have conflicting ideas about how to improve the school. Mr. Bevington still seems to be convinced the whole process is just for show, and we just need to play the game and all will be fine. This doesn't feel like a game to me.

We reluctantly decide to meet again the next morning at the school. It reminds me that my dad used to say, "I like to hit my head against the wall. It feels so good when I stop." When will this feel good?

Joey In The Tub

There's a terrific bookstore near home, where Grace and I have purchased dozens of books for ourselves, for Joey, or as gifts. Finding a new bedtime book I can read to Joey tonight is a diversion on my way home after my frustrating day.

After wandering the aisles for a while to clear my head, I end up in the familiar children's section. I find the only Calvin and Hobbes book I have not read to Joey. He loves these cartoons. Calvin, who is about Joey's young age, is always causing trouble for his parents and Suzie, the girl next door. He makes evil snowmen in his yard, he uses big words to talk with his stuffed tiger, Hobbes. I read one of the sophisticated things Calvin has precociously said, laugh, then ask Joey if he knows what one of Calvin's big words means. Joey says no, so I tell him. He thinks about it, and two seconds later laughs because now he gets the joke, too.

Mission accomplished, I head to the checkout area. Standing in line by tables of calendars and coffee mugs to buy on impulse, there's also a table of clearance books. One title jumps out, Why Our Children Can't Read and What We Can Do About It. Hmm, maybe this is the universe reaching out, saying, "Look here for some answers." Imagine, whole books about this reading thing. I pick it up and flip through it as I inch toward the cash register. It's from 1999. No wonder it's on clearance. In the middle of the book, I spot a section of tests to use to see if your child is on-track or not, starting at age four. I wonder if Joey's on-track? "Next customer," says the clerk. Okay, looks like I'm buying two books today.

*   *   *

Grace made a delicious dinner. I wash all the dishes afterward as Grace plays with Joey in the living room. She's really gentle and patient with Joey, letting him engage her in his imaginary world of trains and robots and toy army men. I hear her giggle. They move to the couch with a book.

I want to do my new book's tests with Joey tonight during his bath time. I looked at them in the car outside the store. They seem simple enough.

"Time for your bath, Joey," I say, after Grace closes a book and Joey asks her to read it again. Grace looks up at me from the couch and silently mouths, "Thank you."

Joey likes bath time, so I have no problem getting him out of his clothes and into the tub full of warm water and bubbles. As he's settling into his routine with his tub toys, I have a few minutes to look again at the tests in my new book.

"Let's play a new game in the tub," I say, as he sinks two army men and their boat beneath the water.

"Sure," he says. I pick up my materials.

"I'll say a word you've never heard before, and you say it back to me. Got it?"

"A word I never heard before?" Joey asks, sounding a little confused.

"Let's call these Mars words," I say, using the book's suggested explanation, "because they are words someone from Mars might say. That's why we've never heard them before."

"Oh," he says, now fully paying attention. Maybe he thinks I'm going to turn into a Martian when I talk like one. Or a Martian is going to pop through the door and start talking. Who knows what's in that little head of his?! He's got curly red hair, just as I did at his age, and he's full of curiosity, especially here in his bubbly tub universe.

"Here's the first Mars word - DAP," I say.

"That's not a word, Daddy," Joey says, incredulous.

"It's a Mars word, remember?" I say. If this doesn't work, what might that tell me about Joey? "Say what I say - DAP."

He looks down at his toys, then says it just the way I said it, "DAP," while crashing two boats into each other.

"Good one, buddy," I say, delighted. "Here's another - FIM." He repeats it and giggles.

We go through the whole list. The words get longer and more intricate. My favorites are toward the end - jozipesh and chibbyreenom. Joey has no trouble repeating any just the way I say them. Check hearing off the list of things to worry about.

Next test, I say real words. I start with "pig." I ask him to repeat it, then I ask him to say it without its first sound. No response, except an exploding sound as he crashes two more boats into a floating dinosaur. Following the book's directions, I say "Pig without the 'puh' would be 'ig'," to give him an example. Once I give him that little bit of help, he gets the idea and can do about half the words on this test. The book says that's okay for a kid Joey's age.

I pick one more test from the book. It's a list of single letters, then combinations of letters. I start with the letter b, and I read the directions to Joey. "If you saw this letter in a word, what sound would you say?" I ask. Joey just looks at me like I'm now really from Mars.

"Daddy, I don't know that," he says, not seeming too concerned. Good, I've managed to keep this a game, not a test.

"Oh, good, I can teach you," I say, genuinely excited. "If you saw that letter in a word, you would say 'buh'. You say it now."

"Buh," he says, looking at me.

"Good, now what about this next one?" I ask, pointing to the next one, letter c.

"I don't know that one," he says again. I point to the d, then the f, then the g. He's just looking at me each time, no response. It seems we haven't taught him anything yet about letters and what sounds they represent. Rather than this being a failed test for him, I'll make this a teaching opportunity.

"Joey, if you saw this letter in a word, you'd say 'kuh,' like in cat," I say, pointing again to the c on the list. "Can you say 'kuh, cat'?" He does say it, so I do the same with d and f and g, and on down the list.

We stop when we have done half the consonants and all the five vowels. I decide not to do the rest of the consonants nor combinations like sh and ch, which come next on the list, as Joey seems to be losing interest by the end.

"Daddy, read Calvin now, in bed." So, I help him out of the slippery tub, dry him off and get him into his pajamas. We go into his bedroom and lie down next to each other on his bed, him under the covers and me on top of them. I love the smell of Joey after a bath, all soapy sweet and bed sheets sweaty. I pull out the new book I got today. After three or four cartoons, I'm falling asleep and Joey's nudging my shoulder to wake me back up. Reading to a child from a reclining position is hard work.

"That's it for tonight, buddy," I say, then get up and tuck him in as he rolls onto his side and snuggles into his blankets. I kiss him on the ear, then turn off the lights. Quietly leaving Joey's room, I see the lights in the rest of the house are now out, too. Grace is already in bed and asleep, so I undress, turn off the remaining bedside lamp and slip silently into bed, wrapping an arm gently around her.

Team Meeting After The Central Office Lady Meeting

Tuesday, January 25

"Looks like we've lost a few." That's Mr. Bevington. This is totally out of control -- meeting at Central Office one afternoon, and right back at the school to meet at 8 the next morning. The Central Office lady is letting a deadline sort the good schools from the bad.

"Let's review," says Mr. Bevington. "She told us to analyze our data and decide our school's biggest issues. Then we present a plan to address these issues. All this in five months."

"That's what I heard," says Ms. Peterson, looking amazingly spry for the early hour.

"I also heard we could get closed down," says Mr. Bean. Doesn't look like he's lost any of that beer gut nor shaved those fuzzy ears since I saw him last. Was he there yesterday?

"We all heard that," says Ms. Peterson. "We've got some work to do. Eighth grade reading comprehension comes to mind."

"Well, I'm the 8th grade language arts teacher," says Ms. Zara. "If we got students who were more prepared from 6th and 7th grades, we'd be fine in 8th grade."

"I'm one of the 6th grade teachers," says Mr. Bean. "We're doing our job. We'd like to get better readers from 5th grade. It's hard to engage students with chapter books when many are still learning to decode words."

"Let's not forget that lots of students in those grades transfer in from some other school, where who-knows-what was being taught,"

Ms. Grabowski says. "We see them for the first time in 3rd grade and we're expected to get them all caught up before they take the tests in the spring. The public sees the scores and says our school is bad."

"How about attendance?" asks Ms. Grabowski. "I'm missing at least two of my 3rd graders every day. Several of my students are missing at least a day every week."

"It's a long and boring day here," says Ms. Peterson. "We need some arts and other engaging things. That's all been cut."

"We need teachers to look forward to coming every day, too," Mr. Bean says.

"Can we divide up these issues?" I ask, thinking about a process.

"Makes sense to me," says Ms. Peterson. "Divide and conquer. I'll take 8th grade. Who's got 3rd-5th, to find data that shows what our main problems really are?"

"We don't only want to show them how bad everything is," pleads Mr. Bevington."

"They've already got enough bad data to put us on their list," says Ms. Peterson. "Now they're checking to see if anybody here can spot the problem, own it, fix it."

"Yeah, but why haven't we done that already?" asks Mr. Bean.

"Sometimes it takes a spotlight shining on you to get you focused on fixing the problems that are right in front of your nose," I say.

"Right," says Ms. Peterson, winking at me. "Who's got attendance to investigate more?"

"I'll do that," says Ms. Grabowski.

"I've been gathering reading scores in the younger grades," I say. "I can finish that."

"And I'll tackle student mobility," says someone. I think it's Ms. Grabowski.

"Okay, somebody has every topic for now," says Ms. Peterson, while Mr. Bevington is flipping through some papers in front of him. "Keep a list if you think of more problems we need to solve. Five months seems like a long time, but it's not. Let's plan to meet again in one week. Send me your work as you get it together, and I'll put everything into one document."

Everybody disperses, leaving just Ms. Peterson and me in the room. I'm suddenly feeling as though we just wasted another meeting. I tried to contribute some process questions, but it didn't seem to help. My head is going to explode.

"A list is not a strategy," I blurt out to Ms. Peterson, as she is grabbing her pile of papers.

"Say what?" she asks, reacting.

"We rehash the same stuff and make lists. A list is not a strategy."

"Why didn't you say that in the meeting, instead of now to me?" she asks.

"I just realized that's what was bugging me," I say. "Aren't you frustrated?"

"I sure am," she starts. "Suddenly it looks like I'm running this thing. Nobody tells me I'm running it beforehand, I just notice no one else is leading. That's okay, I love leading. So I fall back on my science training and go with first gathering lots of data to use. That just creates a list, which is not a strategy. That's a valuable insight. Come on, let's hear more like that."

I suddenly remember what Veronique asked me. "We need one or two key things we are going to do, things with leverage to get the school rolling in a positive direction again."

"You're making sense now," she says, putting down her pile of papers.

"Here's what I've been asking myself. What's stopping this school from having lots of kindergarten and 1st graders reading at level?"

"What kind of question is that?" she asks. "We've got a whole school to fix."

"First, what's stopping this whole school from being great?" I begin. "Reading is the answer. If students can't read, they can't do math, science, or anything."

"Okay," she says. "I was arguing for 8th grade comprehension just now."

"So, what's keeping 8th grade reading from being great?" I continue. "Eighth grade relies on 7th grade, which relies on 6th grade, all the way back to K and 1st grade reading."

"Okay, maybe," she says.

"So, what's keeping us from having great readers in K and 1st grades?"

"Let's say I go along with that being the most important question. What's the answer?"

"I don't know," I respond. "It's driving me nuts. I finally had to talk to someone about it."

"I'm that lucky someone, right?" she says, with a small smile.

"I'm sorry," I say. "You seem like someone who cares. I should've kept my mouth shut."

"Hey, wait. It's Patrick, right?" It feels like she is seeing me for the first time. "Don't apologize. Just say it in the meeting next time." She grins more broadly now, then grabs her stack of papers and dashes out the door.

Nearly Every Student Can Learn To Grade Level

Wednesday, January 26

"Half of our students can't learn to read," says Mr. Bevington. "It's their fault we're on that bad list." He saw me sitting in the teachers' lounge, typing a note on my laptop in the five minutes before I need to leave for a rehearsal downtown.

"What do you mean," I ask, irritated that he might make me late.

"When I was teaching, 50% of my class was never going to learn to read at their proper grade level," he continues. I'm not sure he realizes that could be an indictment of his teaching. "I bet 30% of students in this whole school should be special ed, what they now call 'diverse learners.' But the district doesn't want that, because of the costs to put special ed students in smaller classes." He suddenly switches to a kind of administrative monotone voice. "Ten to 12 students per room, depending on type and severity of disability, according to section 226.731 of the Illinois Administrative Code."

"So what?" I ask. "Why do you care how many students are called one thing or another?"

"If 30% of students in this school are special ed," he says, "they shouldn't count in our results. You can't expect us to get any more than 70% of our students reading at grade level."

Sounds like an excuse to me.

"Let's look it up on Google and see how many students are special ed. Okay?" I'm hoping facts will bore him and he'll go away. Pulling up my browser, I type: "How many students in the US are in special ed?"

Click on this one," he says after a moment of looking at my screen, pointing to a link. Darn, I hadn't expected him to engage with this. "It says it's got state-by-state numbers." I click on the link to Disabilitycompendium.org and start looking.

"Look at this," I say. "In 2014, 8.4% of school-age children in the US were special ed in some way. Hawaii had the smallest percentage (6.3 percent), while New Jersey had the largest percentage (11.6 percent). In Illinois, the percentage was 9.1%." That should be enough to end this discussion and get out of here. "That 9.1% is a long way from your 30%."

"So, in rich communities such as Winnetka it might be 5%, and in poor Chicago or East St. Louis maybe it's 15%, for the Illinois average to come out to 9.1%," he says. "And if the total is 15% in our whole district, maybe that means it's 5% in middle class neighborhoods and magnet schools, and it's 30% in schools like mine."

"I don't know," I say, now doubly-irritated by his made-up facts. "Aren't you letting teachers off the hook for not teaching all students to read?" I'm just imagining Grace's response if Joey is having any trouble learning to read and she thinks it's a problem with the teacher, say Mr. Johnson in 1st grade, God forbid. So she and I go to Mr. Bevington and he says "Thirty percent of our students should be special ed. Maybe we should have your son tested." Grace would go through the roof, and I'd be right behind her!

"I just think a lot more students qualify to be tested and labeled as special ed," he says. "Yes, it would take a lot of pressure off teachers and me. Let me see your fancy computer for a minute," he says. He sits next to me, bringing a strong odor of some cologne I have not smelled since junior high. I reluctantly move my laptop toward him.

"This one looks like it will have more numbers," he says, clicking on something called https://www.naset.org/2522.0.html. We both look at it silently for a moment. Putting his finger on my computer's screen, he reads aloud to me: "Since 1975, when the category of LD was first included in public law, the number of students identified as having a learning disability has grown by almost 250%, from approximately 800,000 students to almost 3,000,000 students (U.S. Department of Education, 2002)."

"That sounds like lots more students already are being labeled special ed," I say. I read down the page. "It goes on to say there are four reasons for this growth, one of which is misdiagnosis." Mr. Bevington clicks out of that page and back to search results. I see a promising-sounding link from September, 2010 in The Guardian: http://www.theguardian.com/education/2010/sep/14/half-special-needs-children-misdiagnosed. I click on it and it opens to this: "As many as half of the children identified as having a category of special educational needs (SEN) are wrongly diagnosed and simply need better teaching or pastoral care instead, a report published today finds."

"I don't know what the Brits mean by 'pastoral care,' but the rest seems to say many children are misdiagnosed as special ed, and really just need better teaching."

"I still say it was always more in my classroom, at least 50%, misdiagnoses and statewide averages be darned," he says.

"For the committee, should we use that number as our goal for this school then -- 50% of students will be reading at grade level. The rest are special ed?"

"We could never say that to Central Office," he answers. "Fifty percent is too low."

"What about 90.9% then? That's 100% of kids minus the 9.1% state average for special ed. Or we could round down and say 90%, to make it easier to remember."

"That's too high -- we'll never get there, and we'll all get fired!" he says, bringing it all back to his job security. "Let's just say 'nearly all' students can learn to read at grade level. Okay?"

"Sure thing," I respond, and I type that in my computer, so I'll remember it later.

"I can tell you that in this school, the little ones come to the front door for the first day of kindergarten and lots of them are not ready to do the stuff we ask them to do," he says, a little pink in the cheeks now. "They can't hold a pencil. They have never seen a book, and they don't know how to hold one right side up and turn its pages. We have students who drop the first book we give them because they are not even coordinated enough to hold it. No wonder so many eventually get diagnosed as special education. Sometimes it's lead poisoning or some brain thing. Maybe those are your 9.1%. But lots of our low students just weren't ready on day one. That's why the reading scores are not 90% at this school."

"I gotta go," I say, standing and putting away my laptop. He looks relieved.

"You keep thinking about this, and we'll discuss it more with the committee," he concludes, then he walks out of the room and starts down the hall. Of course, that's not a response to this question, not setting a clear goal that his whole team can embrace. This suddenly feels too much like my "bad burger joint" experience from the weekend: one bit of indecision leads to a work-around, which leads to chaos and, eventually, the worst burger joint ever. Only this one doesn't just inconvenience a few hungry customers. It hurts the futures of hundreds of children who are given no choice in the matter.

Cocktail Party

Wednesday evening, January 26

"You're going to this tonight," Grace demanded.

"But I have a million other things I need to be doing," I responded. Then came "the look" that told me I'm going to this thing after all.

"This thing" is a house party fundraiser for the local private school. Why can't we just send a small check? Or is Grace going in order to schmooze for a scholarship for Joey next year?

"I'm so glad you could come, Grace. Let me introduce you to a few people," says our hostess for the evening as we walk in the front door of her lovely home. I wasn't aware Grace had been researching private schools enough to have made friends who know her by face and name. Our hostess proceeds to introduce us to several well-dressed people standing with little sandwiches and plastic drink cups in hand. She then slips effortlessly back into the crowd.

My cell phone buzzes in my pocket. While Grace engages in idle chit chat, I see it's Ms. Peterson calling. Did I give her my cell phone number?

"I've got to take this," I say to Grace and her new friend. "I promise I'll be right back." I slip into a side room that is quiet.

"Patrick, sorry to call you. It's official. They are saying they'll close 20 schools that don't comply," Ms. Peterson says .

"I heard that same thing."

"Sure, Patrick. Have a good evening." The phone call ends.

"What did I miss?" I ask, rejoining my visibly irritated wife.

"Mrs. Morley, this is my very busy husband, Patrick. Mrs. Morley was just telling me about her volunteer work with the local high school near here on Western Avenue."

"Patrick, your wife is perfectly lovely. I was telling her about our family's work with high school juniors, coaching them toward applying for college and supporting them once they are in college to keep at it. You know, that high school has students from all the neighborhoods around here. Very diverse. It needs our help."

Grace is looking at me expectantly. I'm guessing she's silently thinking, Step up, Patrick. Ask a question. Tell her what you are doing in schools. Show her we'd be great to have as parents in any school. My cell phone is buzzing again. Grace is looking at my pocket. Ignore it!

"Your volunteer work sounds rewarding," I say, trying a non-committal approach. "Is that the high school where your own children go?"

"We looked at it for our two, after nine years apiece of private school tuition. But they got accepted into magnet schools, one for her arts interests and the other for her math skills. We figured they should get to pursue those talents to their highest levels. We feel a little guilty at not supporting the local high school by sending our children there, so we do this volunteer work."

Well, that's a hot topic in our house, too: should we work to make the local school "worthy" of our precious child, or should we try for somewhere that is already pretty good or even great? In our case, we don't have the money to pay private school tuition. I shoot a quick glance at Grace. She gives me a non-committal look. Maybe I need a slight change of direction.

"How exactly do you go about helping those juniors in high school?" I ask.

"Well, we find those with the grades to get into college, yet who say they are not really thinking about it. Or they say they are thinking about getting a job and saving money so they can go later. They tell these things to their counselors at school, and then their counselors tell us."

"So, you are getting the students who are doing fine in school?"

"Yes, but they might not go on to college. We're saving them," she says.

"What about the ones who have mediocre grades and won't be able to go to college? Who's saving them?" I ask. Glares from Grace.

"Those children will have to figure out some other way to make their way in life," she answers. "They didn't put the effort into school earlier on. It's so sad. We focus on the ones who are, you know, on the bubble, just on the cusp of advancing to college."

"How many students do you work with then?" I'm getting bugged now.

"I work with two students myself," she says. "The program works with 26 students per year. It's a classroom of juniors, basically. We get 80% of them to apply for college, and 90% of those get accepted into some kind of college or university."

"How many students in the junior class?" I ask.

"Roughly 900 students, or thereabouts," she answers. "It's a really big high school."

Grace knows me well enough to see my brain at work calculating. I know to keep my calculations to myself, or risk sleeping on the couch tonight. So, 26 students out of 900? Big high school! And 80% of those 26 apply for colleges. So that's about 21 students. And 90% of those 21 get accepted - that's about 19 students. So, 19 of 900 students is about 20 percent. Wait, move the decimal point. That's about two percent of the school's entire junior class. They are "saving" two percent of all juniors, by working with the students most likely to be savable. I don't think they want to put that number on their annual report, though! But maybe they're thinking "gotta start somewhere, do something."

Maybe it's all volunteer, so it costs nothing? I'm not likely to find that out from her this evening. Best to try a different track for finishing this chat.

"Sounds like we agree on one thing" I say. "The problem starts early."

"What do you mean?" she asks, starting to back away a step or two and looking around for anyone else she knows.

"You said 'They didn't put the effort into school earlier on,'" I remind her. I say this in my sweetest voice, but Grace is looking like I'm about to take this woman apart limb by limb. "That says the problem starts earlier than junior year in high school. I wonder how much earlier?"

"That's right -- earlier." She's back to her perky self. "I did some volunteering last year in freshman rooms, too. Some of those students seemed disengaged already. They aren't going to end up in our program unless they make a stronger effort. Even freshman year is too late for some."

"Right. When does the problem start, if we wanted to fix the problem at its start?"

"Oh, gee, I never thought about that." She eyes me, not sure again where this might be going. Grace slips her hand around my arm and gives it a squeeze.

"What about 8th grade?" I say. "That's the grade that gets students ready for high school."

"Hmm. But that seems silly," she says, "to think students come into high school ready or not to succeed because they had a great experience in just 8th grade. Right?"

"Then what about 5th grade?" I ask her. "That's right before junior high school. Or even 6th grade? That's the start of junior high, when lots of things are going on in students' bodies, and schools schedule students to move from room to room all day, just as in high school. Maybe that's where some students start deciding to disengage and stop putting in the effort."

"Maybe 6th grade," she says, sounding a little unsure. "I remember 6th grade being a difficult time for me when I was that age."

"Okay, let's say 6th grade. Is it just the new schedule and their changing bodies that causes this sudden loss of interest in school?" I ask. "If so, why are some students still engaged at that point and beyond, even into high school and even up to junior year when you see 26 semi-motivated students, most of whom go on to apply for college? Why don't all the students disengage, if it's just about schedules and hormones?"

"That's a good point" she says. "Sounds like you've been thinking a lot about this before tonight! So, what do you think?"

Steady, Patrick, I say to myself. You've been under a lot of stress. She doesn't want a lecture. Grace doesn't want you to give her a lecture.

"Well, I don't have all the answers. But I did read a study recently that says that a student's reading level at the end of 1st grade is, 88 times out of 100, where he or she will be as a reader in 4th grade and all the way to 11th grade, relative to other students. The good readers stay good, the struggling readers stay struggling. Other research says math textbooks in junior high are 80% words and only 20% numbers. So, reading seems pretty important to success in all subjects."

Silence. Grace is holding tightly to my arm. Is she trying to pull me into the other room? She knows how geeky I can be with research, and she's trying to make a good impression here.

"How are the students you see? Are they good readers?" I ask, trying to get to some end of this without Grace killing me in public.

"Oh, yeah, they read just fine. For some of them, it's not their favorite thing, so much, but they can read well enough," she answers.

"There you go -- a little evidence." I say. Grace is squeezing my arm super-hard. "Well, nice meeting you." I almost stumble over a potted plant nearby as Grace pulls me into another room with her. I see a portable coat rack there.

"What the heck, Patrick? You're so busy and your phone's always buzzing. Then you have to pick a fight with that woman?" She seems more than a little steamed.

"From where I stand, she's doing everything we said we would never do -- send your own children to an elite private school and then a magnet school across town, abandoning the neighborhood schools and all other people's kids." I start, feeling the anger rise at having to defend this with Grace. "We always said we were going to make the world right by our own actions. We said education was one important way to do that."

"That was a fine idea in theory," she replies, looking ready for a fight. "But now it's for real, and our local school is a mess. This is not some theory any more. It's our child's future. Don't you see that? Or are you just too stubborn to open your eyes? You personally are going to make all schools perfect for everyone? Get over yourself, Patrick."

"Our local school has some problems," I say, trying to take her hand. She bats my hand away. "I'm trying to help folks work on those. But you're not even giving it a chance." Out of the corner of my eye, I see people looking from the other room to see where the raised voices are coming from.

"I'm not interested in experimenting with Joey's future," Grace says, having found her coat on the rack. Now she's buttoning it tightly and getting ready to leave. "Can you fix that school by next Fall?" She is steamed up and ready to protect her young cub to the death. I've seen her like this before and I should have seen this coming.

"Can we even agree that I should keep doing work at our local school, even if it's just for other people's children?" I ask her.

"You do whatever you want for other people's kids," she spits back. "But don't be experimenting with Joey's future. I'm calling our hostess tomorrow to apologize for your behavior and try to rescue a scholarship for Joey. Charters, magnet schools, private schools, suburbs -- everything is on the table." With that she turns and is gone. After a moment to collect myself, I go in the same direction. I find her sitting in the cold car, staring straight ahead. The drive home is also chilly.

Kindergarten Emergency

Friday, January 28

This morning, after Grace left early to cook at the soup kitchen and I took Joey to pre-school, I just needed to drop off one thing for Mr. Bevington, then scram to a brass quintet rehearsal. Up the stairs, turn left, down the hall, reach for the office doorknob. Turn it gently, almost there…

"Patrick!" Familiar voice from behind me. Keep moving and pretend not to hear? "Patrick, we've got an emergency." Mr. Bevington is now standing beside me with his hand pressing on the upper door to keep it closed.

"I just stopped by to drop off that study you wanted," I say. "What's the big emergency?"

"Come in and I'll tell you," he says in something of a whisper, as he opens the door with his other hand on my back, ushering me toward his inner sanctum. I haven't been in his office since the first day I ever set foot inside this school. I see again that it is more like a closet than a grand office for the leader of 30 teachers and 650 students and the keeper of the hopes of however many parents. Dividing the tiny space is an old wooden desk, piled high with papers and binders and what looks like what's left of yesterday's lunch. On the wall over the desk is a plaque with an eagle on it and words too small to read from a distance. The largest type is a date, which I can read clearly - June 10, 1979. Perhaps this plaque has been here longer than this office's current tenant?

Behind the desk, Mr. Bevington sits in a wooden rolling chair with a large green foam pad on the seat. He gestures for me to sit in the one other piece of furniture that could fit in the room, a plastic guest chair on the other side of the desk. "Just move those papers to the floor over there and close the door," he says, gesturing toward the area behind the door.

"Sure, but what's the emergency?"

Last night I looked at kindergarten enrollment stats for next year. They are way down. I asked a couple of parents dropping off their children this morning, and they tell me parents heard things are really bad here. So they're waiting to decide if they'll enroll their children here for kindergarten next year. We've got to do something, and fast. The enrollment deadline is in five weeks. That might as well be tomorrow. If we don't have students entering kindergarten, we've got big problems. Central Office doesn't need more ammunition."

"What could they do?"

"They've already mentioned shutting us down. I've got this year and next until I can file for my pension and get out of here. The plan was just to keep on keeping on, don't rock the boat. Now I've got this enrollment thing. Your child could enroll here next year, right?"

"Yes, my son will be in kindergarten next year," I say.

"What do parents want?" he asks.

"I can tell you what my wife and I want. Good teachers."

"Good teachers in every classroom? What about we put iPads in every classroom? And good after-school options?" he says, as if he's going down some list he read in Principal PR Weekly.

"Those might impress some parents," I say. "But what has them so riled up doesn't sound like it's the lack of iPads. There's been one story in the paper about low reading scores, with links to this school's scores. That gets a negative buzz going pretty quickly. A bunch of iPads is not going to stop that buzz."

"What will_stop that buzz?" He's sounding desperate, as he imagines his sweet future melting and then dripping onto his well-worn penny loafers.

"Good teaching. Good teachers. Classroom visits to confirm good teaching, and happy children learning in happy ways."

"You know our teachers. That's not Mr. Johnson. That's not Mr. Ferris," he says.

"Well, keep parents of potential kindergartners out of the gym and away from Mr. Johnson's 1st grade room." I say, somewhat sarcastically. He looks at me silently for a moment. Turning serious, I start again. "How about you have a community meeting, to tell the potential kindergarten parents about the great things we have planned for here next year in kindergarten. Maybe we just have to build the future one grade at a time, starting with kindergarten, and build parents' trust as we go."

"But we don't have great things planned for kindergarten, do we?" he asks, bewildered.

"Not yet we don't," I say, quickly and somewhat flippantly. I will probably regret this. But the adventurer -- and the parent of a next-year kindergartner -- in me has jumped up and raised his hand. "You get the community meeting announced for five weeks from now and get parents there. We'll sign them all up that night. Ms. Peterson and I will figure out the plan for kindergarten."

Ms. Peterson Kindergarten Emergency Meeting

"You said what?" That's Ms. Peterson's reaction when I find her in her empty classroom. "You and I are going to plan the kindergarten program for next year? But I'm the 8th grade science teacher, and you're a community member. Who's our team?"

"Just you and me and five weeks of time. We just have to simplify, simplify, simplify," I say, channeling something Eric says constantly in brass quintet rehearsals when we're in over our heads on some musical piece.

She is just staring at me.

"Look, you and I both agreed we don't need a list. We need one simple strategy. I think that strategy begins with kindergarten."

Ever since the bad burger joint, I've been thinking about that diarrhea book I carried around all junior year in college. Instead of finding doctors to give expensive and easily spoiled shots to millions of people sick with cholera in one of the poorest countries in the world, they created a potion that used ingredients every household would have. Then they trained low-paid but dedicated community members and sent them to train parents to make and administer it. There were roadblocks to overcome, but it worked. One simple strategy.

"Assume I'm going to play along for a moment," Ms. Peterson says, sounding more like her usual chipper, efficient self. "What do we do in those kindergarten classrooms?"

"I told Mr. Bevington that parents just want to see good teaching going on."

Ms. Peterson puts down her pile of papers, sits at a desk and closes her eyes, then gently massages them with the palms of her hands. After a few moments she stops and pulls an old-fashioned paper weekly planner from the pile. She thumbs through the heavily marked pages until she gets to the lesser-marked future weeks. She takes a deep breath and lets it out slowly. Looking at me, she asks, "Okay, team. When exactly is this community meeting?"

"I'm saying Thursday, five weeks from now," I answer cautiously. "The deadline for kindergarten enrollment is that Friday, so that would be the final moment to influence parents."

"Five weeks sounds just dandy, if we don't have five months," she says with a small wink. "Sit, Patrick, you're making me nervous. Do you have a specific picture of what you mean by 'good teaching'? Or is it just 'you know it when you see it?'" She seems worried.

"I used to think I'd know it when I saw it. After observing several classrooms at another school, though, I'm not so sure," I tell her. "Is it going to be harder than I'm thinking to promise good teaching to parents for next year's kindergarten?"

"If we can't even define it, it will be easy to promise but hard to deliver. Are there things besides good teaching that you'd want to see as a prospective K parent?"

"I guess I'd like a bright and colorful classroom for the kindergarten. Maybe lots of books. Seeing happy children in there learning and reading."

"That's a lot to promise and actually be able to show parents," she says, matter-of-factly.

As a creative person, a learner, a puzzle-solver, and social justice advocate, I'm feeling a quiet excitement rising in me. Not only is this what I want for my child. It's what I want for every child.

"Well," she says before I can share, "I've got to go pick up my students from gym now. How about this -- you go see what's happening in our kindergarten. Come back with what 'good teaching' looks like, and if any of our kindergarten teachers are doing it."

As she stands, I stand. She turns and looks me right in the eye. "Bring some more ideas, too, for how we're going to make this happen. If kindergarten is our initial strategy for improving this whole school, it had better be strong."

After The Fight

Saturday, January 29

I haven't been looking forward to this weekend, but here it is, Saturday morning. Grace and I have barely seen or talked to each other since the cocktail party on Wednesday night. I've been leaving early in the morning to get to music rehearsals. Grace had a dance thing in the evening Thursday, then was gone early yesterday morning to the soup kitchen and out with her girlfriends in the evening. Maybe that's been just as well, sort of a cooling off period.

I find my way to the kitchen, pour some cereal and milk in a bowl, and sit. Grace is at the back door, knocking snow off her boots. Time for a chat, perhaps.

"Good morning, Patrick. We got a light dusting of snow, which I was brushing off the car for you," she says, as she closes the outside door and takes off her winter jacket and gloves.

"Thank you. Am I forgetting something I'll need the car for today?" I ask.

"I'm pretty sure you said you had a brass quintet gig with Eric and the others this afternoon," she says, peeling a banana and sitting at the table with me to eat it.

"Wow, thanks for reminding me," I say. "I guess my mind's been on other things."

"Mine, too," she responds, then pauses. "I'm sorry I got upset with you at that cocktail thing the other night. I've been thinking a lot about that since."

"I'm sorry I was upset, too," I say. "The whole thing kind of caught me by surprise."

"What do you mean?"

"You know, me getting so upset. You getting so upset. I don't want to be upset about anything with you."

"Me neither," she assures me. "But I still am, even though I'm sorry."

"Talk about it?"

"Maybe. You go first," she says.

"Well, I don't even remember why I was upset. I've been so busy since then."

"I remember exactly why I was upset, and you being so busy was part of it," she says.

"You mean someone calling me in the middle of the party?"

"And your phone buzzing multiple times and you always being out at that school."

"That reminds me what I was upset about, too," I say.

"One more thing – you were rude to that woman. I was trying to get Joey a scholarship."

"That's what bugged me – a scholarship to go to that elite private school for rich kids? That's not the Grace I thought I knew."

"Being rude to other people is not the Patrick I thought I knew," she responds.

"Okay. You're right. I was a bit in-her-face and I am sorry for that, too. Anything else that got you so upset, besides me rude and me busy? Let's get it all out so we can try to move on."

"Well, yes, there's also you putting all our eggs in that local school basket for Joey. You can't fix some broken school by next fall. But you get your mind set on something and, by golly, you'll do whatever it takes to show you're right."

"You used to think that was a good trait of mine, not a character flaw."

"Your stubbornness and bull-headedness?"

"No, my dogged pursuit of truth and justice for all."

Her eyes look up from the table and catch mine. She smiles slightly.

"You're right, when you put it that way. Really though, Patrick, this school thing won't work by fall."

"Someone waves a red flag in front of me that says, 'This can't be done,' and I'm all the more determined to make it happen. Oh, that's another thing bugging me. You are writing off whatever

I'm doing in that school, while you are trying for a free membership deal in the private school club."

"What can anyone do in a few months, Patrick?" she asks, softening slightly. "It's nine grades to fix and however many teachers and hundreds of kids."

"What if it's not the whole school we need to fix by fall? What if it's just kindergarten?"

"Then what – he transfers to another school for 1st grade?"

"Then next year we work on 1st grade, then 2nd grade, all the way up," I say. "Our simple plan is to fix kindergarten for next fall, then build on that."

"I don't know, Patrick. It sounds too simple to me."

"Just keep telling me it can't be done," I say.

"I'll keep telling you I'm looking for other options for Joey's kindergarten."

"Please stop telling me elite private schools are one of them, at least?"

"Okay, I didn't like those people, anyway," she says. "There must be better options."

Meeting Ms. Armstrong

Monday, January 31

Just the person I need to see is walking toward me down the hall as I head toward the office on Monday morning -- Mr. Bevington.

"Patrick, the community meeting is scheduled. It's in five weeks, the evening before the district's enrollment deadline. Your plan going to be ready?"

"We'll be ready. I need to observe the current K rooms first, see what's going on," I say.

"Fine with me," he responds. "Go see Ms. Armstrong's class. She's in room 104. She's one of our mid-career teachers, a little jaded maybe, but she'll show you the ropes."

As I turn and walk toward Ms. Armstrong's room, I realize I can't just say, "I'm here to see what's going on in kindergarten, to determine if it's any good."

Time's up. The door is open, lights are on. I walk in. No students are in the room.

"Hello?" I say into the seemingly empty room.

From behind a file cabinet stacked with boxes comes a female voice. "Just a minute." A moment later, a head pokes out. "I need to find something before the students get back."

"Are you Ms. Armstrong?" She's maybe 40, stocky, built for a fight but now out of shape. She's wearing a dress, a formalness that's unusual at this school.

"Yes, I am. Don't mind me if I keep doing stuff. My students will be back any minute from music," she says, grabbing a book off the

87

floor and placing it back on a shelf as she walks toward a large desk at one end of the room. "Who are you?"

"I'm Patrick Fitz. I'm a community member, and I'm helping out some with planning for next year." She gives me a quick glance, sizes me up, keeps moving. "I heard the music teacher got cut."

"It's a special thing, some musicians working with our students. I get a break for a few minutes, so I'll take it."

"Did your students get to see the brass quintet concert in your gym last week? That was my group."

She stops and looks at me. "That was really good. My students were talking about that and drawing pictures of your instruments for days after that."

"That's nice to hear." Students start clomping back into her classroom and noisily start sitting on a brightly colored rug area right by where we are standing. "Would you mind if I just sit and watch for a while?"

"That's fine. We have reading time next," she says, pushing a little chair toward me and sitting in a larger rocking chair to face her students. "Sorry we don't have any other real chairs in here." I take the small chair and sit behind the students, who are now seated cross-legged on the rug.

"Students, we have a guest this morning," she says. "Quiet down and let's get going again. I'm going to read you a new story this morning."

She reads a story from a colorful book she pulls from a rack near the rug area, holds a tissue for one boy to blow his nose, stops two girls near me from braiding each other's hair, asks students some questions about the story she just read, goes to her desk to get some papers to hand back to students, and tells a student who is being disruptive that he must go sit back at his desk, which is way off to one side. For 20 minutes she is a blur of motion.

At the end of all that she sends the students back to their desks and gives them a worksheet about the story to work on individually. Most begin coloring on it. I get up and put my jacket back on, signaling I'm going to leave.

"I need to get back to my other work," I say to Ms. Armstrong as she comes over to me. "I really appreciate you letting me watch some of your class today."

"The students were a little rowdy today. We've got some handfuls here," she says, with as much affection as affliction in her voice. "Plus, Ms. Orr and I and several 1st grade teachers took the students from Ms. Gage's room this morning, to help her out. Could you bring your musical instruments next time?"

"Oh, maybe." I say, thinking about my immediate goal of gathering information and ideas for my next meeting with Ms. Peterson.

Back in my car I still have no better idea than when I visited Clover Elementary of how to think about what I just saw. There's just too much going on in a classroom of kindergartners for me to be able to say, "This is good, that other thing is bad."

I've got to figure this out so Ms. Peterson and I can create a plan. That's when I remember Veronique.

1200 Hours

It wasn't hard to find a phone number for my former college professor-turned-consultant from the coffee shop encounter. I just put her full name into Google and searched. Up came five or six hits, one of which was nearby. She wasn't just visiting town when I ran into her recently - she lives here. So, I call her number and she picks up!

"Yes, I remember you," she says. "You're lucky to catch me at home. I'm headed out of town for two weeks. What color was my hair when you saw me?"

"That's easy, it was bright red," I say, having no problem recalling the exact shade.

"Good. It's bright blue now," she says. "Have you figured out what's stopping your school from being great?"

"I think so," I say. "For a school to be great, reading skills must be great, all the way through 8th grade. This can't happen unless there are strong 3rd grade reading skills, which means you need a strong pipeline of K-1st reading skills being built, then maintained and furthered in 2nd and 3rd grade."

"Good start, Patrick. You've nailed the first thing you need. So, what else can I do for you, before my driver gets here?"

"I'm stuck when I get to the level of what a good classroom looks like, what good teaching looks like, to produce those good reading skills," I respond.

"Twelve hundred hours," she says.

"Huh?"

"The answer is 1,200 hours," she repeats.

"How is '1,200 hours' the answer to my questions?"

"The first filter you can use to decide if good things are happening in a classroom is how many hours a child is being exposed to reading and its instruction. By the end of 1st grade, that should be 1,200 hours."

"First of all, where do you get that number?" I ask. "Second, that's just an amount. What about the quality of that so-called exposure? What counts toward that number?"

"Ok, my driver is late. Your last question first: what counts toward that number?" she says, and I can hear her sit. "At home, before schooling years, being read to is what counts. Once the child goes to school, instruction counts, along with more hours of being read to at home."

"Wait, is there any research to back-up this idea of yours?" I ask.

"Well, there's a study that says reading to your child 20 minutes per day produces better readers. Then there's Hart and Risley's work from the 1990's saying poor children hear 30 million fewer words than middle class children by the time they are five years old. You can see why other studies show that children enter kindergarten at greatly varied levels of reading readiness. This is the start of the "reading gap" we all hear so much about in later grades. I just put it all together and did some simple math to come up with that 1,200 hours idea. But there's not one study following children from birth to the end of 1st grade and comparing their reading performance and the number of hours of reading exposure. Maybe you should do that study!"

"I'm a musician, not a reading researcher!" I say, a little too loudly. "And how do you know all this stuff? You were a music professor, right?"

"I was a 'world music and community building' professor, remember? That's a lot more than just music. We talked in class about community, including education and jobs and civic dialogue. That got me into looking at reading research pretty quickly. It all pretty consistently says early reading skills are the key. Even the economists are saying that now."

"I get that, I guess. Then what about your number? Why not 10,000 hours?"

"Got a pencil? Research says 20 minutes per day of being read to is good. So, assume 20 minutes per day from birth, times six days per week, just to give the parents one day off per week for good behavior. That's 20 minutes times six days times 52 weeks times seven years until the end of 1st grade." As she speaks, I am writing on a sheet of paper:

Reading Experience at Home = 20 minutes per day

x 6 days a week = 120 minutes

x 52 weeks a year = 6,240 minutes

x 7 years = 43,680 minutes by end of 1st grade.

She continues: "Then add in-school instruction in kindergarten and 1st grade. That should be 80 minutes per day for 40 weeks for every child, to move ahead a year in reading skills."

"At the same time the student is being read to at home?" I ask, trying to keep up.

"Absolutely. Continue the reading at home," she says. "So, the school portion is 80 minutes per day for two years."

I scribble on paper:

Reading Experience at School = 80 minutes per day

x 5 days per week = 400 minutes

x 40 weeks per school year = 16,000 minutes

x 2 years (K-1st) = 32,000 minutes

"Add the time at home and at school. What's that all total?"

"Let's see. Looks like 75,680 minutes."

"Right. Now divide by 60 to get hours."

I get out my iPhone and punch the numbers into its calculator. "Looks like that's 1,261 hours," I say. I write the equation on paper now, to keep it straight.

Total Reading Experience Time by End of 1st grade

43,680 minutes at home

+ 32,000 minutes at school

= 75,680 minutes total

Divided by 60 minutes per hour

= 1,261 hours total

"Right," she says. "Let's round down to 1,200 hours, just to keep it simple."

"Now I see how you get that total," I say, a little dazed.

"Not to freak you out any more than I already have," she continues, "but we can extend this idea out through high school and it needs to total 10,000 hours, according to Benjamin Bloom. That's how many hours he says it takes to be a true expert at reading. So, this 1,200 hours is just the beginning. Let's call it the essential foundation."

"But what do you propose a teacher should do with all of this?" I ask as the idea sinks in.

"Remember Nancy Reagan?" she asks.

"Say who?" I ask.

"As first lady of the whole United States, Nancy Reagan's slogan was, 'Just say no.' Or are you too young to remember her anti-drug program? So forget Nancy Reagan." She moves on. "The idea is that 1,200 hours becomes the way for a teacher to judge the value of any initiative or program or even moment to moment classroom activity - and then say no to any that do not produce more instructional time for the students, especially for those who need it most."

"And who are those students who need it most?"

"They're the students who didn't get the minutes of reading exposure every day at home."

"Wait. So, are you saying the teacher should make up that time? Teachers are not going to like that. Do you want them to stay after school for this?"

"It can be done during the regular school day," she says. "Oops, my ride is here."

"Wait, I've got a million questions for you. You didn't say anything about the quality of that reading exposure," I plead.

"I've got a plane to catch. When you can tell me how teachers can find more instructional time during the school day, call me. Then you'll be ready for more."

Patrick Tries Tutoring

Tuesday, February 1

I desperately need some direct experience with students. My latest bathtub time with Joey has shown me lots about how one smart little boy figures out sounds and letters. Does that tell me anything about teaching 30 students for a whole day?

Ms. Armstrong is game to let me try tutoring students individually. "I've got a student or two you can have for as long as you want!" she says when I approach her the next day about volunteering in her classroom as a non-teacher, under her guidance. "So long as they're not bugging me and other students for awhile, I don't care what you try teaching them. How about you start right now?"

First up, she gives me Robert -- short for his age, wiry, beautiful smile. "Try sitting over there at that table with him," she says, pointing. "Practice these letter cards with him, why don't you? And read one of the books in his basket."

Robert and I walk the ten steps to the table, and sit on small chairs, facing each other. "Hi, Robert," I say. "My name is Patrick. Do you like to read?"

No response from Robert. He just stares at me with his gigantic brown eyes and cartoonishly-long eyelashes.

"How about we play a game with these flashcards your teacher gave me? I'll hold up a card and you tell me the name of the letter. Can you do that?" No answer from Robert, so I guess we'll just have to do the game and hope he says something. Otherwise, this is going to be a short session.

"What letter is this?" I ask, holding up a B card.

No answer from Robert. He starts fidgeting. I tell him it's a B. After three cards and no answers from him, he starts looking around the room. Another three cards and no answers. He is not even looking at me or my cards anymore.

"All right, Ms. Armstrong said you have a basket with some books in it," I say to Robert, as I abandon the flashcards and move on. "Get one of those books and I will read it with you."

"I don't read", says Robert, finally letting me know he at least has a voice.

"Okay, then. I guess I can read it to you, instead," I say, as Robert goes off to get his book. While he's gone, I start organizing the small pile of letter cards that Ms. Armstrong gave me to use. Robert has not returned after a moment, so I look up. He is not by the book bins. My eye catches him kicking the Legos that two students are building on the rug, causing a commotion.

"Robert, go back to the table with Mr. Patrick. Right now!" comes the disapproving voice of Ms. Armstrong. Robert has a book in his hand, too, and heads back toward me with that book. He sits back down when he reaches the table, putting the book between us, facing me.

"Can you tell me this book's title, Robert?" I ask, attempting to get another peep out of him.

He shakes his head, but says nothing.

"Okay, then I'll read the book," I say. "Can you tell me what the book is about or why you chose this one?"

"It's about trucks," Robert says, not indicating whether that's why he chose it or not.

"Great. I like trucks," I say. "Let's start with the front cover, which says Trucks, trucks, trucks as the title of the book." I proceed to read the whole book to him. It's just 10 pages long, each with about three words on it. That takes all of about two minutes.

"You want to try to read it to me?" I ask, thinking maybe he can read it now, since I just read it to him. He looks at me with those big eyes and incredible eyelashes, looking as though I just asked him if he'd like to ice skate. "No? Okay, just go back to your seat. Thanks for spending time with me today," I say, as if he just did something wonderful.

Ms. Armstrong has the rest of the class sitting on the rug, and gestures to Robert to join them. "That was fast! Ready for another student, Mr. Patrick?" she says, sounding a bit surprised we're talking again so soon.

"Oh, sure," I say, "as ready as I was for Robert!" I guess that doesn't sound very confident. But, frankly, I'm not feeling very confident.

The next student she sends to me is a girl named Roseanne.

She sits right down, picks up the pile of alphabet cards and starts putting them into alphabetical order. As she does this, I just watch. It's as if I am not even there, and she is playing a game of "organize the loose cards". She starts with the card with an A on it, says its name, then looks for the B card and says its name, and so on until she has them all in order. OK, so much for my first activity! I ask her to go get a favorite book to read, which she does without messing with other students along her path there and back.

"I'm gonna read you a story," she announces when she sits back down. She opens her chosen book and slowly turns each page, pointing to colorful pictures on each page and telling me the story. The words she is saying don't match most of what is printed on the page, but she is telling me a version of the story that the book and the pictures are about.

After she's done "reading" me her book, what can I say or do? "Thank you for reading to me," I say, sounding very lame.

I go through the "Robert charade" with two more students who can't do anything, and then Ms. Armstrong announces it's time for a bathroom break. I'm off the hook for the moment.

"Want to come to the bathroom with us, Mr. Patrick?" asks Ms. Armstrong.

"No, thanks," I say, wondering what the protocol is in kindergarten when asked by the teacher if you want to go to the bathroom break with them all. "I've got to get back to being a

musician. I'll see you tomorrow, after I maybe figure a few things out."
I grab my jacket and head to the door ahead of the messy lines of
kindergarteners ready for potty break.

As I get in my car, I'm thinking: Ouch! What am I doing here?
One student reads to me and organizes my cards. Three students give
me silence. I read to them, about six minutes apiece. Not so hot. What
did I think I could add to this scene?

Am I learning anything about how students learn, how classrooms
work, and what good teaching looks like? No, no, and not really.

Student Data Is Crucial

Wednesday, February 2

"Yesterday wasn't so great," I say to Ms. Armstrong the next morning before her students arrive. I seem to be getting into a pattern of spending most mornings at the school.

"I wondered," she observes. "It seemed to go pretty fast with each student. I appreciated that bit of time without those students turning everything inside out. I was also dealing with having a few of Ms. Gage's students again yesterday."

"You said that the day before, too. Is that some special program?"

Ms. Armstrong lets out a little harrumph. "I'm just helping her out some days when she needs to be late. She's got some issues at home. Don't we all?" I move on, aware that her students could come in at any moment, and I need some advice from her.

"Instead of me working with any students today, I could use some pointers about what else to try, so I can make a better plan for next time," I plead.

"I'm sorry we didn't have more time yesterday morning before you got started," she says. "Time is always against us! I could easily just give you more activity options."

"That would be helpful," I start. "But it also feels as though I need some kind of information about these students. That little boy, Robert, who you gave me first yesterday, couldn't do anything with me. He couldn't say the names of letter cards. He couldn't read the book he picked out. Nothing. He barely talked."

"I'm not surprised," she responds. "Still, I'm sure he was getting something out of just being read to by you for even a few minutes."

"I'm not so sure," I say. "The next little girl was just the opposite - - chatty, put all my letter cards into alphabetical order, then totally read me her favorite book. Wow! Made me feel like a huge success! Except it had nothing to do with me!"

"I sent you that girl, Roseanne, after Robert because you looked so dejected," Ms. Armstrong responds. "She's one of my stars, and a real classroom leader. She'll run the world someday, don't you think?"

"Oh, that explains a few things!" I say. "Thanks, I guess. Still it just made me realize that I don't know anything about what students know and how to teach each of them, when some of them are like Robert and some are like Roseanne. How do you do it? Is there some kind of information you look at?"

"What kind of information do you mean, exactly?" she asks me, seeming skeptical.

"I don't even know," I respond. "I hear schools do a lot of testing. Would any of that tell me something?"

"There's a big pile of tests and reports I keep in a file over there," she says, gesturing toward a beat-up file cabinet by her old wooden desk. "Go for it. Look at whatever you want here. But, for student confidentiality, you can't take any of it with you."

She goes and opens the top file drawer, revealing many manila folders stuffed with paper.

"Is this all on the computer somewhere, too?" I ask, not wanting to go through all that paper.

"Sure it is, but I'm old school and I print everything so I have a paper record in case a parent comes in or whatever. They make us test every student first thing in the fall, and at least two more times during the year," she says. "I have twenty years of experience. I know what a child can do once I've been his or her teacher for a few days. Tests only measure a small portion of what's really going on with any child."

"That's true, I'm sure," I say. "But I don't have your 20 years of teaching. Might it be good for me to have some idea of the test and what it might tell less-experienced people like me?"

Suddenly students are at the door and moving into the room, flinging backpacks on the floor by desks, chattering to each other excitedly, hugging Ms. Armstrong's legs.

"Okay, give me a minute to get things started with the students," she says, "then we can do a little testing demo for you to see. The bosses downtown will like that. More data they'll ignore or use to torture me."

With that, her day has begun for real. A flurry of activity gets morning routines taken care of: lunch money collected, attendance done, permission slips handed-in. She calls over the intercom for an aide to come from the office in ten minutes. Once the aide arrives, Ms. Armstrong puts the students to work coloring a drawing of the American flag.

"Now, we've got a few minutes. Let's test Billy first," she says to me. "Billy loves books and can read anything I put in front of him from our classroom library." Then she turns and is heading toward a boy working by himself at a table.

With the aide in the room to manage students, we take Billy out in the hall to a small table with two chairs at it. "I'll just stand," I say as Ms. Armstrong sits across from Billy.

Ms. Armstrong shows Billy a list of words, printed one word per line down the page. "Billy, start at the top and read down the page. Read any words you can. Don't worry about any words you can't read. Just do your best."

Billy reads the first word, then the next. He reads the whole list. I can tell, as he reads, that the words are easier at the top, then longer and more sophisticated as they get to the bottom. He reads them all, one by one down the page, occasionally slowing before saying one aloud, but marching surely to the bottom.

"Very good, Billy. Now let's look at a different list. These are not real words, not words you ever heard before. We call them nonsense words, because they don't make any sense. So, you just have to sound them out and say them, even though they don't make any sense. Ready?" He nods. "Good. Let me read the directions to you." She looks at her sheet and begins. "I would like you to read these make-believe words. Do your best reading. If you can't read the whole word, tell me any sounds you know." She places a sheet in front of Billy. "Put your finger under the first word. Ready, begin."

Billy looks at the list but says nothing for a few seconds. "I don't know any of these," he finally says.

"I know you don't," says Ms. Armstrong. "They are not real words that you have ever heard or seen before. Just try." Silence from Billy. After a few more silent moments, Ms. Armstrong says, "Can you tell me what sound any of these nonsense words begin with?"

"That one begins with a T," says Billy. "And that one starts with a B."

"Yes, thank you, Billy. That's all for now. You did great. You read lots of the words on that first list. How did you do that?" asks Ms. Armstrong.

"We have a reading game on the computer at home. All those words are on it."

"How much do you play that computer game?" asks Ms. Armstrong.

"Every day after school," says Billy. "It's really fun."

"Good, Billy," says Ms. Armstrong, running her fingers through his mop of blond hair. "Go back into the room and ask Melissa to come out next, please."

Once Billy is out of sight, Ms. Armstrong mumbles, mostly to herself, "That was weird. Billy can read anything in my classroom library, including books for 1st grade level readers. He read that list of real words with no trouble. Those last words on the page are 2nd and 3rd grade words. But he couldn't read any of those nonsense words." She seems perplexed. Then she looks at me, as if she had been talking to herself and just realized I was even there. "It doesn't really matter. Central Office makes us use that test. Why should we be testing 'nonsense?' We'd never teach nonsense. He was just confused, after we tell students all day that school is where we learn important things. Nonsense is what that test is!"

I'm pretty sure there's more going on with that test than just Billy being confused. But this is all new to me, and she's already moving on.

"Let's test one more student, so you can see another example." Ms. Armstrong says. "I haven't seen this girl read anything yet this year. I'm pretty sure she doesn't even know her letters. So, I'll use a different test for her initially, then try the one we used with Billy.

"Melissa, come work with me for a minute, please," Ms. Armstrong says in a friendly tone, popping her head back into the classroom.

A bright-eyed girl with one ponytail on the side of her head comes out in a moment and Ms. Armstrong ushers her over to the table. They both sit down.

"Melissa, we are going to do some activities to help me see how your reading is going." Ms. Armstrong gets out a set of cards. "Tell me the sound this letter makes," she says, holding up an "S" card.

"Ssss," says Melissa, quietly.

"Very good, honey," says Ms. Armstrong. "Let's do another," and she proceeds to go through the whole deck, probably 30 cards in all, with Melissa accurately saying the sounds for about 3/4ths of the letters she sees. Ms. Armstrong looks over at me at the end, eyebrows raised.

"You did that very well, Melissa," she says, as she puts away the letter cards and gets out the same sheet of words she showed to Billy. "Let's read some words now."

She shows Melissa the list of real words, and points to the first word at the top. Melissa says that word, slowly but accurately. "Very good. Now the next one?" Melissa sounds out the first letter of the next word, but does not say the whole word. She says the third word, slowly but accurately like the first, then can only say the first sound of the fourth word. Losing confidence as the words get harder down the page, she soon stops saying anything but the sound of the first letter of each word, as if that was the actual assignment.

"You are doing a good job, Melissa. Let's do one more activity, then we're done," says Ms. Armstrong, picking up another sheet with print on it. "I would like you to read make-believe words. Do your best reading. If you can't read the whole word, tell me any sounds you know." She places a list in front of Melissa. "Put your finger under the first word. Ready, begin."

Melissa looks at the list for a moment, concentrating on the first word. "Buh - i - mmm" she finally says, then waits a moment.

"Try to read the words as whole words. Keep going," says Ms. Armstrong. Melissa repeats the same process, slowly saying the sound of each letter in the next make-believe word. She continues this response for four or five more, until they get longer and harder. Then she stops. Ms. Armstrong waits three or four seconds, then prompts her again with, "Keep going." Melissa, now silent, looks up at Ms. Armstrong.

"Very good job, Melissa. Go back and get ready for math," says Ms. Armstrong.

After Melissa has left, Ms. Armstrong turns to me and says, "Well, that was a surprise, too. She knows the sounds that go with letters, pretty consistently. And she knows to at least try to sound out words by their letters, like she did in those nonsense words."

"If I was working with Billy vs. Melissa," I ask, "what would you tell me to do with them? The same stuff for each of them? Or different activities for each?"

"I'm still in shock at how those two students performed. I'll have to think some more about what I'd have you do."

"Okay," I say. "I'm out of here. See you in two days. Thanks for showing me the tests."

Analyzing Data

In college I sought out Frank Crisafulli to be my trombone guru. He was the legendary second trombonist of the Chicago Symphony. Old guy, didn't even own a computer. I had to call him once a week for three months until he finally said yes to scheduling a first lesson. Once I was trying to run my brass quintet after college, I found business consultant Ed Crego for monthly leadership coaching, which Grace took to calling "trombone lessons" in honor of Crisafulli. I know what it's worth to track down the best. To a person, they've generously rewarded my tenacity with their time and sage advice.

When I get home, I try Veronique, who may be my next source of "trombone lessons."

It takes me three calls, an email and two text messages to track her down this time. She finally has me call her back in ten minutes, so she can finish a call with someone in California. Or maybe her text is saying she's in California? Either way, once I get her on the line she apologizes and says she thought she'd hear from me again.

"Can you help me make some sense out of what I saw today?" I tell her my whole tale.

"I'm happy to talk, but I've got a call in 10 minutes with a Hollywood producer. Did you figure out an answer to the last question I asked you?" she asks, ignoring my current questions.

"Well, no. I'm working on that one by getting into some classrooms and seeing what's going on. I'm asking you new questions, as I work on your other question." I've really got no chance of answering her first question until I get some better idea of what I'm looking at in real classroom terms. Wait... Hollywood ?

"Okay, I've got ten minutes, or now only eight minutes," she starts, talking quickly. "From what you told me, including the part about that boy's mom and the computer program at home, that teacher and you learned something quite important today, and it's something the teacher didn't know by just teaching and observing in the classroom."

"What did we learn? Please, tell me!"

"For starters, you learned that individual student data is crucial to teaching, that without it even an experienced teacher may misdiagnose a student's reading skills. Then that teacher can't give that child what he or she specifically needs in order to progress."

"Huh?" I respond. "That boy today could read! Flat out, he was reading that list of real words. Even the 2nd and 3rd grade words. I think what we learned is that nonsense words are just that -- nonsense. They didn't tell us anything about that child's reading ability."

Veronique snorts. "You better research that some more. There's more there than you have figured out. Call me when you've got the answers next time."

"No, please, don't hang up on me," I say as quickly as I can. "I need a few more answers or I'm going down the tubes here. Give me a little more to work with, please!"

"Fine. It's right in front of your face, but you can't see it," she says. "When the teacher first showed you the testing, what did that student, the boy, struggle to do?"

"He couldn't read a single nonsense word."

"Right. And why not?"

"Well, he didn't say," I respond. "I have no idea, other than nonsense words are, uh, nonsense."

"Says you. And what did he say, about his computer game?"

"He said he could read all those other words because his computer game showed him words and told him what they sounded like."

"Right. I forget that you are not my undergraduate student anymore, just wanting to know if this will be on the final," she says, her voice softening just a bit. "You're not one of my consulting clients, either, getting paid to do this. You're doing this in your spare time, as if any of us has any spare time."

"I'm in way over my head, clearly. I'd appreciate any help you can give me." I say this in the most grown-up pleading voice I can muster.

"Well, it's likely that boy is very bright," she says, now sounding like she's my mother, "so he has memorized the connections the computer game showed him between the words he saw and the words he heard. He thinks that is all that reading is about.

But that's not reading, that's memorizing word shapes and spitting back the sounds. Those nonsense words are something he has never seen nor heard before. What happened with them?"

"He couldn't do any of them," I answer.

"And do we ever need to be able to see a new word and figure it out for the first time?"

"Not very much any more as adults," I say. "I know 99% of words I encounter. It would be incredibly slow to sound out every word I read these days."

"Sure. But when children have just started learning to read, they encounter hundreds of new words every day. Maybe thousands of new words, come to think of it. They have to be able to sound out lots of words and then match the sounds with words that might be in their spoken vocabulary. It's laborious for a child at that point. But the books are not War and Peace. They're short and high-interest about things a child loves to explore and think about, such as dogs and trucks and princesses. So, they're excited to do it, once they figure out that's how reading works. Then they memorize more words they've sounded out a first time or however many times it takes. More words in the repertoire means more books to read, which means more practice reading and more encountering new words. That adds more words to the repertoire. It's a virtuous cycle. Your little guy today thinks it's about memorizing without ever sounding out. What'd he say when the teacher asked him to tell her the sound of any of the letters in those nonsense words."

"Hmm. He said they started with a T and a B."

"Yes. Those are letter names, not sounds. That computer program probably has a game for letter names, too. But he had no idea how to connect individual letters to individual sounds. He just recognizes whole words he's memorized and their sounds. That's why the nonsense words are perfect for testing the concept a child must have, namely that letters represent sounds, and you can sound out a word you have never seen before."

"I think I'm beginning to see what you're talking about," I say. "What does all this mean for the teacher? She's still thinking nonsense words are nonsense. What does she do with these test results tomorrow in her classroom?"

"Those are great questions. Do you have any ideas for what it means for teaching that one student?"

"Geez, are we back to you having only questions?"

"You were never a lazy learner in college, Patrick," she says, pushing back. "Work for it."

"Okay, sorry. What do today's tests mean for teaching Billy? The teacher thought Billy could read just fine. But it turns out Billy has only memorized lots of words and their sounds. So, Billy needs to learn how to sound out words. How the heck does the teacher teach that?"

"You are making progress, so I'll give you one bit of help for that. Start with spoken sounds without any written letters. Can Billy hear the individual sounds in a spoken word? Say a word, maybe 'bat', with nothing written to look at. Ask him to tell you the first sound he hears in bat. If he says "buh," do some more words to determine if he just got lucky. Then ask him to tell you all three sounds when you say bat."

"What's the point of doing anything without written letters or words to look at?" I ask. "After all, isn't this about learning to read things that are written?"

"Yes, that's the real goal, of course," she responds. "But first it helps to have another concept firmly in the child's mind. To a young child, 'bat' might sound like one sound - 'bat'. But it's actually three sounds - the initial sound "buh," and the middle sound "a" like apple, and the ending sound "tuh". Understanding this, the child can more easily understand that individual letters represent those three sounds, rather than it's one spoken sound and there's no connection to printed letters."

I guess that makes sense, though I had long ago forgotten this.

"Once he can hear spoken letter sounds and segment them fairly rapidly, go back and show him flash cards with letters printed on them, and tell him what sounds they represent, one at a time. Have him echo you. Later, mix them up and ask him to generate the sounds without you saying them first."

"Generate?"

"Yes, say them out loud, in other words, without having just heard them from you."

"Okay, work with Billy on sounds, then letters for those sounds, then, let me guess, words?"

"Correct."

"Cool, and going from echoing to generating. Got it. But that teacher's got a whole room of students, maybe 25 or 30 kids. Do we have to test every student in order to teach everybody in the classroom? Or can a teacher just test the students she is not sure about?"

"Was that teacher unsure about Billy?"

"Good point. She was actually very sure about Billy, until she sat one-on-one with him and gave him those two tests. Then she was suddenly unsure about Billy."

"From our little talk here, can you help her be more sure about what that nonsense word test is telling her about Billy?"

"I think so," I say. "I hope so, at least. She's sure that she knows everything she needs to know, just from her 20 years of experience and from interacting with students in her classroom."

"I hope so, too, because she can teach Billy better if she realizes that the testing has given her teachable information about Billy. Her little testing demo for your benefit may lead her to be more willing to test all of her students."

"I agree," I say, trying to sound thankful. "That was all very helpful."

"Hold on," she says to me. I hear another phone buzzing, then I hear her say, "Hello, Marcello. Yes, this is Veronique. Can you hold while I end my other call, please?" Then she returns to talking to me.

"Good, Patrick. Call me again when you have figured out how the teacher can get more instructional time during the school day."

Band Rehearsal

"You promised you'd go to that community band practice tonight after dinner. Don't forget," says Grace as she is putting on her coat and heading out the door.

"I'm too busy for that," I say, trying not to sound like a jerk. I need a quiet evening to process the million thoughts swirling around in my head. I have been falling behind in brass quintet work, too.

"This was part of how we were going to become part of our new neighborhood, by you joining the community band and meeting some people there. I've got to go to a magnet school thing with Joey," and she's gone. Wait, she's going to magnet school meetings and taking Joey?

"What about dinner?" I mumble to myself. I know I'm crabby. I hate it when I'm crabby. No food in sight. I'll have to grab something later.

I trudge to the local high school, then wait for community band practice to begin, poking at my smart phone to try to catch up on a few quintet-related emails. Yes, I like playing in a group and making music. But I should be playing with other professionals, getting paid, not here with retired band directors and high school students.

The community band's conductor, Bill Camphouse, is new this year, I was told. He's even younger than me. He looks like he has never shaved. Woodwinds player, I hear. I've talked to him several times, scheduling dates for rehearsals. He is earnest, but I'm not entirely sure he has a firm grasp of what mostly-amateur musicians should be able to do in a band, nor how to get them to do it. As I look around after finishing an email, my suspicions are confirmed.

Everyone is either a high school student or a grey-haired retiree. I have not played with a group like this since I was in high school myself back in Oregon. Why did I come?

"Our first concert is next month, so thank you for being here," Bill says to the group. It looks like nearly everyone is here, judging from the numbers of players in each section versus the few empty chairs that remain. "Let's start with 'March in B-flat' to warm up."

The group plays through the whole piece under his direction, start to finish. Every now and then a unison section sounds like it needs some work to be more unified, or individuals are clobbering notes, or some portion is sadly out of tune.

When we end the march, the conductor looks intent. "That was pretty good," he lies, "but there are a few places where we need to do some work. Let's start at the top and I'll stop you when there's something we can do better." We begin again but don't get very far.

"Okay, stop everyone. Clarinets, in bar 16, you sound like you are playing some wrong notes. Or maybe it's the trumpets, who are supposed to be playing the same melody as you there. Let's start at measure 14 again and see if we can work it."

They start again, but now the playing sounds truly awful, like some have started in the wrong measure, and others are just playing the wrong notes.

"Ouch! That didn't help anything, did it?" says the now-frustrated conductor. "Clarinets, let's hear you all starting in measure 14." They start again, sounding like they are all playing different parts of a somehow-related melody. They stop after a few bars.

"Which is measure 14?" one of the clarinetists asks.

"That sounds like one of the problems. While you five clarinetists figure that out, let's hear the trumpets play the same melody, starting in measure 14."

The trumpets play, sounding a bit better than the clarinets. At least they are all starting on the same measure, but the melody is out of tune in several places. By this point, 15 minutes have gone by, just working on six or seven measures of this one piece of music.

"This was not at all going to be the focus of our rehearsal here tonight. We're supposed to be just warming up with this easy march so we can spend some real time on that fugue that is much more difficult. We don't have time to spend on the clarinets and then the trumpets and then the flutes for everything we're going to be playing tonight. Let's take a short break and try again in five minutes."

At the break, the conductor comes over to introduce himself to me in person. "Hi, we spoke on the phone. I'm Bill." He extends his hand. "Nice to meet you. Most of these musicians have been here before, so I wanted to make sure I introduced myself to you this evening. It's nice to have a real pro in the group. As you can hear, we've got some work to do before we can play our first concert next month. If you have any suggestions, I'd be all ears."

"I'm glad to meet you," I say in response to his kind introduction. His deference to me as a "pro" in the group is a good reminder, after spending my days at the elementary school encountering lots of things I know practically nothing about, that I know a thing or three about music and how it gets practiced and prepared for an audience. "It's your band. I don't want to step on your toes, or anybody else's, as the new guy in the group."

"No, really, I'm all ears," he says again. I guess he means it. "We can't afford to go over every eight measures of every piece with the trumpets, and then the same with the clarinets, and then the same with the flutes. We'll never get a concert ready."

"You've got quite a range of skills in each section," I say. "They all need different things. I'd be happy to take the trumpets and trombones for 15 minutes, to woodshed a few key parts of the march we were just working on, and even look ahead to the fugue. You could take the clarinets and flutes and do the same. Then we could put them all together again. That might help us work through a few rough spots with the various skill levels in each section."

"That sounds like a great idea," he says. I'm glad he likes this idea, given how many skill levels there clearly are in the band. Of course, now I have to work harder. That's fine.

So, after the break, he announces this plan to the group. I take the trumpets and trombones into a room nearby. They seem a bit skeptical - this is my first rehearsal, after all, so what am I doing suddenly leading a session with them. I quickly put any doubts to rest by starting right into a methodical working of the troublesome measures of music from the march.

"Trumpets, start at measure 14. Everyone know which measure that is? Rodney, can you show Maria? Tommy, you got it?" I'm so glad Bill had us put on name tags when we came in tonight. "Let's take it at half-speed, just to get the notes. Ready?" I count it off, nice and slow. The group plays a decent version of the next 12 measures of music, the same bit that had been bedeviling them and the clarinets in the whole group rehearsal. "That's more like it! Still some intonation issues in about bar 18 or so. Let's hear you one at a time, starting with Rodney." I picked Rodney, one of the only middle-age looking trumpeters, because he seems to be the one I hear playing the most-confidently through this passage when they are all playing at once. I figure he'll set a good example for the others.

"Very nice, Rodney. Maria, you next?" Maria looks to be a high schooler, probably less experienced. Maybe Rodney's example will have given her something to rise toward. Indeed, she sounds very good when she plays the passage. "Very nice, Maria."

We continue like this through the five trumpeters. I point out any sour notes or places where they need to watch the tuning. "Now let's do it all together again at half speed, then we can speed it up to full speed." It sounds much better at half speed this time, and we manage to do it several more times at increasing speeds until it sounds pretty darned good at full speed. When we stop, everyone is smiling and high-fiving each other.

"Very nice, folks. Let's go through a couple of other spots with the trombones, and take a quick look at any hard spots in the fugue, then go back in and show those clarinetists what we can do! Hopefully, they're ready, too!"

The rest of the rehearsal goes better than before, focused on refining the march and the fugue that we had practiced in our smaller trumpets and trombones group. Afterward, Bill Camphouse and I congratulate each other. "I sure hope you're coming next week, because your help really made a difference," he says, enthusiastically.

"Yea, that was fun," I say, "and it reminded me of some things I'd forgotten I knew."

After Rehearsal Chat With Grace

"Did you go to the practice?" asks Grace when I get home. I nod as I eat some cold pizza I found in the fridge. She continues, "How was it?"

"Really helpful," I say, trying for a friendly tone. Grace and I have been tip toeing around every conversation with each other since the cocktail party blow-up, neither of us wanting another fight.

"Helpful? You mean the band was good, and you met some neighborhood folks?"

"Well, sort of. The band is not very good, so that's kind of a drag. And the conductor's really young. He right away put me in charge of the brass section. That's going to be more like work than play at every rehearsal."

"What's the helpful part then?" she says, sounding skeptical. "I'm not even sure it matters, but it might be good to meet some neighbors. If we decide to move, they might know someone to buy our house."

She looks at me. I look at her. I pause a moment, then try again. "I did meet some neighbors, and I think some of them now think of me as a helpful kind of guy because I jumped right in and led the brass section rehearsal." I pause again, wanting to air my concerns but not inflame the conversation. "I wish we could stop moving so fast on this school thing. I feel pressured. Now it's a house thing, too. For me, that goes way beyond being just a real estate transaction."

She glances at me, then away. In all the time we've known each other, we have both prided ourselves on being good listeners, and on being willing to use what we hear to change what we think and what we do next. Sometimes it takes a few days. This whole thing is maybe the biggest rift we've ever had, and it's taking us longer to walk back to our normal selves.

Finally, I start again. "What I found helpful about band practice was that it showed me something about making our neighborhood school better, whether we send Joey there next year or not."

"Patrick, the chances of that are not good, based on what I've been hearing about that school." She's tiptoeing, just like me, keeping her voice calm. "I'm looking for other options."

"It's good for you to research other options, in case things aren't fixable at our local school. But are you open to hearing what the rehearsal reminded me of, and how it might be helpful at our local school?"

She looks at me, longer this time, and her face relaxes just a little. "Okay, but I'm not going to stop looking for something else just because there's some small chance that school will get fixed and everything will be just great there."

"I get it," I start. "What I've been struggling with is what could anyone do to help that school to improve? Let's face it, I'm just a trombone player. What do I know about how a school works, or even one classroom. I was in one yesterday, Ms. Armstrong's Kindergarten room, and I had no idea what I was looking at. There were students moving around doing this and that. It all seemed pleasant enough. But the school's scores are not good."

"First of all, you are a really smart and talented trombone player," Grace says, emphatically. "But those scores are what parents out here in the neighborhood see and how we judge the school. They freak us out, Patrick."

"I get that, too," I say quietly, gently taking her right hand in mine. "It's been really bugging me that I've somehow gotten myself involved at this school and I know nothing about how schools work.

Tonight's rehearsal was helpful, I'm saying, because it reminded me of what I do know in this world, which is music and how to properly rehearse with a group of musicians so they all get good at it. Maybe some of those same things might work for helping students get good at reading."

"I know we both love music, " she replies, and I see in her eyes the woman I married, full of love for me, for music, and for all the arts. That gruff mama bear confronting the threat to her only cub, our son, recedes for a moment. "What else did you want to tell me about the rehearsal?"

"I really was looking forward to talking with you about tonight's practice," I start, hoping we are ready to have a real conversation. "Here's what it got me thinking. A school has to teach students to read, right? And each teacher has 25-30 students she has to teach to read. That's a lot of students to be managing all day, trying to give all of them what they need."

"But what's the connection to band?"

"Tonight, the conductor had this same issue -- 30 people whom he is supposed to help move ahead and help learn to do something individually, yet together. So, like the teacher, what is the conductor to do, especially in a community band with so many levels of players? Helping one player while 29 others wait is a waste of time for 29 people. But just having all 30 do the same passage over and over and not stopping to give feedback is also a waste of time."

"So, what's the solution?"

"Small groups, or what musicians call sectional rehearsals," I answer. "Take the three or four who are similar, say the trumpeters, and work with just them, while the rest of the band does something else, such as have a woodwinds sectional."

"I think I see where you're going with this," Grace says.

"Here's what else I remembered. There are ways to run those sectionals that make them more-productive than just running through the notes in a smaller setting."

"Like what?"

"For one, tonight I had this capable older guy named Rodney play first during the sectional, to set a good model for the other, less capable players to hear. Then I had the other players try. Here's another thing. I gave the players feedback after they each played a short piece of the music. They got immediate feedback. Other players could hear the playing and hear the feedback before they then played, too. So there were lots of practice and feedback loops."

"This takes me right back to my dancing days," Grace responds, looking wistful.

"One other little music trick that was helpful," I say, playing to my now-receptive audience, "is that we went from doing any section slowly, then speeding it up until we could play it at the speed it was written to go." I'm feeling again like I actually know something and have made an important connection.

"Sounds like you did have some fun at band practice," Grace says. "How, exactly, are you going to apply that to the school?"

"Basically, I want to see if what I remembered about how 30 people learn to play a piece applies to how 30 students in a classroom might learn to read," I say. "Ms. Peterson, the upper grades science teacher, challenged me to figure out what good teaching looks like in kindergarten and whether that kind of teaching is going on or not at our school. We're making a plan for how to entice more parents to send their kids to our school's kindergarten next fall."

"It's not 'our' school until they convince me it's good enough to send our only child, our Joey Jomo, there next year," Grace insists. But she's smiling, finally. She'll be customer number one to sell.

Small Groups

Friday, February 4

"Mrs. Armstrong, I want to try something in your classroom today," I announce two days later as I enter her room before students arrive.

"Instead of one student at a time, can I have four students at first today?"

She looks at me a moment longer than usual. "If that's what you want, it's fine by me. I'll just keep doing my thing, either way. You've got a plan?"

"Yes, this time I've got a plan," I say. "It's based on my experiences as a musician, plus a few ideas from the Internet."

It actually feels like trying a new cooking recipe. I created it by reading other recipes and combining ideas. Of course, it's the first time I'm making this, and I've invited 30 little people over for dinner.

"Want me to look it over before you try it?" she offers.

"Thanks, but I think I'd like just to learn by doing this time," I say, wanting to jump in and give it a try. Besides, I haven't seen her doing small groups in her classroom, so I'm not sure what she'd have to offer me there.

"This should be interesting then," she says, taking a step back and sitting on one of the small student chairs.

I want to try teaching students as if they are a "band," and use "sectionals" to do it. For content in these small groups today -- these "sectionals" -- I'll show students flashcards with something written on

119

them and ask them to say what's printed there, similar to what Ms. Armstrong showed me for tutoring.

I've written some words I want them to know onto the flashcards, from the book we'll be reading. We'll practice those words, one flashcard at a time. Then I'm going to have them play a simple game: see the flashcard, say the word on it, you get the flashcard, and see who has the most cards at the end of the game. The Internet says kids this age like games. At the end, we'll read the book together that I've picked, as relaxation after the hard work. Skill practice, then a game about that skill, then read a book. Skill, game, book. Let's do this.

"Can I have Billy, Melissa, Robert and Roseanne for my first group?" I ask Ms. Armstrong.

"Sure. Are those just the four students whose names you know?" she asks, somewhat sarcastically. Hmm. She's not usually sarcastic.

"I figured I know them a little, so I'll start with my best foot forward," I say, feeling a little defensive. "I can take other students next time, once I work out any kinks."

"Okay," she says, "it's your plan."

"Thanks," I say, glad she's not hassling me more about missing pieces of my plan.

"What do you want to do with the other students during your plan?" she asks, sounding as though she had more to say but decided not to. Geez, I hadn't even thought about the other students.

"Good point," I say, trying not to be too defensive. "I guess I figured you'd be doing something with them anyway during this time, just like when I'm tutoring. No?"

"All right then, I'll just carry on as usual." She gets up from her small chair and heads toward a group of students who just entered the classroom. I head to the table where I planned to work today and begin laying out materials for my lesson.

The students all arrive, she settles them into their desks and chairs, does the morning routines of attendance and lunch money and homework papers getting handed in. Now it's time for her to start some teaching and for my first small group.

Ms. Armstrong calls out the names of the four students I requested, and they head to my table at the back of the room.

The four sit. Roseanne right away starts organizing some cards I have out. Robert is quiet, as are Billy and Melissa, whose shoe Robert has accidentally kicked.

I lead them through the first part of my plan, which introduces the skill I want them to work on today. I show them a flashcard, I say the word on it, and then they say that word. I'm guessing this is a lot like Billy's computer game. The four of them seem to be doing fine with this part, though Roseanne is definitely leading and loudest in her responses, while Robert is quickly looking around the room. I have to say his name to pull his attention back to the task at hand.

"Students, let's use these same cards to play a little game," I say to introduce the next portion of the day's plan. "I'll hold up a card and whoever says the word first gets to put the card in your pile of cards. Ready?"

I shuffle the order of the cards from before, then show the first card.

"Balloon," says Roseanne.

"That's right," I say and hand her the card. She beams, while Robert scowls and kicks her shoe again under the table. Melissa and Billy wait for the next chance to guess.

"Woman," says Roseanne, again beating the other three to the right guess.

"That's right again," I say. "Roseanne has two. You other three pay attention and you'll get some next."

It goes on this way for the remainder of the deck of flashcards, with Roseanne getting ten cards in her pile and the others getting none. I even try slanting the cards away from her and more toward Billy and Melissa and Robert, but she still wins them all. Roseanne is regularly offering to give Melissa some of her cards. Billy is sitting quietly and looking around the room. Robert is routinely kicking all three other students under the table, and I have twice had to pull him back into his chair when he has started to get up to leave.

The final part of my lesson plan is the reading of a book. I am especially looking forward to this part. After all, what kid doesn't like being read to or even getting a chance to read along?

"Students, I have five copies of a favorite book of mine. We are going to read it together." I glance at my watch. Twenty three minutes have gone by. I planned for each group to take 20 minutes, and to do two in a 40-minute time slot. "We only have a few minutes more, so let's just all read it one time through."

"What's this book about?" asks Roseanne, always wanting to take charge.

"Well, let's see what we can tell from the front cover," I say, trying to pre-engage them in the story by looking at the picture of three people, two animals, and some balloons. Roseanne's question starts a flood of questions about the book and the front cover picture. I finally just have to open the book and start reading.

"Read along with me," I say after the second page. None of them is reading aloud with me, except Roseanne. I read the next page and nobody reads aloud with me, except Roseanne. Oh, well, no time to stop and fix that today, we're already at 28 minutes. Actually, it's just Roseanne and Melissa now. Robert is back in the main group with Ms. Armstrong, causing trouble with another boy who is crying. Melissa is still gamely turning the pages of the book we are reading whenever she sees me turn a page. Billy? Where has Billy gone to?

"The end!" I say after six more pages. I close my book, then reach to collect the students' books. "You two can go back to your seats."

That was much harder than I thought it would be. The whole thing took 29 minutes, so I'm stuck without enough time to do another small group today in my 40 minutes. That will have to wait, if Ms. Armstrong gives me another chance to try. Here she comes toward me.

"That didn't go exactly as planned," I say, as I pick up my small group materials and try not to come off as discouraged as I feel. I had a plan, it didn't work, and I'm wondering why not.

"I figured," she says. "Robert was over with me about halfway through and Billy came too by the end."

"Right, and Roseanne was the only one who could read the words and the book I took the words from," I respond, hoping Ms. Armstrong will have some kind of answer to what went wrong and how I might do it better.

"Can I see the book?" she asks. I hand her a copy. "There's your first problem. This is not a kindergarten book. It's too hard for all of them, except Roseanne, who shouldn't have been in the same group as those other three anyway."

"I was hoping Roseanne would be a good model for the other three," I say, thinking of Rodney the trumpeter at last night's band practice, "and she'd help them all rise to the challenge."

"How'd that go for you?" she responds, slightly consoling but slightly "I-told-you-so."

"Not so well, for sure," I say, feeling chastised. "Sounds like you've got some ideas for how my plan could be improved?"

"I like your spunk, and your willingness to jump right in and try. I'll give you that, Mr. Musician," she says with a twinkle in her eye, honed from years of encouraging young learners who have failed in their attempts to do something harder than they thought it would be. Great… in her eyes I am just another kindergartner.

"I've been thinking about our testing the other day and how confusing the results were for me. I've got a couple of possible ideas for how to make your plan work better next time," she continues.

Well, I'll be darned! She's already made me realize I forgot all about what we discussed from Veronique about using student test data. I shouldn't have put those particular four students together. Then I chose a book that was too difficult. Probably I chose words for my flashcards that were too hard. It all took too long, so that's another thing to fix somehow.

"I'm actually, well, excited about your small groups idea," she continues, "just from watching you from across the room this morning. I've been wanting to try that myself, but somehow never actually got around to doing it. Maybe now I will."

The big shocker is that she seems to be interested in my little experiment.

"Come back on Monday and let's try it again, with a few changes," she says with a little lilt in her voice. "Still game?"

"That would be great, but I can't Monday," I respond, trying not to squash her enthusiasm. "I'm on a road trip for a music gig at the beginning of the week. How about later next week?"

"That'll work," she says. "Maybe I'll try a few of my ideas."

"Of course," I say. "That would be great. I'll be back on Thursday morning then."

"Good. See you Thursday," she says, almost skipping across the room.

Serving The Homeless

Friday, February 4

I couldn't stay in Ms. Armstrong's classroom because I promised Grace I'd help out at the soup kitchen where she volunteers. I'm on the road a few days this coming week, so I'm trying to be helpful to Grace wherever I can.

I'm a willing volunteer, don't get me wrong. My parents were big on helping others. They dragged me along to all sorts of their volunteer gigs when I was young. In high school, I found my own ways to make the world a little nicer, such as playing Christmas carols at the senior center on Christmas Eve. Somehow it all became my thing instead of my parents' thing. Once Grace and I were a couple in college, it became something we eagerly did together.

"Hi, hon. You're serving guests today," Grace says, giving me a quick kiss. "Grab an apron and wash your hands. We're just about done cooking and ready to serve."

"What's for lunch today?" I ask, putting on an apron.

"Beef stroganoff on noodles, green beans and a salad and roll," Grace says. "Plus cake and ice cream for dessert. No food for the servers and cooks, just good karma." Knowing they never let volunteers eat the food, I had grabbed a sandwich on the way over.

On a budget of $210 per week, Grace and others cook and serve a three course meal to 64 homeless men and women. The money comes from two churches, a synagogue and a mosque, one per week of the month. I find that low cost for so many meals remarkable. Grace helps chop and wash and cook most weeks. I am always a server, when I can be there at all. I like taking plates of hot, delicious food out to hungry and appreciative people.

A rabbi says a heartfelt blessing over the guests and volunteers and food. Someone then rings a little bell and we servers begin delivering eight plates of food to each table. Not only do the guests get delicious and nutritious food, but they get it served to them just like a restaurant, a real treat. This respect for the guests is returned – mostly – by all of them waiting to take their first bites until everyone has their food in front of them. Of course, I've been told more than once to be careful not to drop any bread rolls on the floor, lest they disappear, leaving us short.

The guests have to register in person on Monday for the Friday lunch. That level of personal organization and self-management means this lunch program gets the higher functioning homeless, Grace has told me. I'd say about half are regulars whom I see every time I'm here. Grace says many sit in the same seat every week. It makes sense, I suppose, to find people you can get along with and then stick with them.

"Young man, can you help me?" asks one of the older female guests near me, as I am clearing the first plates so we can deliver salads next. "I just got this new medicine from the clinic, and I don't remember whether I take one or two pills three times a day."

She gestures for me to step closer and bend to her seated level. I've learned to be cautious in this kind of situation, as the guests often have pungent odors from many nights on the street.

"Can you read this for me?" she says, quietly, once I have knelt and my ears are at her level. She hands me a prescription bottle.

"If your eyes are bad, we could get you a referral for an eye exam and some free glasses," I say, thinking of the free clinic nearby. I start looking at the small type for a dosage amount.

"My eyes are fine. It's my reading – never had any," she says quietly.

"I can't read neither," says the woman sitting next to her, matter-of-factly.

"Well, you've got me for that for the moment," I say. "This bottle says take one pill just once per day. It has a warning – don't take more than once per day. And take them for ten days, even if your symptoms go away first. Good thing you asked. Did they tell you this when you got these pills?"

"That's one thing that has gone bad -- my memory," says the first woman again. "I don't remember what they said."

"How are you going to know to just take one pill per day, if you can't read and your memory's bad?" I ask. "Am I going to have to worry about you now?"

"Oh, aren't you sweet," she says, blushing slightly. "I've had to remember stuff all my life. I reckon I'll tie a string around my finger or something."

A tap on my shoulder makes me stand. Grace is there with salad bowls for eight. "Time to stop flirting with my husband, ladies, and let him clear your plates for salad." With that she begins putting bowls in front of guests, and I take my tray of dirty plates to the kitchen.

I go back out and stand to one side, watching the guests all eat their salad course. After a minute, Grace comes and stands beside me. "You really charmed those two ladies, young fella."

"They scare me," I say. "One's got a prescription that she's only supposed to take once a day. But she can't read and she can't remember. She could get hurt."

"Do this work long enough and you realize you can't fix all these people's problems," Grace says, moving a little closer to me and looping her hand around my arm.

"Could someone have fixed it when that lady was Joey's age?" I ask, not really expecting an answer.

Small Groups Success

"I couldn't do small groups by myself unless there was something else for the other students to do," says Ms. Armstrong as soon as I walk in the door of her classroom on Thursday morning. It's like she's been standing by the door, waiting for me to walk in. "So I created some learning stations for them to go to and do work by themselves or in small groups of two to six students."

Small groups? Learning stations? I should go away more often!

"That sounds terrific," I say, as I take off my coat.

"The students were a little confused at first and were just goofing around at the learning stations," says Ms. Armstrong, sounding eager to tell me all about her past few days. "That was with me walking around to monitor them and all. I wasn't even trying to do my own small groups on that first day or two. So I stopped them, and we had a class meeting about it all. I helped the students set some simple rules and guidelines for the stations. We decided that they should be for work, not just play. So, we renamed them 'work areas' to make that clear. Then we started again."

Class meetings? I've not seen her do that before. She's like a changed person. I am already learning a lot from her.

"Wow, how'd that second try go?"

"Well, we didn't go as long -- just ten minutes," she says. "We've worked up to 20 minutes at a time, but it took a couple of days to get there. They just needed some practice. We talked about it after each time. I hated that it took several days that I could've been doing other teaching. Hopefully it'll be worth it, now that they can work on their own and I can take a small group by myself."

"That sounds amazing!" I gush, unable to hide my enthusiasm.

"Of course," she quickly points out, "there are several students who are often trying to cause trouble, but even they're getting better. You want a group, Mr. Traveling Musician?"

"Can I just watch today, before I try again?" I ask, humbled by all she has done.

"Sure," she says readily, "but I've only been getting to do my own small group since yesterday, so I'm sure there is a lot left to figure out. For one, I haven't had any who got to do the book part at the end. We always run out of time. That's a shame, since I think actual reading is the most important part!"

"Why not do the book at the beginning?" I ask. "You make sure it gets done that way."

"That might work," she says, seeming a little surprised by my simple suggestion. "I guess I was just doing the sequence you did. Good idea, partner!"

So, I watch her get her students into their new work area configurations. Some are at tables working with paper and pens. One group is on the rug with a bin of blocks building a tower.

Then she calls the names of four students and has them join her at the table near the back of the room. She sits where she can see the whole room, while the four students have their backs to the other students working and moving in the rest of the classroom. Smart! She can intervene in any classroom problems that come up, and her four students are less-distracted by the rest of what's going on in the room.

None of these issues came up when I led the brass sectionals at band practice. We just went into another room. Of course, they were all at least high school age and they had all chosen to be there to do something they enjoyed. Classroom management turns out to be critical with a bunch of 30 five and six year olds. Duh!

Her small group runs much smoother than mine did, with each student paying attention, four students all reading a book together at the start, then competing for a share of the flashcards. It takes 24 minutes by my count, but what a big success!

Afterward, we talk about what I just saw. "Really great, and in just the few days since I was last here. So much better than what I tried," I say, again feeling humbled.

"Well, your attempt inspired me," she replies. "I could see what I'd change, which made me excited to try it myself. So, thanks for the inspiration."

She tells me she used the data from the tests, like the ones I saw her give Billy and Melissa, to form small groups that needed work on the same skills. She found multiple copies of some books and other materials that pretty much matched her first few groups' learning levels and needs.

"If you come back tomorrow, I can give you your own small group," she offers, looking eager to see me try again.

"I'm up for that," I say.

That's how it began. We spent the next week implementing small groups together in her room. It felt good to be succeeding, finally. It's not what I went to music school to do, but it has many satisfying moments to it -- when a child figures something out for the first time and has a look of profound happiness on her face, when a child "wins" who has never won at anything before, when two children cooperate to help each other learn. It's all truly good.

What's The Whole Day?

Friday, February 18

"What are you and Ms. Armstrong doing?" says Mr. Bevington in the hallway following a week of success in Ms. Armstrong's room. He doesn't look happy. Not that he ever looks happy.

"We're doing lots of small groups for reading instruction," I say. "Is something wrong?"

"Her students' scores on the monthly test are not good. Whatever you're doing isn't working. Figure it out or I'm pulling the plug." With that, he pushes by me and down the hall.

Strange to hear, as Ms. Armstrong and I have been working so well together. I thought I was seeing real improvement in my four students, and we were ready to move to the next skill.

Instead, I'm headed to her room to share bad news and figure out a solution.

"I don't know what he's talking about," is her response. "I've been seeing good progress with my students, especially the ones you and I are meeting with in small groups."

"I agree. Could it be something about the other students that are dragging down the reading results? Could it be something about the test he mentioned?"

"I have no idea," she says, sounding worried. "Maybe these small groups are not enough."

"I don't know either. He's going to pin all bad things on us and our small groups. Plus, I was thinking we might showcase our small groups and work areas at that parent night."

"Maybe it's something else," she confides. "Could you sit in my classroom on Monday morning, from the start until lunch, and see what you notice?"

"I'm not sure your confidence in my ability to spot things is justified."

"Sometimes another set of eyes, even a naive set like yours," she says with a surprising fondness, "is all that's needed to spot something."

"You are too kind," I answer. "But I'm game, if you are."

"Ok, let's do it then," she says, sounding confident.

Grace's Computer

Grace is at the front door when I get home Friday evening. "I'm so glad you're home, Patrick. Can you help me with my computer? I'm trying to register for evening classes."

"You're doing what?"

"I'm trying to register to complete my master's," Grace says again.

"Wow, that's huge," I say, not aware she was thinking anymore about finishing her master's. She started it right after we both graduated and got married. But then Joey came along, and some things got put on hold. "Why now?"

"You mean why now, it's dinnertime? Or why now, it's five years since I last attended any classes?"

"Five years since you last attended."

"I'd like something more stable than being an artist-in-residence the rest of my life."

"Don't you need the flexible schedule of freelance gigs?" I ask.

"Joey will be in school, somewhere, in the fall, Patrick. I want to be ready for whatever comes next. But I can't get the registration website to load."

"Let's take a look," I say, still grasping what she has just said. A lot will change when Joey goes to kindergarten. Grace has never said she was tired of doing dance work in schools.

"I have to write a letter asking to be re-admitted because I've been gone so long," she says. "I have to upload it onto the college's registration site."

"That doesn't sound hard," I respond, as sweetly as I can muster after an exhausting week. Things have been better between

133

Grace and me lately, and I don't want to screw that up again.

"Something's not working. You're more patient than me," she admits.

"Let's just do it together," I say, trying to get to the relaxing part of my evening -- taking off my coat, sitting down, sipping a beer.

"That works for me," she says. I do take off my coat, as she pulls another chair over to the table where she has her laptop open and a bunch of papers laid out.

"You've got Donna, who you can call any time something's not working. That's what I need, too," says Grace. Donna's my friend from college who's a computer whiz.

"I'm just willing to stay with it longer than you are. And, yes, I have Donna," I say, as she pokes a few keys and her screen lights up.

"I need my own Donna!" she says, as I sit next to her.

"I'll be your Donna," I offer, and give her a little squeeze. "Show me where it hurts."

"Aren't you sweet," she says, punching me in the arm as she calls up a very complicated-looking college website on her browser. "Here's what hurts. Can you fix it?"

How To Observe A Classroom

Saturday, February 19

After my first good night's sleep in a while, I'm lying in bed late on Saturday morning. I can hear Grace and Joey in the living room, playing together. I lie here a bit longer, enjoying the happy sounds and the chance to think.

After a pleasant reverie, my thinking turns to the practical. What else is going on all day in that classroom? Sure, I am working with my four students for 20 minutes, as is Ms. Armstrong with her four, and we both see it's making a difference for those students. But her principal says whatever we're doing isn't working, because he's not seeing any test progress. Why is that?

I have no idea what to look for and what to make of what I am seeing. I decide to call Veronique again, even though I haven't got an answer for her last question yet. I quietly dial her number on my cell, hoping to ask a quick question before Grace or Joey know I am even up.

"Hmph... hello," comes an unfamiliar female voice.

"Veronique? This is Patrick," I say softly, wondering if I have a wrong number.

"What time is it?" the voice asks, sounding a bit more like Veronique, but sleepy.

"It's ten o'clock," I say. "I have another question I need..."

"In the morning?" she asks, sounding like the real Veronique, but upset. Silence. "I told you not to call again until you have some answers. I'm hanging up..."

"No, please. I need to observe in a classroom to find your answer," I plead as quietly as possible. "How do I do that?" I feel so subversive, hiding away in the bedroom, using my covert-ops voice.

She waits for about ten seconds, all while I'm holding my breath hoping she won't hang-up. I hear sounds like she's rolling over in bed, then what sounds like the clicking on of a lamp.

"It's 2:00 in the morning on Sunday here," she says. There's another long pause. She's mumbling something under her breath that I can't understand. Finally she says, "You've got three minutes. Any more and I'll be too awake."

In my same covert-ops voice, I explain that I'm going to observe Ms. Armstrong's classroom on Monday. Then I whisper my question: "What should I be looking for when I observe this classroom?"

"Look for who is actually doing what," she says. "What is the teacher doing? What are the students doing? All the students or just some of them?"

"How do I do that with 30 students?" I ask, hesitantly.

"Simple Excel chart, with all the students' names across the top and five minute increments down the left side. Sit in the back of the classroom and record which students are being taught by the teacher at any time. If only one or two students are being taught, put an X in the boxes of those one or two students. Draw a line straight across the page from left to right if all the students are being taught."

"What if some kid is looking out the window while the teacher's teaching?" I ask. I'm not hearing any sounds from the living room anymore. Perhaps Grace took Joey outside?

"You are recording what the teacher intends to be teaching, and I mean directly teaching, not handing out worksheets and then sitting at her desk and correcting papers. Got it? Nighty night." That was very helpful.

Joey Reads In The Car

"Let's go for a drive," says Grace, about 1 o'clock that afternoon. I finally got up, we had what Joey calls a "French toast morning," and now the day must begin for real. "Get some groceries, get out of the house, maybe look at a new sink for the powder room. That one's still not draining right."

Grace and I several years ago made an agreement, for her sake and for my sanity, that I can have all kinds of crazy hours during the week, between playing school gigs and professional rehearsals and trombone practice at home. But weekends are for two things only: family time and whatever paying performing gigs either of us get called to do in the evenings. If I don't have a paying gig on a weekend, I squeeze in some more trombone practice, trying to keep my chops together and ready for any orchestra audition that might show up. But the rest of the weekend is for each other.

We pile into the car, strap Joey into his booster seat in the back, and we're off. I'm driving and Grace is looking at some mailer from the grocery store for what's on sale. Is this how it's going to be for the next 30 years -- work hard all week, jump in the car and do errands all weekend, play music gigs at night, collapse into bed, repeat? I could get an orchestra job someday and be mainly working at night, with days off. Joey will be a teenager in eight more years, so he probably won't want to do this anymore then. So, basically, no. This is not how it's going to be for the next 30 years. "So, enjoy it while you can, folks," I hear my dad's voice saying to me.

As we are driving along, Joey is quietly singing some song in his car seat. I hear him every now and then stop singing and start going "buh, buh" or "puh, puh" instead, still fairly quietly. Then he goes back to singing. As we approach the next stop sign, he says "Dad, what sound does the letter on that sign make?" This startles me. We have done the reading games in the tub several more times since I introduced them two or three weeks ago, but that's just in the tub. Plus, the games so far don't have any words, just individual letters and their sounds.

"Which letter, Joey?" I ask, exchanging glances with Grace in the front seat.

"That first one, on the red sign," Joey says, pointing out the right side window.

"That's an S," I say. "It makes the Ssss sound."

"What about the next letter?" he asks.

"It makes the Tuh sound," I say, realizing what he's doing in his little head now.

He says "Ssss, tuh, aww, puh." Then he sits quietly for a moment, as someone honks a horn behind us and I start through the intersection.

"That sign says 'stop', Daddy," he says. I look again at Grace, who is smiling.

"Yes, it does, buddy," I say proudly. "You just did reading."

"I did?"

"You sure did. Want to do it some more?" So we do, with Joey finding signs along the road and on storefronts. Pretty soon I'm turning down new streets just to find more signs for him to read. When there's a letter he doesn't know yet, he asks and I tell him the sound it makes. When there's a weird word that is too hard for him -- he can't do Lee Street or Lemoy Plumbing, it turns out, on his first day of reading -- I point him to an easier sign nearby.

After 30 minutes of this, Joey suddenly says, "I'm tired," and conks out in his car seat. Grace and I silently high-five each other. Our kid is reading! Maybe the next 30 years just got a little easier.

Ms. Armstrong Observation Morning

Monday, February 21

Monday morning here I am, walking up to the school with my brand new chart in hand, ready to observe Ms. Armstrong's classroom. It's maybe 8:35. I figured I'd see what happens even before the students show up, and talk to Ms. Armstrong to make sure she's still comfortable with my sitting in the back of her room.

The clerk at the main office seems a little surprised to see me. "The teachers are all in the library for a meeting. You want to see Mr. Bevington instead?"

At that moment he walks out. "Hello, Patrick. You here again? Can't get enough, right?"

"Remember how you weren't sure what's going on in Ms. Armstrong's room? Well, I'm here to see what I can detect by observing for the whole morning."

"If that's what you want to do, go ahead. But it's not working, from what I can tell. Sorry, gotta run. The teachers are all waiting for me in the library for my 8:30 meeting." I look at my watch after he turns to leave – it's 8:40 now.

I may as well go to the classroom and get set, so I can grab Ms. Armstrong for a minute before the students show up. I head to her room. It's locked. There are two students standing outside already, though I know they are not supposed to be in the building until the bell rings. I don't know either of these students, so I don't put them on the spot with any conversation or "probing adult questions."

It's five minutes before the hour, then 9 o'clock straight up, then five minutes past. So I go up to the closed library door on the second floor, to see if the teachers and principal are all still in there.

They are, from what I can see through the tiny window. I turn and go back downstairs. As I pass the front door of the school, I look outside – students are all out there, throwing their coats at each other like weapons and generally running wild.

At about 9:20, I hear adult voices and start to see teachers coming down the stairs. Eventually, Ms. Armstrong appears at her classroom, where I am standing by the door with the two of her students who somehow got into the building. A bell rings, and more student voices can be heard from down the hall and around the corner. Ms. Armstrong has her keys out, unlocks the classroom door as all her students suddenly are upon her and opening and slamming lockers in the hallway and chattering noisily. "Put your coats away and let's go. We are already late, so hurry it up and be quiet about it," she says, assuming command.

"Ms. Armstrong, remember I'm going to sit in your classroom this morning and just watch? It would be helpful to have a list of your students' names and reading scores, so I can keep track of which students are doing what. Okay?"

"I remembered you were coming. Everything is a jumble at the moment. Do whatever you want and I'll do my thing, too. Here's my class roster, organized by reading scores already, not alphabetically. Need a chair?"

"I'll just find a chair in the back, out of your way." I wait for Ms. Armstrong to get all the students in the door. Then she heads to the front of the room by her desk. I grab one of those mini kindergartner chairs from a desk in the back row, and pull it to the very back. As Ms. Armstrong takes students' homework papers from them, and records attendance on the computer by her desk, I write each child's name across the top of my chart, highest readers on the left and lowest on the right, one per column.

Finally, Ms. Armstrong tells the students it is time to do the "daily routines." She starts with the Pledge of Allegiance, then they all sing the national anthem as the accompaniment plays through the school loudspeakers in every room. She asks the students to change the little weather and date and day of the week signs on a pre-made board she must have bought at some teacher store.

At 9:30 she tells them all to move to the rug, "to start our reading lesson." Moving takes five minutes, I note, while then noting that it is 9:35 and I have not yet written a single X for direct instruction in any child's little square.

She begins the lesson from her perch on an adult-sized rocking chair that looks very comfortable while her students sit cross-legged on the floor. Several girls are very close to me at the back of the rug. Ms. Armstrong opens a large textbook, teacher's edition it looks like, and begins to read from it. It is a reading lesson, something about a story. She asks the students questions every now and then as she reads.

One student, Jeremiah, is causing Ms. Armstrong all kinds of trouble from the moment the lesson begins. I have not seen him in her classroom before, so perhaps he is new, or has been absent a lot? After five minutes, at about 9:40, she stops to deal with Jeremiah. She moves him back to his desk, which I notice is all by itself by the front blackboard. She then starts putting materials of some sort onto several tables all around the room, apparently abandoning her other lesson. I note this takes another five minutes, and I cannot put any X's into boxes while she does this. (So far, I have put an X in the 9:35 box and drawn a line straight across, indicating she was teaching all students at once for five minutes.)

With nothing to do but watch, my eye catches things about Ms. Armstrong I had not noticed before, including a long thread that keeps dangling onto her big book. This leads my eye to the source of that thread, a frayed seam on one sleeve. Looking farther, I see her shoes are scuffed on the toes, and Ms. Armstrong has a nasty-looking bruise on one arm. I write a note: Teaching takes a physical toll.

Ms. Armstrong announces, "It's small group time." The students seem to know exactly what to do when they hear this. They set about rearranging the room, putting desks into groupings of four to create new "tables" around the room and start doing things together at each new table area.

Ms. Armstrong calls out "Anjari, Anasia and Jeremiah, join me at the small group table." Anjari and Anasia leave their tables immediately and come to her kidney-shaped small group table where there are four child-sized chairs on one side and one teacher-sized chair on the other side. Jeremiah does not move from his isolated desk at the front of the classroom, so Ms. Armstrong goes on without him, teaching the other two students with flashcards and small books, as I've been seeing her do for the past week or so.

I find the two girls' names on my chart and start putting X's under their names at the 9:45 row. Jeremiah joins the small group at 9:50, after he is beckoned again by Ms. Armstrong with a threat to call his mother if he does not comply. Once at the table, Jeremiah is not at all cooperative and is causing disruptions to the two girls who were putting some effort into what they were being asked to do until Jeremiah showed up.

Looking for their names, I see that these three are the three lowest readers in this classroom, occupying the three columns on the far right of my sheet. Ms. Armstrong hands out three copies of the same small book, and she reads it to them as they try to put their finger on the words she is reading. Next she shows them flashcards with individual letters and asks them what sound each represents. Ms. Armstrong and these three students know the drill -- whoever answers first gets to put that card into a pile in front of them, like a prize. "I've got the most," says Anjari at the end of the activity. This upsets Jeremiah, and he knocks his smaller pile of cards onto the floor. Jeremiah soon leaves the small group table and starts pestering a group of students nearby. Ms. Armstrong again threatens to call his mother, so he stops momentarily and returns to his desk at the front of the classroom.

At 10 o'clock, Ms. Armstrong rings a small bell she has near her and all the students in the room move to a different station, while a new group of four come to Ms. Armstrong at the small group table after she calls their names. Interesting, as I have not seen her do two small groups in a row before. The students seem very familiar with what they are supposed to do when the bell rings. This is rather remarkable to me, as I know Ms. Armstrong has only been working with small groups for two weeks. I find the students' names on my

142

chart and note these are the next four lowest students, though they are incrementally higher than the first three she called.

Jeremiah stays at his desk with a piece of colored paper and a blue crayon from one of the tables and looks to be drawing. It takes five minutes for this transitioning of everyone to be completed, so it is now 10:05. Miraculously, all is relatively calm for 15 minutes in this configuration, and I put X's into the four students' boxes for three five-minute time chunks.

One girl in this second small group, Brenda, is very attentive and is trying hard, but she does not get many correct answers. This seems to make her sad, but she continues to try, as if propelled by some stubborn internal force.

It is 10:20 and there has been, after an hour and twenty minutes of the school day, five minutes of instruction for all the students in Ms. Armstrong's classroom, and 15 minutes of instruction for the seven students in her two small groups (if we count Jeremiah).

At the end of the second small group, Ms. Armstrong again rings her little bell and tells the students to start cleaning up. It is whole group time on the rug again. As the other students assemble on the rug, several students eagerly go about the room cleaning up the little piles of colored papers and pens and other materials at the various tables where students had been working these past 40 minutes. This continues for those several students even as Ms. Armstrong begins at 10:25 to read a very large book to the rest of the class, assembled on the rug. As she reads to the students, she stops sometimes to ask questions or to show them a word and point out that it is spelled with a CH or an OU.

Toward the back of the group, several girls braid each other's hair. Another student keeps messing with the contents of a nearby desk, which are at eye level to the rug-seated student, causing pencils and larger textbooks to slide out and fall to the floor.

I mark three X's (for the 15 minutes she spends on this) and draw lines straight across for all three, signifying that all students received 15 minutes of instruction during this whole group instruction time.

At the end of the book, Ms. Armstrong gives directions for a spelling activity related to the story and hands out a worksheet for them to complete for this spelling activity. She tells the students to go back to their desks. They do, and she circulates around the room, giving help and putting out fires caused by rowdy students. No X's get recorded for teaching time now, as per Veronique's strict instructions.

Near the back of the room where I am sitting, one girl is causing problems during the spelling worksheet time. Ms. Armstrong notices and asks her to stop distracting others and get back to work. Once Ms. Armstrong's attention is elsewhere, the girl asks me a question about the worksheet, gets my answer and completes the assigned page in about three minutes. That done, she then goes back to distracting other students.

At 11, Ms. Armstrong announces it is time to go down the hall to the bathroom together. The students seem to know to stand by the door, in one line for boys and another for girls, until all are ready. Getting into these lines takes five minutes to accomplish. I decide to stay in the classroom and clean up my chart.

I have plenty of time for this and even have time to look at email on my phone. The whole crowd reappears at 11:25 and immediately goes back to working on the spelling worksheet for the next 10 minutes. At 11:35, Ms. Armstrong announces it is time for lunch. Again they line up by the door, as she hands out paper lunch tickets by name. This all takes five minutes and the students all depart at 11:40. Ms. Armstrong asks me if I want to go with her to drop the students at the lunchroom and then talk in the teachers' lounge while she eats her lunch for ten minutes. "Sure," I say, realizing this must be the end of my observation for the morning. She grabs a plastic bag from her desk, full of carrots and apple slices and half a sandwich, then we head out with the students.

As we walk, I think through the morning. She taught one five minute whole group lesson at first, and another later for 15 minutes. That's 20 minutes of instruction for all students. In addition, she taught two small groups, 15 minutes each for seven students altogether. So those seven more students got a total of 35 minutes of instruction each. To accomplish all this, she taught a total of 50 minutes in the three hours I was observing.

In the course of the morning, here are several things I noticed, even as I was mainly concentrating on my time chart. First, Jeremiah is a royal pain in the neck for his teacher and for other students such as Brenda who are less able. I suspect he is much brighter than his reading scores would indicate. He is energetic and quite mischievous, with a twinkle in his eye. He certainly has Ms. Armstrong figured out. His favorite trick is to sneak out the front door of the classroom, which is not far from his desk. At one point Ms. Armstrong goes out in the hallway to find him after five or six minutes and can be heard speaking quite sternly to him about his behavior. Other students listen intently from across the room.

Ms. Armstrong's main remedy for Jeremiah's misbehavior was to ask him to stop, then to threaten to call his mother and bring his mother down to the school for a meeting. As far as I observed, she never followed through on this recurring threat. All of this took considerable amounts of Ms. Armstrong's attention and was a clear drain on her energy and enthusiasm as the morning wore on.

Once we get to the teachers' lounge, I see there are already two other teachers seated there, eating their lunches, along with several other adults who do not appear to be teachers – maybe parent helpers or classroom aides? That will make candid conversation about the morning harder.

I show Ms. Armstrong my chart tracking the time observations I made this morning. It feels a little uncomfortable, in the company of other teachers and staff from the school, to have much of a conversation with her about the morning. But I manage to ask her, at the end as I am putting on my coat to leave, "Was that a typical morning?"

Ms. Armstrong's reply is immediate, "Yeah, pretty much."

How To Get More Time

"I think I've got part of the answer," I say into the phone.

"Nice to hear from you, Patrick. What was the question?" Veronique responds. She doesn't sound like she just woke up, but the connection sounds as though she's on the other side of the world.

"I asked you what a teacher could do to get all her students reading at grade level."

"My answer was 1,200 hours. Right?"

"Yes. Then you said the teacher could make up any hours a student had missed and catch them up, during the school day."

"I remember that. I'm still in Canberra, Australia, and it's 16 hours later than Chicago," she says, sounding even farther away. It's late-afternoon in Chicago, so that's morning for her in Australia. "Did you know Canberra is the capital of Australia, and it is closing 39 of its 140 schools?"

"I had no idea," I answer. "What are you doing there?"

"Later I'm giving the keynote. Right now I'm being driven to breakfast."

"Have you figured out how a teacher can provide enough instruction during the school day for all students to get their 1,200 hours?"

"Maybe. I spent yesterday morning observing in a classroom. I can tell you it's possible for the teacher to waste two out of every three hours not doing instruction of any kind."

"That's a good place to start," she says. "That's what we can call the difference between 'scheduled time' and 'actual instructional time.'

146

You can be sure that teacher had created a schedule and given it to the principal that showed three hours of instruction. We don't count all scheduled time, just actual instructional time, toward that 1,200 hours."

"I saw lots of stuff that was not instruction -- 25-minute bathroom breaks, taking attendance, transitions from one subject to another, student reprimands. Today the teachers all started 20 minutes late because their principal kept them in a meeting. So, that's got to be part of the answer. Eliminate time-wasters."

"Good observations," she says. "The principal's meeting sounds unusual, but wasted time is probably a daily occurrence in that classroom. Imagine if some of that time was used for instruction. You can't eliminate all transition time and bathroom breaks, but even ten minutes more of instructional time per day for a student is 33 hours more per school year."

I quickly scribble a calculation on a scrap of paper:

10 minutes

x 5 days/week

x 40 weeks

= 2,000 minutes

Divided by 60 minutes in an hour

= 33 hours

Yup, her math checks out.

"Once we fix the time-wasters, it seems like the quality of all instructional minutes should be part of the equation, too," I say, warming to the positive feedback. "In the classroom I observed, some students were paying attention, but there were girls during whole group who were braiding each others' hair. Do those minutes count toward your 1,200 hours?"

"Very good. You've found the difference between Actual Instructional Time, where there is the attempt at instruction by the teacher, and Engaged Time. That's when a student is paying attention, the student's eyes are on the teacher and that student's brain is engaged with the content. Actually, we can count 'engaged time' as double toward our 1,200 hours. That's how valuable it can be."

"Cool. Combine that with figuring out ways to use more of the school day for instruction," I continue, excited, "and the teacher can make up time students didn't get at home, right?"

"That's right. There is one more level, too," she says. "It doesn't sound like you saw any of this highest level in that classroom, so I'll just tell you it can exist and is worth trying to create. We call this level 'academic learning time.' It happens when a student is engaged and is performing at a high level of success, say 90% successful, during that engaged time. This can be done by assigning tasks at the right level and by monitoring progress and giving feedback immediately to students. Small groups, as you said you saw, are a great format for doing these two highest levels."

"I think I'm getting it," I say. "Let me try to process your levels in response to the classroom I observed. First, I saw two hours of time wasters that would not count as any form of instructional time."

"Yes, that's right."

"Then, I saw the teacher actually teaching, some whole group instruction and some small groups. Some of it kept the students' attention, and some of it didn't. So, using your language, the first was 'engaged learning time' and the second was just basic 'actual instructional time.'"

"Good work, Patrick. Here's how I say all of that:

Scheduled Time = what a teacher puts in her calendar for the day

Actual Instructional Time = time the teacher is actually instructing students

Engaged Learning Time = time students are paying attention, eyes on teacher

Academic Learning Time = student responding accurately at least 90% of the time."

"Thanks, very helpful," I say.

"Before we go further," she says, "we should clarify what we mean by 'instruction.' If the teacher hands out a worksheet for the students to do independently, or even in pairs or a small group, would that be instruction?"

"Well," I start, not sure I'm on firm ground here, "the students are reading the worksheet and having to fill it out with answers they are creating. I guess I'd count that as instruction."

"I disagree, not toward that 1,200 hours," she responds. "Worksheets are 'practice' of a skill. Practice is good and necessary. But 'instruction' is what goes on before a student can practice a newly-forming skill. Instruction is also what occurs, many times, after the student has practiced a new skill for a while and needs additional help to fix some misunderstandings or incomplete information. 'Instruction' is a full loop, consisting of the teacher providing information or questions directly, the student being stimulated to respond, and the teacher completing the loop by immediately telling the student whether the response was correct or not. In that definition, students doing worksheets doesn't count, because there's no last step. But the teacher flipping flashcards in front of a student, the student saying the sound of the letter on the flashcard and the teacher saying 'right' or 'wrong, the answer should be this instead' -- that is engaged learning time, as I am defining it."

"Since we're clarifying," I say, "do you also mean teachers have to count every minute and keep track of who's paying attention and who's looking out the window?"

"Good one. This 1,200 hours theory is not some scheme where we must count every minute," she responds. "That would be impossible. It's just a way of conceptualizing the overall idea that the amount of time a child is engaged in literacy activity between birth and the end of 1st grade really matters, and that it should be approximately 1,200 hours. More would be better, and less will be detrimental."

"That's good," I say. "because I'm thinking teachers would hate counting every minute."

"Time for a pop quiz," she says. "If the teacher you observed yesterday had 180 minutes of 'scheduled time' for reading instruction on the calendar she submitted to her principal for that day, should we count that as three of our 1,200 hours for every student in her class that day?"

"No way!" I say quickly. "She taught just 50 minutes all morning. It was discouraging to see."

"Quiz question number two: should we count that as 50 minutes of actual instructional time for all of her students?"

"Well, not exactly," I say, starting to understand what this quiz is about. "By my count, all of her students got just 20 minutes of instruction that morning, counting the one whole group session of five minutes and the other of 15 minutes."

"Good. Question number three: how much 'engaged learning time' should we count from that morning?" she asks, continuing her quiz.

"Some were engaged, from what I could tell from my perch in the back of the rug area," I say. "Others were distracted."

"So, her whole group instruction was not all that engaging. Make a note: that teacher should work on that, so more of her whole group instruction will be truly beneficial to all her students, and we can count more of it toward that 1,200 hours goal. I ask again: how much time that morning could count as 'engaged' instruction?"

"During the small groups, some students were paying close attention. Those were 15 minutes each, four students in each," I say. "Though one student who I had never seen before that day, Jeremiah, was not engaged even in small group."

"Hold on. I'm getting out of the limo and headed inside," she says. "Give me a minute. Just hold on the line." I hear her walking across pavement, greeting someone, maybe a doorman, then walking across more hard surfaces and opening and closing a squeaky door.

"Where were we? Oh, right, the morning you observed in that classroom, every student got 20 minutes of actual instruction, and seven of them got 35 minutes. Nobody got even the basic 80 minutes that day. So, if that goes on day after day, they all fall farther behind, instead of any of them making enough progress, let alone catching up a bit."

"I still need to know how a teacher can make up the difference, during the school day."

"Very good, Patrick." she responds. I can hear her pacing back and forth, her heels clacking on what sounds like wooden floors in a big, empty room. She's all wound up. "Some smart folks in Kennewick, Washington wrote a great little book on how to do this during the school day. It's called Annual Growth for All Students, Catch-up Growth for Those Who Are Behind. Snappy title, right?

They got 90% of their whole district reading at grade level. Eighty minutes of actual reading instruction per day was the foundation for that achievement. For students who got less reading and language experience before they start school and are far behind, we've got to play catch-up with them, so they make more than a year's worth of progress. Kennewick gave those students 20 added minutes per day of intensive small group instruction. I say small groups count as two minutes for every one minute of instruction, because most are at least 'engaged learning time.' Even if we do good regular instruction every day, plus good small group instruction every day, for two years, some still need about 400 more hours to catch all the way up. So, just like Kennewick, we give them another small group session per day."

"That's a lot during the regular school day."

"It's a lot, but it's totally doable by schools," she says. "If some students need even more, pre-K gives them 200 more hours, conservatively. There's also summer school and after-school. But I said this can be done by teachers during the regular school day, and I mean it. If you want to see the math, I'll send you my PDF of this all."

"Please do!" I practically beg. "I think I'm getting this, mostly."

"Good," she says, "because that teacher you are working with needs you to understand this, so you can help her understand it. If we want some students to be 'catching up', they'll need more instruction every day."

"Could any of this be done by the parent or some adult at home with 20 minutes per night of reading to the child?"

"It could, yes," she concedes. "But if time for reading was not provided before kindergarten, we have no reason to rely on that environment to be providing it once the child is in school. A home under stress does not suddenly start behaving more positively just because a child starts school."

"My wife has been checking out other schools for our son, and she says some schools have active and successful parent-engagement programs," I say. "They get parents to start providing that 20 minutes of reading each night."

"Yes. But that can't be your first line of attack for this problem," she adds. "We must, as the professionals charged with getting every student reading at grade level, make a plan for what we can do to make sure our goal is met, regardless of what other adults might do."

"Some people have been telling me that schools could do a good job if only parents did their job better and sent us better students."

"Parents send us the best babies they have," she retorts. "It's our responsibility to those students to teach them well, make sure they all get 1,200 hours by the end of 1st grade, and get results. Now I'm sorry but I've got to get off the phone."

"Thanks again. I wish I could hear your keynote."

"You just did," she replies.

Explaining Time To Grace

"How does the teacher know which students are missing some hours already?" Grace is asking, having just heard me recap the concepts I've learned from Veronique. Good practice, as I will want to explain it all to Ms. Armstrong soon.

"Well, we can't go to every child's home and watch each one 24/7 for five years before anyone comes into our classrooms," I answer. "We can't count every minute and every hour of language and reading experiences they get. So I guess we have to use a proxy. For instance, at the start of 1st grade, if a student is testing at the level he or she should have been at to start kindergarten, we can approximate that student is one year behind."

"But teachers will say they don't have another 40 minutes per day to focus on each of their low readers," Grace says. She is picking this all up lots faster than I did! I guess I'd forgotten how much experience Grace has from doing dance work in schools during her college days and up to the present. "Especially if they have more than one of those lower-level students."

"Right you are," I say. "So, let's put four of the lower students into a small group for engaged instruction. Now that teacher needs just 20 minutes per day, not 80 minutes, to help four students get what they need in order to catch up. That's what Ms. Armstrong has been doing."

"That's what band directors do to help a section of the band get better. They work with them in a small group. They get lots more chances that way, in band or in reading class."

"I understand as a dancer, too. We work with small groups to perfect technique outside of the general rehearsal. Now you need to convince a bunch of teachers at that school," says Grace.

"Would teachers doing small groups help make it okay to send Joey to that school then?" I ask, sensing a chink in Grace's armor.

"It might help, but it wouldn't be enough by itself," she responds. I've checked out magnet schools and several charters, so far. From what I've seen, classrooms are rarely all they should be, especially compared to some of what you've been telling me about instructional time and small groups and all. It doesn't matter if it's charter or magnet or whatever. I'm seeing some good things, but I haven't seen the perfect school for our Jomo yet."

"Are you open to seeing for yourself what's going on at the school where I've been helping? It's not perfect, either. Not yet. But I think it deserves a chance."

"Look, Patrick, I can see how excited you've been about this work at that school. It's like I've gotten my husband back -- that idealistic, talented, creative, funny guy I married. So I want to support that. But is that school going to be good enough for Joey? Or will it hurt his future somehow?"

I shut my mouth, suddenly realizing how good it feels to get feedback filtered through the eyes that know me better than any others. "Do you really think I'm that different now?"

"Yes, I do," Grace says. She pauses. "But, there's still that core issue with that school."

"Yeah, I hear you," I say, relieved to hear a real opening. I continue, cautiously. "I think you should come and see what's happening at this school. I didn't think there was even a chance you'd say yes, so I haven't told you about this. But there's a night coming up for next year's potential kindergarten parents. It's next week. I'd like you to come with me to it, to see what's going on there in kindergarten."

"This is so hard, Patrick," she begins, her tone softer from before, less sure. "I don't want to move to a new neighborhood, let alone the suburbs. All the idealistic reasons for staying here are still there for me, just as we always talked about. But parenting really sent me for a loop. Primal instincts kicked in to protect my baby from harm. Wacky, but there it is."

"I used to like your primal instincts, when they were more like 'Me Jane, you Tarzan.' Those primal instincts were good."

Grace smiles for a moment, then continues. "I also have begun to realize how bad it would be for you if we moved to the suburbs. There's no way we could afford that on what you make. So that would mean a new job, probably not in music."

"You could get a job once you get your degree," I say. "The pressure shouldn't all be on me."

"That's the idea for me going back to school," she says, matter-of-factly. "But that won't be completed by next fall when Joey starts kindergarten." We both sit silently.

"Your dad always said he could get me something at his place," I say, half-heartedly.

"That would be the worst," she says. "Suit and tie every day, 9-5, sit at a desk. That would be the end of anything with music for you. You'd be utterly unhappy."

"You are right about that," I say. Working a straight job would be about as far from why I went to music school as is possible. At my 25th college reunion, I'd be saying "I work in an office. I'm a 'suit.' I don't do music anymore." Just shoot me right now and save me the misery of the years from here to there.

"So, what does that all mean for us and Joey?"

"I don't know," says Grace. "Maybe it means I should at least come to see your parent night, see what's got you all jazzed up again. But that can't mean we're making any decision yet to send our own child there next year. It's just being fair and taking one tiny step."

"Deal!" I say, startling her. "No pressure… except on me and the kindergarten teachers at our neighborhood school."

Every Minute Counts

Wednesday, February 23

"So, what insights do you have from your morning of watching my classroom, Mr. Trombonist-becomes-teacher?" says Ms. Armstrong as I enter her classroom the next morning. "Do you have the solution to why my students' test scores are not soaring the way our dear principal would like?"

"I saw some things that might play a role." I'm starting slowly. She's my pal now, but what happens if I criticize what I saw?

"Mr. Smarty then, aren't you?" she says. She seems a little nervous about this feedback thing, now that she's invited it. "I'll just forget your first try at small groups and only remember the great trombone playing you did. I could never give you any feedback about that. And I'll remember how great our small groups have been going lately. So, I know you are a capable adult. It's just nerve-racking to have someone watching me teach."

"I can understand that feeling," I say. "In music school, every semester we had what they called 'juries.' You'd prepare a piece to play, then go into the recital hall and play it for the five or six brass faculty, who were all sitting there silently, staring at you, and they'd then give you a score. Is it like that?"

"That sounds easier. You could practice exactly what was going to happen, right?" She distractedly rubs a yellowish area on the back of one hand.

"Good point," I say, just trying to keep the conversation going until she relaxes a little. "But listen, those brass faculty were pros, with power over me. For you, I'm just a trombone player from Oregon. Of course, we didn't have 30 little people on stage with us, who could suddenly do whatever they wanted to screw it up. Yeah, I guess music school was easier."

"I'm picturing your brass thingy with 30 six-year-olds on stage with you. One throws up, one hits another kid, one starts crying, and you're supposed to keep playing something beautiful and also corral them the whole time. Pretty different."

"That's the mash-up of music school and teacher's college, right?" She chuckles along with me at this image. I know her students will be here shortly, so I need to press on to give her a few notes from my morning of observing in her room.

"Watching your classroom at work was very helpful for me, so thanks for letting me do that," I start again. "We've had some successes with your small groups, but I didn't know anything about the rest of the school day. So, let's just say we're brainstorming here."

"No problem," she says, still looking tense, but a little less so.

"I'll tell you that I called someone I know from college days. She's like my education guru, helping me think about what I might see in your classroom or any other classroom," I say. I then proceed for ten minutes to tell Ms. Armstrong about Veronique, the instructional time model, and what I saw in her classroom in terms of time usage that one morning.

"I never really thought about teaching in terms of instructional time," she says after I'm done. "I have my things to get done, the students respond, it's lunch time, repeat in the afternoon, go home, repeat tomorrow, end of story."

"Does it make sense that time is important, and something you have some control over?"

"Now that you've reflected it back to me as part of what you saw in my classroom," she says, "I can start to see it as super-important. It's embarrassing that you saw me wasting so much time. It was a pretty typical day," she trails off.

"Could it be part of the answer for fixing the scores your principal cares about?" I ask her, as gently as possible.

"Hey, let's take this away from being about my principal," she snaps at me. "He's not the reason I show up to work every day. I want to do good work regardless of him and his retirement plan and all of that."

"Okay, then."

There it is - the same basic impulse as the creative types with whom I usually hang out. It's about personal integrity and control and expression. It goes all the way back to those ancient humans who painted pictures on cave walls that said, "I was here. I did good things. I mattered." That's a lot different from, "I was here to collect a paycheck. I did what I was told by my boss and the bureaucracy." Are teachers closer to musicians and dancers and visual artists than I'd thought? Or is it just Ms. Armstrong who's like this?

"So, what's your so-called 'guru' say we can do about it?"

"How about we start with bathroom breaks?" I ask.

"That seems a little bit inconsequential to me," she says, with a kind of harrumph in her voice. "Why not start with how little time I made for actual instruction?"

"We'll get there," I respond. "Let's do a little calculation. I watched your students take one bathroom break. How many of those do they get per day?"

"Oh, I don't know. Probably three on most days."

"If every bathroom break is the length I saw, 25 minutes, and you do that three times per day, how much time is that per day?"

"That's 75 minutes."

"And if we do that every day for a week, how much time is that we are using to go to the bathroom?" I continue.

"So, that's five days multiplied by an hour and a quarter each day. That's a little over six hours a week."

"And how much is it, if we do that every week for the whole year?" I ask.

"There's maybe 40 weeks in a school year. Multiplied by six hours, roughly, that's 240 hours. That's ridiculous," says Ms. Armstrong.

"Think about bathroom breaks as a drain on your potential instructional time. Maybe, with practice, you and your students can get half of that 240 hours back."

She has that look in her eyes again. "I'm just thinking about this on a daily basis, for today and tomorrow and every day, never mind what it adds up to all year."

"It gets us 37 and a half more minutes per day, every day," I say, "for reading instruction."

"I'm ready! Sign me up! How do we do that?"

"Let me come tomorrow and try an idea I have."

Time Graphing Activity

Thursday, February 24

"Students, I have something I want to talk about, as a group," I say, sitting in Ms. Armstrong's big rocking chair this morning and looking at all her students' faces as they sit attentively on the rug. It reminds me of the first time I ever tried to conduct a band. That was scary. There's a big difference between watching and holding the baton.

"How long do you think it takes for our whole class to go down the hall to the bathroom and back?" I ask. Hands shoot up.

"Five minutes?" comes the first answer, more like a question. "Two minutes?" comes the next. "One hour!" comes a third. Possibly they have no firm idea of time. This is a rich area for exploration, I'm sensing, beyond just solving the instructional time problem for Ms. Armstrong and me. The realization comes over me that I'm creating teacher puzzles in my head, as I sit in front of a group of children. Weird.

"Put your hands down." Students wait expectantly for my next move. "I have been timing your class when you all go to the bathroom each day. It takes you 25 minutes, usually. Your class goes to the bathroom as a class three times every day. That adds up to more than one hour of time each day, just to go to the bathroom. That is a very long time."

I realize multiplication, and even addition, is not what any kindergartner can do, so I am trying to make this easy, without needing any fancy math.

"What could you do that is fun, if you had even an extra hour each day in Ms. Armstrong's classroom?"

Again hands shoot up. "More free time... Draw pictures on the easel... Blocks work area... Ms. Armstrong reads to us... Learn stuff."

"Yes, you could do more of all of those things," I say, "if you spend less time doing your bathroom breaks each day. Want to see if you can do it?"

Now I get some students saying "Yes!" and others looking at me with puzzled expressions. I'll go with the yes votes and hope the others figure it out by participating in something they can see and feel.

"It's time for your morning bathroom break," I say. With that, Ms. Armstrong gestures for all to stand and line up. As they do, I go over to the white board by the door and write the time from the clock. "I am going to time you, to see how long it takes. I am writing '25 minutes' up on your white board to remind all of us how long it usually takes. Let's see if you can be back here as a class in less than 25 minutes this time. Do you think you can?" Lots of yes's from students.

"Here we go, students," says Ms. Armstrong, and they march slowly out of the classroom. I stay behind, with one eye on the clock and the other on my email.

The first student pops her head in the door 19 minutes after they left, with all the others right behind her. Not exactly earth shattering improvement, but a good start. I ask Ms. Armstrong to gather them all on the rug by her big chair again.

"That took 19 minutes," I say, once they are all settled again. I write "19 minutes" on the white board next to "25 minutes." "That means you have six extra minutes of something fun. Is that very much extra time?" I hear some no's and some yes's from the students.

"What could you do next time to be even faster?" I ask the group. They respond with a variety of ideas, along with complaints about who is going too slow, and who made a mess that needed to be cleaned up, and other issues. "Do you think you all can help each other next time to fix all these things and do it faster?" Lots of yes's this time.

"Mr. Patrick," says Ms. Armstrong now, stepping toward the white board and picking up a marker pen, "Is it all right with you if I draw something up here?"

She draws a tall bar and writes 25" at the top of it. Next to it she draws a slightly shorter bar, and writes 19" above it. She draws one more bar, slightly shorter, with no number above it.

"This is a bar graph. You will learn about this in 1st grade. But I think you are ready to learn a little about it right now, to keep track of our bathroom times. The first bar is your 25 minutes, the second bar is what it just took you, 19 minutes, and the third bar is for next time. We can see if the bar gets shorter and shorter. Thank you, Mr. Patrick, for helping us get more time in our day for all the fun learning we love to do. I am sure we'll be even better next time."

Ms. Peterson Meeting About K Plan

Thursday afternoon, February 24

Ms. Peterson and I have tried to meet about the kindergarten parent night, but we keep missing. We've exchanged several emails, but it feels like we're behind, with only a week before the event. So Ms. Peterson got Mr. Bevington to give her someone to cover her class for the afternoon so we can meet. I suggested a little family-run Mexican restaurant that has good food.

"So, here's the whole enchilada, Ms. Peterson," I start, after we're both seated in a booth.

"Pun intended?" she asks, picking up the menu.

"Absolutely," I respond, happy to make her smile.

"Before you launch into your 'whole enchilada' speech, I wanted you to know Mr. Bevington and I have agreed that I'll be running the committee from now on, and I've decided not to have any more of those meetings for awhile. Instead, I'm collecting everyone's homework and using it to create some slides. Mainly, I'm doing that 'one simple strategy' thing you and I discussed, focusing on K-1st as the big stick we'll use as our lever to move this whole school."

"Physics metaphor intended?" I ask.

"Absolutely," she responds with a twinkle in her eye. "So, you were going to visit our kindergarten classrooms, then tell me what good teaching looks like and if there's any going on there. Is that what your enchilada speech is about?"

"Yup. I've been spending a lot of time in Ms. Armstrong's room."

"What have you decided good teaching looks like?"

163

"Well, it begins with having enough instruction going on, so all students can get the amount they need."

"Is that happening in our kindergarten rooms?"

"No, it's not," I respond, bluntly. "So, that should be the first plank of our plan."

"There's not enough instruction? That's really upsetting!" The waitress looks over from behind the counter, stands and starts walking toward us. I stay silent as it sinks in for Ms. Peterson. "We can't stand in front of parents and say that. They'll laugh us out of town."

The waitress interrupts to take our order: huevos con chorizo for me, homemade chicken soup for Ms. Peterson.

"No, we can't say our plan is to have enough instruction," I agree. "But we can say we customize instruction, so every child gets what he or she needs in order to read at grade level or above. That's code, between you and me, for small groups."

"That sounds much better. You realize most of our teachers have never used a small group, right? They think the students will run all over the place and go wild if teachers aren't standing in front of the room lecturing. They want the desks to provide order and discipline."

"Well, Ms. Armstrong is pretty great at them. She's doing them every day lately," I say. "Small groups are the ultimate form of control - - four students right in front of you, learning."

"But what do we tell parents the other students are doing while their teacher is only paying attention to four students, which might not include their child?"

"Well, we tell them about something else Ms. Armstrong is doing really well: work areas," I say. "Picture it -- a whole room of kindergartners working independently around the room in various groupings or solo, with some students reading a beautiful book while sitting in a bean bag chair over here," I say, pointing to that imaginary bean bag chair in that imaginary room, "and other students working together at an easel over here."

"Sounds like the suburbs," says Ms. Peterson, with a touch of sarcasm in her voice. "Parents will eat that stuff up. How about we tell them there will be lots of books in every kindergarten room, purchased with a grant from the Bill and Melinda Gates Foundation?"

"Have you got that grant?" I ask, wondering what else she hasn't been telling me.

"No way, but let's dream big!"

"So, we'll promise lots of books, and we'll find the money somewhere," I say. "Actually, I know a guy who runs a book-donating nonprofit. Frank was in my dorm in college. He can get us all the 'gently used' books we want."

"Now we're talking! What else do we need to do to make parents excited about next year?" asks Ms. Peterson. "I want them to enroll their kindergartners that night, at our parent event. The deadline, after all, is the next day."

"Then we'd better be good."

The waitress brings our food and the busboy brings a pitcher of water to refill our glasses.

"Here's where I need to tell you about 1,200 hours," I say.

Thirty minutes later we've gone all through what Veronique told me. Ms. Peterson seems to move from skeptic to believer, just as Grace did when I first explained these ideas to her. It's hard to argue with the positive effect of time on task. We finish our food and the dishes are cleared.

"Let's summarize," says Ms. Peterson. "Our message includes the following:

Customized instruction, in small groups and whole, so every child gets what is needed in order to read at grade level

Work areas throughout the classroom, where each child can work independently and in cooperative groups with fellow students

Lots of books in each classroom, so students always have a book they want to read, right at their elbow, and

4. Lots of engaging instruction, all day long."

"So we're going to tell them there will be lots of instruction?" I ask.

"Sure," she says, "but in marketing lingo: 'a full and active day for every child, filled with amazing and caring teaching.' How's that?"

"You could've been in advertising," I tease. "In addition, it would be huge, for persuading parents such as my wife, for them to see something."

"Like what?"

"Like a classroom, with students doing actual stuff and teaching going on," I respond.

"At night?" she asks.

I've been thinking about this and I'm prepared to answer her concern.

"Sure, at night," I say. "Ms. Armstrong's students would think it was a blast to 'play school' in the evening. I already talked to her about the possibility. We'll make it great."

"I'm going with your gut on this part," she says. She stands and we both put on our coats and head to the front to pay. "I've got this, since you're doing all the work. Gotta keep you fed."

"Thanks for lunch then," I say, surprised. She pays and we head out the door.

"There's one other thing," I say as we reach our cars. "Shouldn't we check this with the other kindergarten teachers? I'd hate for them to hear it for the first time in a public meeting with prospective parents."

"It's just the three of us," she says. "I can use Ms. Armstrong to help sell it. I'll let you know how that goes. Good or bad, we're going with this message and plan. We are going to boost kindergarten enrollment that night!" She pulls her calendar out and I see her write a large note on next Thursday's date - Bring enrollment forms.

Grace And The Neighbor Lady

Friday, February 25

Grace is talking excitedly and doing dance gestures with her arms as I walk in the door. "Patrick, I found my own Donna! Her name is Graciela, and she lives right next door."

"Your own Donna?" I ask, wondering what she might be talking about as she continues moving across the room with graceful movements.

She shifts to making exaggerated typing gestures with her arms and hands. "For computer stuff." There's something about dancers when they're excited, moving in ways only dancers can do. I could watch her all day, especially when she's obviously so happy about it all.

"Terrific!" I say. "She's even got your name, sort of. I should be able to remember that."

"I made some tsoureki bread today to take around to the neighbors on both sides of us," she continues. "We've been here for several months and not met anyone."

"It's winter," I say. "Nobody's outside in this weather."

"Exactly," she continues. "So I baked some Easter bread, like a good Greek girl always does around this time of year. Joey was at preschool at the church, so I had a little time. I've been dying to bake, though that oven is a disaster, it turns out."

"I love your tsoureki bread," I say, realizing what the wonderful smells were when I first walked in. "I didn't realize it was Easter already."

"Easter's really early this year, last week of March," she responds. "Nobody was home on the other side of us, but Graciela was home, with her three young kids. She right away invited me in when she saw the bread. I apologized six times for the bread not being my best because of the oven. I couldn't tell what the temperature really was. It's so old, all the numbers have worn off. So,

I told her I thought the bread was a little dry inside. Anyway, her kids were coloring Easter eggs, so I sat and colored a few. She and her oldest were also doing this other egg thing, I think she called them cascarones. They take empty shells from eggs they've already eaten and they fill them with confetti and then paint them and glue crepe paper over the open end. I'd never seen that tradition before. It was fun sitting there for a while. I finally got to meet all of them."

"Is there a Mr. Graciela on the scene?"

"I didn't ask, but I assume so," answers Grace. "We had a nice get-to-know-you chat. Her oldest is Carlos. He's the same age as Joey. Graciela volunteers with some community organization I promised to check out. They train parents to help in schools, doing tutoring with individual students. I think it's during the school day. I told her about what you are doing with that school, which sounds similar."

"Not exactly, but that's fine," I say. "I haven't seen any volunteer tutors where I'm at."

"That's the thing," Grace continues. "She said she wanted to help out at that school where you are, because her oldest might go there in the fall for kindergarten. But that principal wouldn't let her organization in there. Something about politics with the alderman, or not wanting a bunch of organizers running around the school. She doesn't have a good impression, as a result."

"I remember she said that before, when the scores first came out in the news," I say.

"She's super nice," Grace says. "We are going to get Joey and her Carlos to the park together, once the weather is a little nicer."

"So, how is she your own Donna?"

"Well, I told her about going back to finish my masters and all," she replies. "I told her how easy they make it, in some ways, but how hard the computer stuff is online. She said if I need help with that kind of thing, she knows a lot about computers. So I asked her if she knew anything about sending photos, and she did. I went home and got my laptop and she helped me send more pictures to my mom, right then. It's done. I love it! Tech is great when it works."

"That's super!" I say, excited. "I'll tell my Donna she's got competition."

"Funny, mister," she says. "How about some praise for my meeting the neighbors and getting my computer consultant lined up?"

"You are so right. Praises to you," I say, grabbing her for a kiss, glad to be reminded to praise, praise, praise. "Did you bake one for us, too? Remember our house rules."

"I remember: I can't make something yummy to give away without keeping some for us." That has been our rule since we got married. "I've got that covered, don't worry."

Prospective K Parents Night

As I drive to the school tonight, I'm filled with a mixture of excitement and anxiety. This feels a lot like pre-concert jitters. I know we are ready, but I also know anything can happen when doing a performance. That's essentially what this is, a big performance. This one includes five and six-year-olds, which is what has me most anxious.

I've never been near the school at night. It's March, so it's dark at this hour. I asked Mr. Bevington to hire someone to direct cars into the parking lot and then stand guard until the event is over, so nobody finds an engine missing when they return. As I pull in, I see the guard is Mr. Ferris, the PE teacher. Must have promised payment in donuts. "Good evening, Mr. Ferris. Working late tonight?"

"I don't know why you all are making such a big deal of kindergarten," he answers. "But if I'm picking up some extra money in the process, who am I to say?"

"Thanks for your help." I pull ahead into one of the many open spots. Grace got a babysitter for Joey, and she'll be coming in a little while. I'm early, to help Ms. Armstrong and Ms. Peterson do anything at the last minute. They're setting up refreshments and signs to direct parents to the large meeting room. All the teachers agreed to straighten up their rooms at the end of the school day, in case any parents wander around and take a peek inside.

The focus we want is on kindergarten rooms, though, especially Ms. Armstrong's classroom. My college friend, Frank, came through with a load of colorful, gently-used books, enough for all three K rooms. As I pass Ms. Armstrong's room, I see her lights are on, her students are already there, and she has displayed all these books to full advantage.

*   *   *

At 7:05 we are ready to begin, with enough parents in seats to feel we can start. Bevington did his job of promoting this, it seems. "Welcome, parents. My name is Ms. Peterson, and I am acting Assistant Principal." Hmm, I did not know she had another title beyond teacher. That's good, as she certainly behaves like the leader of this school. "I also teach upper grade science, and I know I have some of your older children in my classes. Our principal had an emergency and has been delayed, so I told him I would welcome you for him. We are very glad to see so many of you here this evening. Contrary to what you may have read in the news or rumors you might have heard, this school plans to be open next year and to do great things for your new kindergartners and for all of our students."

As Ms. Peterson thanks a few parents who helped her with set-up, I count 51 couples or singles. Hopefully more will be coming later, or else we're in trouble. Ms. Peterson told me that to have three full classrooms next year in K, we need at least 70 students, preferably 75. The union contract says 29 students per room is the maximum allowed, so we could go as high as 87 students total for our three rooms next year. She said some won't show up when fall rolls around, so it's good to have some extras register, maybe five or 10. That brings the total up to 92 - 97 as our ideal enrollment goal. Ms. Peterson said she's afraid of overdoing it, too, because classrooms get too large then, even though we'd love the extra funding that comes with more students. If it's 60 - 69, on the other hand, we probably will be forced to have two really large classrooms of K, which would be bad because we have three this year and three K teachers. That would also mean we'd be losing enrollment in the school overall, which would be even worse in the longer term. This whole enrollment process feels like we're just guessing.

Ms. Peterson hits all the points we planned. She finishes with an invitation to watch a live video feed from Ms. Armstrong's classroom, where we have set up a video camera (manned by me) to watch as Ms. Armstrong and her students (almost all of whom showed up tonight) do their thing. We decided this video feed was the only way to have so many parents see the classroom in action at the same time without freaking out the students.

After a short pause as I walk quickly to the classroom and camera next door, the live feed comes on the large screen we have borrowed for the evening. I give a wide shot of all the students sitting on the rug, waiting semi-patiently. Then Ms. Armstrong tells the parents what she wants them to be watching for this evening. I cross my fingers.

The students do well for the full 30-minute video portion. It's touching to see many of them so dressed up. Their parents knew it was a show and dressed them in the best clothes they could muster, their Sunday best. Even in their stiff dress clothes, they all quickly settle down and do what they always do in class these days. After a short whole class warm-up, Ms. Armstrong runs a small group, while other students work nicely together in the work areas they know really well. I try to keep the video camera focused on the room as a whole, with some traveling around the room from time to time to get close ups in small groups and in several of the work areas. I even catch a moment of one little guy unselfconsciously reading aloud a big book to his best friend, sitting side by side at one end of the classroom. For the last three minutes or so, Ms. Armstrong leads the whole group in a song, and I pan with the camera to show all the students engaged and happily singing along.

After the video feed ends, Ms. Peterson takes questions from the crowd. Ms. Armstrong has to stay with the students until their parents come to get them, so I come back, just in case Ms. Peterson can't answer some question.

When all the questions seem to be answered, Ms. Peterson says thanks and points parents to the kindergarten registration table. A crowd forms around the table. I see Grace off to one side talking to an adult couple. I go over to her and she gives me a peck on the cheek. "Patrick, I'd like you to meet our neighbors, Graciela Rodriguez and her husband Frederico."

"So nice to meet you both," I say. "It's been too cold to see you over the backyard fence."

"It's nice to meet you, too," Graciela says. "I've enjoyed getting to know your wife a little just recently. She makes a great Greek bread."

"I know she does," I say, enthusiastically. "And when you get some, I get some, too."

"How did you think this went tonight?" Graciela asks.

"This was even more nerve-racking than doing a concert at Orchestra Hall," I say. "I thought everyone did really well, especially the stars of the show, our five and six-year-olds. That was not easy to pull off. I have to hand it to Ms. Armstrong."

"I'm sure it wasn't," she responds. "Is that really what they do in kindergarten every day here? Or just for us tonight?"

"Every day," I say, choosing my words carefully. I should say it's what Ms. Armstrong's students do, not every K room. "Grace tells me you volunteer in classrooms regularly at another school. What did you think tonight?"

"Well, as I just told Grace, if that's what kindergarten looks like here, I'm in."

"Patrick and I have been talking a lot about what to do," Grace pipes in. "I got scared by the test scores, and what you originally told me, Graciela, about this being a bad school."

"I think we can't always judge a school by what's in the news," Graciela says. "It is best to go see for yourself, like tonight. Are you going to register your son?"

I look at Grace, who is looking at me. Then she turns to Graciela and her husband and takes a deep breath. "I really liked what I saw here tonight, and it's important to me to know that other parents like you will be here next year." Grace stops and looks at me again. "Patrick and I will be talking about this tonight and making a decision by tomorrow."

"I hope you will join us here," says Graciela. "No pressure, right? I'm just saying it would be better to do this together."

I see Frederico discreetly squeezing his wife's coat sleeve. She looks at him for a second and says to us, "It's time to go rescue the babysitter. We'll see you again soon!" With that they are off to the parking lot.

"You probably have more to do here before you can come home," Grace says to me once they are out of earshot. "Can you walk me to the parking lot, though?"

"Sure, let me grab my coat."

Grace and I walk to the parking lot together. She reaches out and takes my hand as we walk. It is chilly out, though I don't mind, given the warm feelings from the evening. At the car, we stop and Grace turns to me. "You know I'll want to get involved, if Joey goes here."

"I'd love that. I'll be sure the school jumps at your offer, too," I say, excited she's even talking this way. I wait a moment, then I can't wait any longer. "Are you saying this is the place for Joey then?"

Grace takes a big breath and then says with a smile, "I am comfortable signing up Joey for kindergarten here, given what we saw tonight and the fact that other parents like Graciela and Frederico are signing up, too. You've said there's lots more work to do here beyond kindergarten. So, I guess we are all signing up for being willing to work for years as our children move up one grade at a time."

"I'm thrilled!" I say, feeling an immense load of uncertainty being lifted and another immense load of responsibility and commitment being placed onto my shoulders in its place. "Are you sure, Grace?"

"I'm lots more sure about here than about other places I've seen," she says. "If something happens to change our minds before the fall, we'll just have to figure out something else for Joey. Mainly I was impressed tonight, Patrick. You should be really proud of that teacher and her students."

"I am," I say. "I really am." She steps closer and gives me a big hug. She will bring wonderful talents to the table. Goodness knows, we will need them. We kiss warmly, then she gets in the cold car and heads for home.

I head back into the school to see if Ms. Peterson has a count of the night's enrollees. "We got 55 sign-ups tonight for next year's kindergarten," says Ms. Peterson. She sounds excited.

"That's not good, is it?" I feel deflated by not reaching the number we wanted.

"Once all the late-comers were here, we had 60 new families with next-year kindergartners represented here tonight," she begins. "So, 55 out of 60 is fairly fabulous."

"But isn't our goal at least 70 students in K next year?" I ask her. "Don't we need a few extras, too, in case some are no-shows in the fall?"

"Yes, and we're good," she answers, almost giddy. "Parents of current students at this school can enroll any incoming kindergartners they have at home. We had 40 sign-ups in-hand before tonight from those folks. So, that's 95 enrollees now. Let's say ten of those will decide to withdraw over the summer because they find another option, move away or any other reason you can imagine."

"So, bottom-line, what's your projected number for K next year?"

"Being conservative, I'd say we'll have 80 in K next year," she says. "We are back in business, folks, as the place everyone wants to send their children."

Foundational Skills Enable Comprehension

Friday, March 4

"Why am I not seeing comprehension activities when I come in your room?" asks Mr. Bevington. He has called Ms. Armstrong and me to the office. The three of us stand there, with Dorothy lurking nearby.

"Last we talked you were concerned about the results on some monthly test. We think we've fixed that since, by paying more attention to instructional time," I respond.

"Central Office says to improve reading comprehension. I want to see all students doing loads of comprehension, even your kindergartners," he continues.

"What would that look like?" I ask, since Ms. Armstrong is keeping quiet, looking irritated. He's not said one thing about our successful kindergarten recruitment last night. Come to think of it, did he even show up?

"Well, I want to see students reading books and then answering questions about them," he proclaims. "I don't want to hear a student read a passage really well and then I ask that student a question like, 'What color was the wagon in the story?' and he can't answer my question."

"What about the kindergartners who can't read any words?" I ask him, incredulous.

"I don't know," says Mr. Bevington. "You have to figure out what to do to make comprehension your focus. That's what Central Office has declared!" With that, he turns and goes into his smaller office and closes the door behind him.

"What are we supposed to do with that?" she asks me or nobody in particular.

"I don't know," I answer, thinking seriously about going into that smaller office and yelling at him. "Let's get out of here so we can think." She seems relieved and we turn, walk out of the office and start down the hallway back to her classroom. We are both silent for a bit.

"Nice job last night, by the way," I say after about 30 steps, trying to break the quiet. I can see Ms. Armstrong's shoulders relax. The halls are eerily calm at this time of day, slowly recovering their composure after a day with the constant clamor of children.

"Lot of good it does if he's going to just bow to whatever Central Office is telling him to do," she replies. She's been working hard to try new things and really improve her classroom work, then her principal doesn't even acknowledge that.

"We both probably agree with him," I start again, as we reach her classroom door. "The goal we all want is for students to be able to read a passage and know what they read, so they can talk about it. Right?"

"Sure," says Ms. Armstrong, "but, like you said to him, these are babies. They can't read a passage yet. So they sure can't answer questions about that passage. That's just idiotic." I think she's more peeved at him than I originally suspected.

We enter her classroom. She immediately goes over and starts erasing all writing off the whiteboard. Her arm motions are vigorous, like she has to start over with a clean slate that requires a deep cleaning.

I watch her clear the whole whiteboard. It seems therapeutic. It gives us both time to think. I'm thinking about parallels between this experience and my experiences as a really young musician in elementary school. Did we ever see the principal, Mr. Cardiff, in the band room? Did he ever tell our band teacher what to do? As Ms. Armstrong writes next Monday's date and day of the week on the board, I start again, talking to her back.

"When I first started learning to play the trombone, we didn't get to play much real music. It was simple stuff we played. That's what you can do when all you know is where to put the slide to make three or four different notes come out. So, you practice those notes, over and over. Add another note. Yay, five notes now! Play a five-note song. How exciting! Learn to automatically do all the right things every time you see the symbols on paper for those five notes. Buzz your lips a certain speed. Put the slide in a certain position, six inches from the closed position all the way in by your hands. Hold the note for a certain amount of time."

"Sounds boring," she says. Having stopped writing on the whiteboard, she starts across the room, stops, and now kneels by a child's desk, trying to scrape something dark and stubborn off the top with her fingernail. She is really working at it, looking determined to make the blemish go away.

"Not boring for a beginner. That's a lot at first." I respond, watching her. She got the dark stuff off the desk, but now it's all on her finger and nail. She goes over to get a paper towel and works on getting it off herself. "Funny thing is, no principal came around to the music room and heard the beginning band learning single notes. He never demanded, 'I want to hear a lot more real songs whenever I walk by your band room. No more learning one note at a time. I want real songs.'"

"How do band directors keep the principal from saying stupid things like that?" she asks. She goes to her big desk and sits. I sit on the corner of a student desk near hers.

"It's the rare elementary school principal who gives a darn about the beginning band, to be honest, because nobody downtown cares about it," I respond. "The band director gives the principal a plan that says, 'We will be ready to give a decent concert performance on this date, so you will know we achieved this level of performance by this date.'"

"That sounds a lot better than what we just heard," she says. "It wouldn't be so bad if he actually knew what he was talking about, instead of just spouting whatever Central Office tells him it wants. I don't need any more fools in my life telling me what to do."

I stay quiet for a few moments, hoping her anger will dissipate in this empty room where so much good work has been done recently.

"In the music world," I say after a few more moments of silence between us, "Central Office folk care about high school band. They need it for marching around a football field at halftime and playing at basketball games."

"Maybe," she says, sounding calmer than a moment ago, "we need to give him something simple that we think is legit to promise, like your elementary band director gave that principal: 'here's what students will perform at the end of kindergarten.' And, yes, comprehension needs to be part of that performance."

"Once you're talking about 'performance,' you're back in my music world," I say, glad to be anywhere near my true expertise again. "What could we promise for comprehension by the end of the year?"

"We can figure it out. Then we'll have to educate him about what early comprehension skills look like, and how they lead to the kind of skills he just mentioned -- read a passage and answer questions about it. We can't just have him saying, 'make comprehension your focus.' That's not helpful."

"Do you know that comprehension stuff, because I certainly don't?"

"He's such a hopeless case" she says, seemingly to herself. Then she is silent again. After a while, she takes out a small piece of paper from her pocket and writes a note on it. "I'll have to look up the latest research, I guess." She finishes writing and looks up at me. "It has been a few years since I was in graduate school, and I'm sure the research has come a ways since I last looked. But, basically, I know that beginning readers have to be able to do things verbally first, such as repeat stories they've heard and retell those stories' actions in the same sequence as they were in the story they heard. They also have to be able to hear individual sounds in spoken language, the way we've been doing in my classroom. And they have to know the connection of individual sounds in spoken language to individual written letters."

"But none of that is reading comprehension, is it?"

"The listening to stories and retelling them is listening comprehension and oral language skills. They are precursors to reading comprehension," she says. "The other things I just mentioned are foundational skills that lead to comprehension. The students also need to be reading words and then sentences with fluency. That is, with some speed and accuracy. Eventually they can tell us about a story or nonfiction passage they've actually read, not heard."

"And all of that by the end of kindergarten?" I ask.

"Not really," she says.

Are we back to where Mr. Bevington left us then, unable to say what the goal is except for his vague goal of better comprehension?

"Entering kindergarten," she continues, "students should have the oral language skills, like retelling a story they heard or telling a new story. And they should be able to hear and say what the first sound is in a spoken word."

"So, lots of hearing skills, at that point?"

"Right, plus speaking," she says. "Then we start them on making the connection between spoken sounds and written words. Right in there, to teach these skills, we start asking them questions before reading them a story, and during it. We have them draw pictures of what they've just heard, to seal it into their brains and help us see what got sealed, so to speak."

"Can we promise him students will be able to draw a picture of what they've just read by the end of kindergarten?" I ask her, hopefully.

"Hmm. Let me think about that one," she says. "That would involve students actually reading. I'll check some research, like I said earlier."

"Okay." I say. "I'll see you on Monday. Have a nice weekend." We've moved from angry reaction to specific actions we can take. Not bad. I stand and turn to leave.

"I'm sorry I reacted so strongly, Patrick," Ms. Armstrong says to my back as I reach the doorway. I stop and turn to look back at her. She continues, "I keep thinking of something a friend of mine says: 'Be kind. Everyone you meet is fighting a great battle.' Remember that."

"Is your principal fighting some great battle I don't know about?"

"We all are, some in secret and some less so," she answers. "Go home and hug your wife and kid for me, okay?" With that, she stands, turns and begins writing on the white board again.

Pillars Of Reading Success

Monday, March 7 - Monday, March 14

"I did a little research during the weekend, to get Bevington off our backs about comprehension. Remember that little issue?" Ms. Armstrong asks me in the teachers' lounge on Monday. She's carrying an armful of papers, which she puts down on the counter by the small microwave. She takes a bottle of hand lotion from near the sink. I notice she has a big black mark on her arm, which she begins massaging with the lotion. She puts some water in a cup, which she places in the microwave and turns on.

"Yes, I remember the comprehension issue. What did you find out?"

"Well, the latest standards say that by the end of kindergarten most students should be able to ask and answer questions about key details in a text, retell familiar stories, and say who the characters are, the setting, stuff like that, in terms of reading comprehension." She picks up and hands me a large bundle from the papers she was carrying. Then she pulls the now-hot water from the microwave and plops a tea bag into it. "There are some copies I printed of the standards and some studies I found. Used up most of my ink at home on this."

"Interesting, I'll take a look at these." I put the papers beside my laptop on the table.

"I looked on the district's website," she says. "I found out they'll be using some test at multiple times during the school year that has students read a passage and then answer questions the teacher asks them. You can score them on how fast they read the passage, but mostly the district wants a score for the level of text they are reading and the questions they can answer about it. They've been piloting this test in a few schools already this year, including at Putnam west of here and Clover, which is a couple of blocks east of here."

"That explains why Mr. Bevington says he wants to see your students doing that. Right?"

"Bingo! You don't think he thought up that goal on his own, do you?" She pulls out a chair across from me and sits, putting her tea on the table. "The district has set a level it wants all kindergartners to meet. The test generates a letter score that tells us where a child is supposedly performing. The district says kindergartners should reach Level C."

"Whatever 'Level C' means," I say.

"It just means the level that is harder than Level B and easier than Level D."

"It sounds like we've got our goal for him then."

"Right again," she says. "Now we just have to figure out what that all has to do with the research I found and how to teach it. Put that all in a document and maybe we'll get all the adults here and downtown off our backs. Sounds easy."

"I don't know about easy," I say. "Where to begin?"

"How about you do the work this time, since I just researched the comprehension goal. You read all this I printed, then create something that shows what individual skills a student needs to have to comprehend well. Do it as a sloppy copy we can look at together. Do it for first grade, too, while you're at it. I think you can do that, smart guy." She picks up her tea and departs, with a small wave of her other hand, leaving me with her pile of papers to read.

*   *   *

We are going to need to go beyond Ms. Armstrong's classroom, and beyond kindergarten, if we ever want to turn things around at this school. Those parents at the parent night were impressed with one classroom and one teacher. They won't be happy if they get here next year and are assigned to a different teacher's room. So, we've got to get the other kindergarten teachers doing things differently next year, too.

Those teachers won't have time between now and the fall to go through the whole journey that Ms. Armstrong and I have gone through.

We need some tools. The first tool is this list of the skills a kindergartner and a 1st grader need to have in order to be considered successful reading comprehenders at the end of each of those grades. Then Ms. Armstrong and I can create a second tool: how to teach those skills. Maybe we'll even be able to enlist the other kindergarten and 1st grade teachers in that task, to pull together their best methods and lessons.

We've got the end goal for each grade, as defined by the test of comprehension that the district is using. That says they should be at Level C at the end of K and Level I at the end of 1st grade. Hmm, guess I'll need to know what exactly "Level C" means, for starters. Each level is tested with a set of little books the students must read and then answer questions about to gauge their comprehension.

On Tuesday, I got a copy of the books that are used, from one of the teachers whose classroom I visited at Clover Elementary. They are really easy at first, getting harder with each level. The length gets longer, the words get bigger, the later stories have more difficult words using ch and sh and th. Harder, certainly, for a kindergartner. Just like those five-note songs were for a beginning musician -- challenging.

My first take on my task, after seeing the books they use for the test, is to make lists of all the words in those test books and tell teachers to be sure to teach those words. I spend most of the week on this task, amidst everything else.

"That's not how those tests work," says Veronique when I call her on Friday afternoon to tell her what I've been doing. "A student might do fine on the test that way. Might. But teaching that way won't develop better readers in the long run. Don't let your list encourage teachers to teach that way."

"Well, then how and what should we tell teachers to teach?" I ask, a tad exasperated. I put more than a few hours into reading a bunch of the little books and counting up how many times certain words occurred.

"Go back to the standards and see what they say about the full set of skills students need," she counsels me, "not just the words students need in order to read the words for that one test. You're cheating those students' futures, otherwise."

I must admit that, at the moment she's telling me that, I am considering firing her as my guru. What does she know? She's out of touch. She probably hasn't looked at the test as closely as I have. If a child knows the way to read the word "chair," with its ch at the beginning and its "ai" in the middle, won't that child know how to read "chin" and "hair" in other texts? And won't that child be able to transfer those skills to similar letter combinations, such as th, sh and wh? Or ea, ie, or even ay? I ask her this.

"No!" she says emphatically. "That's not the way it works for a young child learning to read. Don't do it."

"How do you know all of this about reading?" I finally am frustrated enough and have to ask her. "What kind of consulting does a former 'World Music' professor do that makes you an expert in all of this? I just spent umpteen hours figuring this out, and you can't just say it's wrong. Maybe my idea is better than yours this time." I'm pissed.

"I was wondering when you'd ask," she says, calmly. "I quit being a professor at the end of the year you were in my second class. I really wanted to change the world, not just talk about it. I then spent several years in a really low socio-economic neighborhood of Chicago, working with teachers in a set of schools on improving their students' reading skills. During that time I read all the latest research on reading skills and how young children develop them. We did amazing and hard work together. I learned a lot in those classrooms, with those beautiful children and their teachers. Those schools' reading scores went up nicely, highest gains in the district for multiple years. Now I've got schools and districts all over the country and even all over the English-speaking world asking me to come to advise them on all of this. So you see, I'm not just a World Music professor anymore."

"Geez, why don't I just have you do this then, instead of me having to figure it all out?" I say, exasperated again.

"No, Patrick. You are on the right track," she says. The sudden compliment leaves me silent. "One of the things I found was that, ultimately, a school has to take ownership of this process. The teachers and parents and principal -- all of them together -- have to become the ones steering the change, or it won't stick. So, it's best if you and the others at that school figure this out together. I'm just here to help every now and then."

She's a lot more of a reading expert than me, and now I have a better idea of why that is. Her advice has been very helpful along this journey. I see the reasoning behind a school needing to own the solution. So it's back to the drawing board on this issue of what to tell teachers to teach. She and I end our call, and I know I have a lot of work left to do.

So, I spend another set of hours Friday evening and all day Saturday reading the research and the standards that exist for reading at young ages. While I'm deep in the thicket of all this, I get three calls from Eric, according to caller ID, which I ignore. Grace and Joey are at her mom's house in the suburbs for the weekend. Grace said they'd be back on Monday before dinner. I miss them whenever they are gone, even for one night, but right now I'm glad to have the place to myself for this huge task. As I'm reading and thinking Saturday afternoon, the light goes out of the day. Dusk later becomes deep nighttime.

The studies I read all agree with what Ms. Armstrong initially told me, off the top of her head while walking down the hall at school:

Beginning readers have to be able to do things verbally first, like repeat stories they've heard. They have to be able to hear individual sounds in spoken language, like we've been doing in my classroom. They have to be able to make the connection of individual letters to individual sounds in spoken language.

The listening to stories and retelling them is called listening comprehension. It's the precursor to reading comprehension. The other parts are foundational skills that lead to comprehension. Students go on to reading words and then sentences with fluency - that is, with some speed and accuracy. They also should tell us about stories or non-fiction passages they read themselves.

Of course, the research and standards go deeper than Armstrong shared in that initial overview, and some folks cal[l] part "oral language skills" instead of just "listening comprehension," but she got the basic structure very right. The more I read it, the more a picture forms in my head of something different from just a list, but I do not know what that should be. It should be simple, preferably all on one page, for teachers who have not been through this whole process with Ms. Armstrong and me. A list could work, but it's not elegant to look at. I need Grace's visual eye, but it's the middle of the night and Grace is not here. I try my usual favorite, a circle. After several versions, I have a trash can full of crumpled paper drawings.

In the fuzzy light before dawn, I stare blankly out our living room window and see vague columns across the street. Half-asleep, I am almost dreaming. Are they trees? Or a building? I count them. One, two, three… seven in all. In this light, they are blue-black columns, tall and statuesque, strong and mighty, telling me to be strong and build something that will stand for a very long time as a testament to this time I have spent alone, digging deeply into mankind's fundamental ways of learning. Nothing seems like exaggeration at this hour, as I drift in and out of consciousness.

When I wake, it is Sunday morning, but just barely. I turn over a piece of paper so I'm looking at a blank sheet. I pick up my best pen and draw a set of "pillars." One, two, three… seven in all -- each tall and strong, meant to stand for a long time. As I draw them, I know each will represent a set of skills that young readers need in order to be good readers. Phonological Awareness (fancy lingo for that listening skill Ms. Armstrong mentioned). Sound to Symbol Correlation (more research lingo, this one for knowing which letters represent which sounds from spoken language). Blending (which means sounding out several letters that make a word). A category I decide to call Advanced Phonics Concepts (I could have called the Sound To Symbol group "Beginning Phonics Concepts," I suppose). Sight words (frequent words that don't follow the regular rules, so you just need to know them by sight). Fluency (speed, accuracy and expression while reading sentences and paragraphs). And Reading Comprehension, finally!

Whew. That's a large bunch of hours of my life that I will never get back. Hey, I don't want them back. Now I've got that visual, that chart that organizes it all. I go into the bathroom, turn on the water, adjust it to warm, and take a shower.

Once I have dried off and put on fresh clothes, I fix a large breakfast of three eggs scrambled, toast with jam, and orange juice. Then I press on.

In each of the pillars, I place a breakdown of the more-specific skills a teacher could see and say, "I saw this student do this skill." For instance, under Phonological Awareness, the pillar has these listed as deeper and deeper levels: "Generate First Sounds in Spoken Words," "Blend Sounds To Make Spoken Words," and "Segment Spoken Words Into Sounds".

Since I did all this reading of the research, putting all these skills under each column will make it as easy as possible for teachers to be able to use this information. I don't want to come back in the fall and try to get my head back to where it is right now on all this research. So, I just did it. It's done. Let me see what the boss says tomorrow morning when school is back in session and I can see her.

*   *   *

This is pretty good, young Patrick. All on one page, too," says Ms. Armstrong after I've given her about two minutes to look at my document. "You could have been a pretty good teacher, if you hadn't gotten distracted by that musician lifestyle thing. I see what I said to you about comprehension research and where you found some interesting, more-current research, too. This is really helpful."

"I figured I was getting the research right. But I had no idea if you'd think the format was useful, with its pillars and all. Such a list could just be irritating to teachers."

"How do you intend for teachers to use it?" she asks me. "Should they teach all the skills in pillar one, then go on to all the skills in pillar two? Or should they teach all the top-of-pillar skills in the seven pillars, then move down the page from top to bottom?"

"Before we think about teaching, think about your boss. He thinks comprehension is this thing that six year olds practice by reading passages and then answering questions about those passages. 'No teaching required, just do it lots of times,' he must be thinking. So, this tool shows the seven skills that must be taught and practiced and developed in order to produce good reading comprehension. This document can be used to educate him about the true nature of comprehension and what 'progress' looks like along the way."

"That'd be pretty great," says Ms. Armstrong. "Now tell me how I use it as a teacher."

"Start teaching the skills that are at the top left corner of the page and go to the bottom right corner where the highest level of comprehension skills are listed," I tell her. "But don't think it's completely linear. You don't have to do pillar one from top to bottom, then go on to the top of pillar two and do it top to bottom. The research says some students will zoom ahead on one skill in the next pillar before they've mastered all the previous pillar's skills. Or they might move down a column to a higher level of that skill without fully mastering something above it on the column. That's all fine. This is an approximation."

"That sounds about right to me," she says. "Kids will always do the darnedest things, no matter how great your model looks."

"Next step is to try it in your real classroom then," I say to her, hoping she's excited enough to want to use it right away, as the next test of my draft and its ideas.

"How about you try it first, since you created it?" asks Ms. Armstrong. "This is going to be work to try the first time. I'm working on instructional time and graphing bathroom breaks in my classroom right now. Let me know how it goes in somebody else's room, maybe Ms. Orr."

Pillars of Reading Success

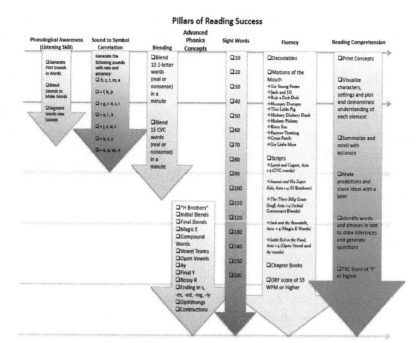

Phonological Awareness (Listening Skill)	Sound to Symbol Correlation	Blending	Advanced Phonics Concepts	Sight Words	Fluency	Reading Comprehension
☐ Generate First Sounds in Words	Generate the following sounds with rate and accuracy:	☐ Blend 10 2-letter words (real or nonsense) in a minute		☐ 10	☐ Decodables	☐ Print Concepts
☐ Blend Sounds to Make Words	☐ b, s, t, m, a			☐ 20	☐ Motions of the Mouth	☐ Visualize characters, settings and plot and demonstrate understanding of each element
☐ Segment Words into Sounds	☐ + f, h, p			☐ 30	◇ Six Young Foxes ◇ Jack and Jill ◇ Rub a Dub Dub	
	☐ + g, r, d, c, i			☐ 40	◇ Humpty Dumpty ◇ This Little Pig	
	☐ + n, l, k	☐ Blend 15 CVC words (real or nonsense) in a minute		☐ 50	◇ Hickory Dickory Dock ◇ Hickety Pickety	
	☐ + j, v, w, z			☐ 60	◇ Bless You ◇ Farmer Trotting	☐ Summarize and retell with accuracy
	☐ + o, x, y			☐ 70	◇ Cross Patch ◇ Six Little Mice	
	☐ + u, q, qu, e			☐ 80	☐ Scripts ◇ Lamb and Coyote, Acts 1-3 (CVC words)	
				☐ 90	◇ Anansi and His Super Kids, Acts 1-4 (H Brothers)	☐ Make predictions and share ideas with a peer
				☐ 100		
				☐ 110	◇ The Three Billy Goats Gruff, Acts 1-4 (Initial Consonant Blends)	
			☐ "H Brothers" ☐ Initial Blends ☐ Final Blends	☐ 120	◇ Jack and the Beanstalk, Acts 1-4 (Magic E Words)	☐ Identify words and phrases in text to draw inferences and generate questions
			☐ Magic E ☐ Compound Words	☐ 130		
			☐ Vowel Teams ☐ Open Vowels	☐ 140	◇ Little Red in the Hood, Acts 1-4 (Open Vowel and Ay words)	
			☐ Ay ☐ Final Y	☐ 150	☐ Chapter Books	☐ TRC Score of "I" or higher
			☐ Bossy R ☐ Ending in s, -es, -ed, -ing, -ly ☐ Diphthongs ☐ Contractions	☐ 160	☐ ORF score of 53 WPM or Higher	

Classroom Management Failure

Wednesday, March 16

Thus, I find myself walking into Ms. Orr's kindergarten room two days later, after taking time to check in with Grace and Joey, who returned on Monday evening to my many hugs and kisses.

Ms. Orr and I had time for a short chat on Tuesday. She liked the idea of me doing comprehension, making it "artsy" and with the whole class, rather than some kind of small groups format. I prepared, but once again I'm on unfamiliar ground.

I've planned a theater-based lesson. In college, I was involved with lots of theater, playing for the musicals, mostly. I also worked with actor friends on pieces that were more experimental and intimate. I even tried writing a few stories for friends to perform.

The connections between theater and reading comprehension seem more direct and useful than something would be with music. Theater's world has words, reading words aloud, making a story visible by acting it out for the non-readers to see it. My plan is that this will touch some of the skills Ms. Armstrong and I put into the comprehension pillar.

"Students, today we are going to read and perform a little play I wrote," I tell the class of kindergartners sitting quietly on the rug in front of me. "Everyone gets a part in this play. And it will be fun, I promise." I've actually written a much-simplified variation on a folk tale I found in the library, and I've made parts for all 30 students, so all have at least a few words to read out loud.

"Here are your parts." I distribute typed scripts to all 30 students on the rug. Ms. Orr has an odd look on her face.

191

"I can't read," comes one little voice from the middle of the group, as I continue handing out scripts.

"Just do the best you can," I say, in my "encouraging" voice. "Ask your neighbor to help, if you don't know a word." I glance at Ms. Orr, who is bending to turn one child's script right side up so she can read it.

"We are ready to begin, students," I say, sensing some restlessness in the group, as their little feet wiggle and their papers rustle in their hands like a flock of birds' wings starting to take off from a calm lake. "You read the part on your script that is highlighted in green highlighter. So, listen as others read, and then read your part when we get to the green highlighted part. Who has the first line in green?"

No student says anything or raises a hand. Looking around the room, I spot the script with the first line highlighted in green, and I point to that student. "You have the first line to read. Go ahead," I say to a tiny boy who is looking at Mrs. Orr for reassurance.

"Okay, Justin, I have a copy, too, so we'll read it together," says Ms. Orr. Justin continues to look at her as Ms. Orr reads his first lines. "Who has the next lines?" she says. We repeat the same search until another student discovers she has the next highlighted lines in her script.

It goes on like this for several minutes, as we very slowly work our way through my script. More rustling of paper, jostling of legs and arms, and confusion as the minutes pass.

Suddenly, a girl shrieks, then begins to cry loudly. "His foot pinched my fingers!" she says as explanation. Ms. Orr looks at the girl and then at me.

The boy next to her on the rug crosses his arms and sticks out his lower lip as protest to these charges. Another boy behind them starts laughing. The first boy reaches around and punches him hard in the leg. Ms. Orr is looking at me. The girl stands and goes quickly to a corner of the room to cry. The whole group is watching all of this now, and another girl gets up and goes to comfort her friend.

"It was an accident," I say, channeling something my mother probably said to my brother or me long ago. "Let's get back to reading our story. Where were we?" In the commotion, several other students who have not had their lines to read yet have crawled away from the group and are fussing with something in another part of the room. They do not seem to be causing any audible issues at the moment, so I let them continue whatever they are quietly doing. I'll have to read their parts when they come up. Ms. Orr catches my eye and raises her eyebrows.

Slowly my script winds to its end.

"Children, line up for lunch," comes Ms. Orr's final pronouncement of my experiment's long-awaited death. "Thank Mr. Patrick for his story today." The students all clap their little hands three times in unison and move to line up by the classroom door.

"Well, Mr. Patrick," says Ms. Orr to me. "We will have to talk later."

Alone in the hallway afterward, I am struck by how good my plan seemed on paper and how quickly it disintegrated in the room with actual kindergartners as my judge and jury. This feels bad, like the first time I taught small groups in Ms. Armstrong's room. Is there no way around this when trying something new with young children? Are lessons bound to fail until they have been tried and adjusted many times? If so, how do teachers ever muster the gumption to try new things that first time (and possibly 2nd and 3rd and beyond) until they work?

I head home, eager to get away from the school and my failure today.

"What's wrong, hon?" Grace asks as I walk in the front door and toss my coat on the sofa. I was hoping she'd be out somewhere and I could sit in the dark by myself until this bad feeling goes away. "Weren't you doing some lesson in a classroom today?"

"It was a disaster," I mumble. "I had a plan, but it didn't work with students."

"Like I haven't heard that same thing from every new teacher I've ever worked with," she says, too cheerfully for my tastes.

"You're being a little too chipper about this, in my opinion," I say, ticked off at how lightly she's treating my failure.

193

"Just trying to counter how gloomy you're being, Patrick," she responds, coming over and putting her warm arms around my waist and her head on my shoulder. "Want to talk about it?"

We move to the couch, her arms still around me, and we just sit silently for a minute. Gradually, I feel like talking. As I do, without her saying anything, I can already see some of what went wrong. "Why did I do it in the whole group? That meant every student only got a small part and spent the rest of the time getting restless." Grace stays silent as more insights come. "In fact, why was I even having kindergartners read? We should have started with them listening."

"You'll learn a lot from this one outing," she says once I've finished and am quiet again.

"I don't want to fail in front of teachers and kids anymore," I say, aware that Ms. Orr, if not her students, now know I'm a phony.

"Seems like just walking through your plan with me was helpful, right?" she asks.

"Sure, but too late," I respond, realizing I'm unfairly shifting a little of the blame to her.

"Next time, let's do that beforehand then," she offers. "I said I wanted to get involved at the school. That's one way I can help, just being a sounding board."

"If there is a next time," I say, gloomily.

"Oh, there will be. I'm sure of that."

Her optimism is probably warranted, knowing how hard I can be on myself, how eager schools are to get outside help, and how resilient and persistent I can be once I have a day to think about things.

Observing Teachers

Thursday, March 17

"What are you writing there?" asks Ms. Armstrong, as I sit in her classroom the next morning watching her teach before our small group time.

"Oh, I'll tell you later," I say. She seems very curious, intensely focused on my notepad.

I was trying an idea -- creating a list of the great things I see Ms. Armstrong doing, that we would want to see other teachers doing. Then we could use this list to observe and work with other teachers here. It certainly would have helped me do better in Ms. Orr's room, in hindsight. That's probably why I started thinking about this.

After a minute or two of her pretending not to be watching me, I say, "I'm sorry. I can tell this is bugging you. Can I just put my notes away and show them to you, I promise, right after we do our small groups? I'll even give you half of my peanut butter and jelly sandwich while we talk then." She loosens a bit around the eyes and drops her shoulders just a little.

"Is that what trombone players eat, PB&J?" she asks, with some tease in her voice. "I don't want your sandwich, but I'll hold you to that explanation of whatever you were doing."

We do our small groups then, same as usual. The whole time I'm wondering what made her so curious. I was in her classroom to observe her teaching, at her invitation, just a few days/weeks ago. No big deal at that time. We even had a conversation about it afterward.

So, I'm continuing -- without notepad -- to document in my head what is working in this classroom that we'd love to see happening in other classrooms.

For starters, student behavior is really good. If a student starts causing a ruckus anywhere in the room, Ms. Armstrong simply says, "Johnny, that's one," and writes his name on a Post-It note. No long speeches from the teacher to all students. Just one little comment and action seems to be all that is needed to get the student back on track. I wonder how exactly this works? That seems worth noting for further investigation and possible inclusion on my list.

Out of the corner of my eye while running my own group of four students, Ms. Armstrong holds up the B card before the D card in her small group today. I have no way of knowing whether the order matters or not, so I just note it for now. As I write the note, it already feels like too much detail to be looking for in other classrooms.

I'm also seeing lots of things around the room that tell me good things are going on. Like Ms. Armstrong has posted a little schedule on the bulletin board, showing when her daily time is for small groups. Next to the time schedule are lists of which students are in each small group and what days they are seen, either by Ms. Armstrong or by me. I'm there as "Mr. P."

Our small group time ends, the students line up and then march quietly to the lunchroom, so Ms. Armstrong and I return to her classroom to talk and eat our lunches.

"I have been thinking about other tools we are going to need for eventually working with other teachers," I say to Ms. Armstrong. "That's what I was taking notes about this morning --what to put in a tool that says what we'd want to see other teachers doing in their classrooms when we come to observe them."

"Whoa!" she says, suddenly getting all prickly. "I don't want any part of that."

"Wait, what just happened?" I quickly ask.

"You said 'observe,'" she says. "That's what principals do once or twice a year to give us a job rating. Teachers are not fond of that whole process. It's threatening and, frankly, disrespectful."

"Why?" I ask her. "Don't you want feedback on your teaching, to help you improve?"

"Helpful, insightful feedback would be great," she continues, "but that's not what this is, usually. More like, our principal tells us he's coming the next day, we pull out our most-successful lesson, one we know will get a great response from students, and he sees our very best stuff. Then we get a rating, no notes, and life goes on."

"Worthless, in other words?"

"Exactly, unless your principal is out to get you," she responds, turning to stare right at me. "Then it can be a very bad thing. Either way, it's a lot of pressure with either no payoff or negative consequences. I won't help you with anything called 'observations.'"

Darn, I thought this was going to be a no-brainer - create a sensible list of what good teachers do, use it to look for those things in a teacher's classroom, and then give her feedback. Simple, right? Again, it sure would have helped me do a better job.

"Well, would you like to know a few great things I wrote down, anyway," I say, knowing I still want some kind of tool for working with other teachers eventually, "even if we can't call it being 'observed' or anything that rhymes with observed?"

"Nothing rhymes with observed," she says back, with a little more playful voice.

"Perturbed. Unnerved, reverbed," I say, trying to lighten up.

"Reverbed is not even a word," she says in response. "I suggest you just tell me what you were writing this morning, specifically, before I get 'perturbed'"

I proceed, happily, to tell her some of what I've written and some of what I collected in my head this morning.

"You've been paying attention, young Patrick," she says, after hearing my many positive notes about her classroom. "I'd forgotten some of those are things other teachers might not do. I just do them out of habit by now."

"And would you agree we should have some kind of list, if we are going to obs…. I mean 'visit other teachers' classrooms and partner with them to support their development?'"

"Yes. It needs to be another one-pager, like the 'Seven Pillars,' so it can be easily used as a reference," she says, warming to the whole idea.

"Seven Pillars, eh?" I say, hearing this name for the first time. "I like it."

"Thanks," she says. "I figured we'd get tired of calling it the 'thingy' or 'our list of content to teach in reading' or whatever. So I made up a name."

"Sounds good. Let's use it."

"About your idea for another one-pager," she says, getting us back on track. "Some teachers will like it best if it says what the students are doing. So maybe we need a version like that. But I also want a version that can tell me what I, the teacher, should be doing, so I can get feedback about what I am or am not doing when someone sees me teaching."

"Like I gave you feedback just now on all the positives I saw you doing in your classroom, even documents you have posted and such?"

"That was nice feedback to get," she says, "even from a trumpet player from Ohio."

"Trombone, from Oregon, but who's keeping track?"

"You've seen one brass player, you've seen them all," she responds. "This list needs some things I don't do, too, that I know I should be doing. I'm not perfect, you know."

"I never said you were," I poke back. "What should we add?"

"I'd add the number of times a student gets to give a response and get feedback in small groups," she says after thinking for a moment. "I've noticed, as we do small groups more, that it's possible to increase those opportunities. I'd like to increase the number per child even more."

"I never thought about that one," I begin. "Naturally I see you over there, as the experienced teacher, going lots faster than I am, at this point."

"So, if I was 'observing' you," she responds, "I guess you'd be getting a lower score, right?"

"Or I'd be getting feedback that told me where to improve," I respond. "Nicely done. This 'non-observation' watching each other would certainly help me."

"My pleasure," she says.

"This makes me remember something I've been wanting to talk about with you," she continues. "Most of what we've been talking about and experimenting with has been about small group instruction. I totally understand how important the small groups are to instructional quality and being able to provide each student what he or she needs -- instructional time and the right content. It's all about those 1,200 hours and all. Fixing bathroom breaks and some other things has meant I waste lots less time, too."

"So, what's the other issue you've been wanting to discuss?"

"Well, what about whole group instruction? Are there opportunities there to do better, to give every student what is needed, just as we're doing now in our small groups? I've been wanting to explore this, so my higher level students who don't get much or any small groups per week are getting better instruction, too."

"Sounds terrific to me," I say, remembering what Veronique said after my morning spent watching Ms. Armstrong's classroom.

"After my rough outing with Ms. Orr's whole group," I say, "I wouldn't say I have much to offer. What ideas do you have for this?"

"I'm just starting to think about this," she admits. "I looked at a few ideas online. Surprisingly, there are some old ideas that make a lot of sense to me. I'd like to try a few of those. Like being strategic about where students sit when we do whole group time on the rug. It always helps to have Jeremiah right by me, but there are others who need that, too. Another interesting idea that seems to be really old is to have students at their desks and give them all mini-whiteboards to write their answers on. Then they each hold up their answer so just the teacher can see it, so I can see who's getting it right and who's still not understanding, and I can do a mini-drill right then with those few."

"How's that work?" I ask, not understanding her idea yet.

"Like I ask the class which letter represents the 'buh' sound," she patiently explains. "Most will write the letter B. A few write the letter D, and I will tell the whole class the right answer is letter B. I can go further and single out one student to quiz a few extra times, if they repeat their error."

"Cool. It's like a small group lesson, but for everybody," I say, excited to be opening up a whole new area of exploration with her and for my own teaching.

"Right. I bet we can find lots of ways to make whole group lots more engaging for all my students," she says, excited just like me.

"Then we can put something about that on this new one-pager," I say.

"Before the students rush back in from lunch, can we decide what needs to be done and who's going to do it to finish this tool for 'visits with feedback,' now that we've got a good start?"

"We need to organize what we have and anything we find to add into a few bigger categories or headings, first, like we did with the Seven Pillars. I've got more ideas, such as classroom management as a category, from my disaster in Ms. Orr's room. Then we need to put everything we have under one or another of those headings, again as we did with the Seven Pillars."

"Does it have to be seven again?" she asks.

"Nope, unless we end up with seven at the end."

"Whatever that means," she says. "How about you do the first draft, since you're on a roll with this thing, and I'll add to it. Here come the students again."

And, with that, formerly-hungry students rush through the door, pushing and shoving as though they've just ingested a large quantity of sugar. Which, of course, they likely have.

New Tool, Draft #1

Afternoon of March 17

Since this morning watching Ms. Armstrong and her class, I've been thinking of practically nothing else but a new tool for spotting what's really going on -- or not -- in other classrooms. I head to the coffee shop where I first ran into Veronique, wanting its good luck vibe. As I sit and get out my laptop, I check my watch: 11:30.

My linear musician brain wants to first get the categories, then fill-in the particulars under each category. This worked pretty well for the Seven Pillars, after all.

I've already got one category: How to Manage the Classroom, from my failed whole group lesson in Ms. Orr's room. One or two misbehaving students took over my classroom. I also remember Jeremiah in Ms. Armstrong's room, pulling her attention and energy all the time, and disturbing all the students and their learning. She has gotten so much better at managing all her students, such as this morning's "Johnny, that's one" trick, so disruption in the classroom doesn't happen as often.

My own small group work in Ms. Armstrong's room often shows me things about student behavior that I don't know how to manage, even though I only have four students to handle. I would love for someone to watch me and give me pointers.

I'm also thinking about little things in Ms. Armstrong's room this morning, such as the schedule she had posted, showing her daily times for small group. They remind me that Instructional Time is another category for my draft.

Teaching the Right Content is important, too. If Ms. Armstrong did really organized small groups, and had a brilliant schedule for them where she saw each student the exact amount of times per week that each student needed, but the content was all math, just to use an extreme example, we couldn't expect that to get more of her students reading.

Ms. Armstrong told me she's getting better at small groups, using Engaging Methods to get more practice and feedback loops into each of her small groups, so students get more practice of the key skills they need. I want that kind of thing on this document, too, somewhere.

I look at my watch. It's 3:20. Time flies. My brain is tired. I have a draft document that's ready to show Ms. Armstrong and get her to help finish it. I bet she's still at school, with no students around, as school lets out at 3 o'clock. I jump in my car, eager to get her feedback.

I find Ms. Armstrong in her room, sure enough. It's quiet and calm without any students around. Sitting at her desk, pen in hand, she doesn't notice me standing in the doorway at first. I stop to enjoy the unusual quiet for a moment. Then I can't hold my enthusiasm anymore.

"Ms. Armstrong, I have a draft," I say in almost a whisper, trying not to startle her.

She looks up. "Oh, hello there, Patrick. Come on, let's see it then."

I proceed to share my draft and its four categories, with some specifics under each. I laid it out quickly in the coffeeshop, very similarly to the Seven Pillars format, so it's not hard to explain it to her and have her immediately know how to "read" it. After 15 minutes, we've made it through the whole thing.

She looks up at me. "This is really good! Nicely done, young man. There's probably some things missing in the details, maybe even a category or two, so we should share it with other teachers. Maybe they'll remind us of something important."

She sits quietly with the document in her hand, thinking deeply, pulling something from some distant recess. I stay quiet and let her do whatever she needs to be doing right now.

"There's one more thing," she finally says. "Can we get something on here about joy?"

This makes me stop. She said it with such seriousness. I want to respond in kind. "What do you mean by 'joy,' in this situation?" I ask her. "Generally, I'm in favor of joy."

"I just mean we've got these great categories and specifics of what we should be able to see a teacher doing and what we'd want to be working on to make a really great classroom," she says. "It occurs to me that most teachers started out in teaching in order to bring the joy of learning to students. After a while, some of us might have forgotten that. Maybe our life got in the way. It'd be good to have a little reminder here, so it can officially be a topic of discussion from time to time, like between you and me right now."

"I like that," I say, trying to keep my voice steady in a tender moment. "I like it a lot."

"It's not a whole category," she continues after a moment. "But just add something about joy and about seeing the teacher smiling and laughing with students, so students see how much their teacher loves the work they are doing together. The joy of learning, in other words."

With that, she stands to pack up her papers and leave, signaling she's said enough.

"It's a good thing we are doing here, Mr. Trombone-player-from-Oregon," she says to me. "We've made a good start of it, so we can keep thinking about it and adjust it in the coming days and weeks. Let's call it our 'compass' for now. Good name for this. I wish I had a compass to help me rescue my lost cause at home." With that vague comment, she is out the door and gone.

Principal Adds Two Rooms

"Hey, Patrick!" It's Mr. Bevington, hollering at me from down the hall as I head away from Ms. Armstrong's classroom and toward the door out of the building. He's accompanied by Ms. Peterson. I stop and wait for them to reach me. He seems very eager to talk, judging by his continually waving arms and relatively rapid movement down the hallway. Ms. Peterson seems equally eager to have a conversation with me.

"What's up?" I ask. "I was just on my way out for the day."

"I hear you and Ms. Armstrong are making progress on that reading comprehension issue," he says. "That would be great news for getting the Central Office folks off my back."

"This is all my fault," says Ms. Peterson, quickly. "Ms. Armstrong and I were talking before school this morning. She told me all about the seven pylons or pythons or whatever it is. I haven't seen her so enthusiastic talking about teaching in years."

"You mean seven pillars, I suspect," I say, feeling ambushed.

"I need you to get into more than just Ms. Armstrong's room," continues Mr. Bevington. "Can you do something for all the kindergarten? That's two more teachers."

"It would fill-out our kindergarten plan for next year," Ms. Peterson adds, a bit sheepishly.

"I'm not sure what would transfer to other rooms, exactly," I say quickly, shooting a not-happy look to Ms. Peterson. "Ms. Armstrong and I have been just experimenting, so far."

"It would be great if you could help those other two kindergarten teachers, too," Mr. Bevington continues. "We need good things in more classrooms. Get the plan going."

Mr. Bevington heads off in search of the next solution to his threatened retirement plan.

Ms. Peterson makes a little motion with her hand that seems to be saying for me to stay.

"I'm sorry about that," she says quietly to me, once he's gone around a corner. "I should never have told him. But Ms. Armstrong is like a new person, and it just slipped out to him before I even knew what I was saying."

"We're doing some good things together," I respond. "I just didn't want to promise him anything more than I'm already doing, not until I've thought about it for more than a minute."

"Of course," she quickly adds. "For what it's worth, I think it's a great idea to do something with the other kindergarten teachers. It's an opportunity to add real meat to our plan."

"Thanks for the vote of confidence," I reply. "But what might I actually do with them?"

"Just my two cents, as a teacher," she continues. "Have a get-acquainted meeting with them. Let Ms. Armstrong say nice things about you. Then teach some whole group lessons in their classrooms. Earn some trust. Then maybe you and Ms. Armstrong can get them to do what she's doing with small groups. They'll trust her, if she says it's worth doing. Maybe it doesn't have to be you doing all the work, times three. Maybe you and Ms. Armstrong can do a training, get the other two teachers doing the work, with you coaxing them along."

"I don't know," I say. "I don't have time to do what I've been doing times three. Besides, I tried teaching a whole group lesson already in Ms. Orr's room, and it was a disaster. I'm sure I didn't build any credibility with her."

"I know Ms. Orr well enough. She'll forgive you your trespasses, if you forgive hers."

"She hasn't had any trespasses with me," I say.

"She will, believe me," says Ms. Peterson. "Get ahead of it with her and others by planning another lesson to do with their whole classrooms. Maybe use some music this time. Get some help to plan it.

Do the same lesson with all three rooms. Start in Ms. Armstrong's room and get really good at that one lesson. They will absolutely love it."

She's got a solid idea. Funny that I'm feeling resistant. A moment before, we were looking at another tool for moving our good work to more classrooms. I guess it's my old "I don't want a boss" thing coming out. It's one thing to have ideas with Ms. Armstrong. It's another thing to have Mr. Bevington coming at me in the hallway, insisting I should do something he wants.

As I walk to my car, it feels more and more like success. Key people are asking -- even begging -- us to expand our work into the rest of the kindergarten. Now I have to "coax" those teachers into believing this is a good idea. I'm glad she had some ideas for how to do that with the other K teachers, as I am fresh out of ideas.

Eric's News

Saturday, March 19

It's the weekend, Saturday, mid-March, and the weather's not bad for early springtime in Chicago. Light breeze off the lake, partly sunny, mid-50's. It feels downright warm.

I'm glad weekends were invented. First of all, regular folks get a break from work. That's how I'm feeling these days -- like a working guy who needs a change of scenery on the weekend. Secondly, weekends give me a chance to be with Grace and Joey. During the week now, it gets dark soon after dinner. So there's not much outdoors time available. It's dinner, bath, stories, bed. Grace and Joey end up being just guardrails for me on that high-speed race track. Final reason that I love weekends is that they give regular folks time to dress up and go to concerts, so I can get paid to be a real musician. My first and my last reason conflict: one's about getting a break from work, the other's about getting to work more. I like them both.

Grace got up early, determined to do something in the yard. By the time Joey and I get outside after breakfast, Grace has a pile of brush she's cleared off the flower beds in front of our house, and the knees of her jeans are wet from kneeling on the damp ground. She looks quite proud of her pile of grey twigs and dead leaves, as Joey and I get our bikes out and prepare to ride. It's been nearly two months since he first successfully rode, with broomstick and then without, and he's been practicing plenty on the sidewalks and alleys.

Our block's streets are nearly traffic free, most days. It's a good day to try a ride together on the street, even if it's just around the block for now. I give him the necessary "dad talk" about street riding, then we're off.

After our third successful loop around the block, I see Grace waving her arms at us from in front of our house. I immediately get Joey to ride onto the sidewalk and I pedal faster to reach her, fearing some calamity has slammed into our pleasant Saturday morning.

"It's Eric," she says, breathlessly, as she hands me the phone and turns to tend to Joey and his bike. The phone reminds me that Eric was calling me repeatedly last weekend as I worked on what became the Seven Pillars. I forgot he'd even called.

"Eric, sorry I didn't call you back this week. Everything okay?"

"Sure, jerk," he begins, though I'm not sure he sounds mad. "I finally have some good news and you can't even call me back. I got the job!"

"The job? The orchestra job in Canada?" Last time I asked him, that audition was coming in a month or so. Time flies when you're not the one practicing all those orchestra excerpts.

"None other," he says. "They want me out there for their summer season, to get used to the place and the other musicians when there's less at stake than during the regular concert season. So, I'll be moving in June, at the latest, maybe late May."

My head is flooded. My best friend since college just told me he gets to live the dream. Yay? So he'll be moving away. Boo!

"That's such great news for you, Eric!" I say, realizing the appropriate response is to be happy for him and sort out my own mixed feelings about this later.

After more congratulations and praise for Eric, I see Grace coming back down the sidewalk with Joey and his bike, and I end the call with promises to talk more about what all this means really soon. Who will take Eric's place in the brass group for school gigs? Who will write new songs for the group and maybe even for classroom work I'm doing? What does this tell me I should be doing about auditions and getting my "real job" act together?

"What's up with Eric?" Grace asks me.

"He got the trumpet job in Canada."

"Oh, ouch," Grace says. "How you doing?" Grace has always read my face very well.

"I'm really happy for him," I say. "It just caught me a little by surprise, I guess."

"Daddy, ride with me more," Joey suddenly says, tugging at my shirt.

"You ride some more with Joey, and we can talk later about this," Grace says, giving me her great empathetic look. She knows I want to be excited about this, and that another part of me is going to feel left behind by the last of my music school buddies getting a full-time performing job.

"That works," I say, grabbing my bike and smiling at Joey. "Let's ride, buddy."

Riding around the block, passing houses I see every day, I am keeping one eye on Joey and the other on those houses, which now seem less familiar. I'm happy for Eric, for his triumph. I'm sad for selfish reasons. After a minute or two, I'm remembering my own reasons to be happy: Joey, Grace, our house, our school begging for more of me. Eric told me once, in his usual rational way, there'd be moments in life when big things happen that shake up the normal and replace it with a new normal. "Pay attention to those moments, and pay them the homage they deserve." With the sun warm on my face, this feels like one of those moments.

Kindergarten Teacher Meeting

Tuesday, March 22

I have a mixed record with the other kindergarten teachers. Thus, Ms. Peterson's idea to meet with all three of them is a good one, but feels perilous. She gets Dorothy to schedule a ten minute meeting before school. Ms. Peterson agrees to be there to troubleshoot afterward, if needed. I had a chat with Ms. Armstrong to enlist her as an ally for things we have been doing in her classroom.

It's the morning of the actual meeting. All of us except Ms. Armstrong are gathered together. It's five minutes before starting time, and I'm feeling unusually nervous. I brought donuts and coffee, to break the ice a little. The one teacher I don't recognize must be Ms. Gage. She's a short woman, trim, in her mid-to-late 50s. I move toward her to introduce myself.

"Good morning," I start. She looks up without any expression on her face. "I'm Patrick. You must be the one K teacher I have not met, Ms. Gage?"

"I am Ms. Gage," she responds, still with no expression on her face. She is dressed conservatively in a tweed skirt, grey blouse and sensible black pumps, low heel.

"You probably saw my brass quintet perform here several months ago. I live in the neighborhood." Does it give me more credibility or less to be part of the community?

"I have been working in Ms. Armstrong's classroom since then," I continue. "I also did some piloting of a whole group lesson in Mrs. Orr's classroom last week."

"I heard about that from Ms. Orr, yes," she says, which doesn't seem overly positive.

"I have a lot to learn," I say, as Ms. Orr comes over to us from nearby. "Ms. Orr can tell you that my drama and reading lesson in her room definitely proved that. Right, Ms. Orr?" I might as well lay some of my vulnerabilities on the table, modeling behaviors I'd love to see.

"Well, it caused plenty of drama in my room, I'll say that," she says with a small laugh. "But I think you've got some interesting ideas. They just need, um… work."

"To be honest, that's generous of you. So, thank you for that," I say, spotting our final participant out of the corner of my eye. "It looks like Ms. Armstrong is here now, so let's get started." With that I head to the seat with my papers on it, and others sit at chairs in a circle.

"Good morning, everyone," I begin. "Our reason for this short meeting is that I have been asked by Mr. Bevington to start working in your other two K rooms, as we finish the plan for kindergarten and this whole school next year."

"What kind of plan are you creating?" asks Ms. Orr.

"I'm sure you've all heard this school is on a list of schools that could be closed next year." I see heads nod. "We're creating a plan to improve reading here and, hopefully, show central office we deserve to stay open."

"That sounds like a heck of a plan," says Ms. Orr.

"Another way to think about this plan is that parents have choices these days for where to send their children for school," says Ms. Peterson. "One of the things parents want, according to a short survey we did at parent night, is small groups, like they saw that evening. So, that's one of the core ingredients of the proposed kindergarten program for next year. We'd like to get a running start by piloting some small group instruction in each of your classrooms this year."

"I'm loving small groups," says Ms. Armstrong, "and any visitor could see me doing those or see them on my schedule. The students are so engaged when there are just four of them in front of me."

"Aren't they hard to set up?" asks Ms. Orr.

"I felt clumsy at them at first," admits Ms. Armstrong. "They took so much thinking to know what to do every moment. But the more I do them, the better they run. So the students get more reps on skills they need, in just 20 minutes."

"And what does that do, other than speed everything up?" asks Ms. Gage, speaking for the first time. "Some children just need time to think about things and not feel rushed all the time."

"More reps," answers Ms. Armstrong, "means more chances for each student to hear a question, try to provide an answer, and get immediate feedback. I believe learning happens in those little moments, what Patrick and I have started calling practice and feedback loops."

"Hmm," says Ms. Gage. "I've never thought of it like that. I'm old school, some people say. I'm going to have to see this in my classroom."

"I hear you," says Ms. Armstrong. "It's been a bit of a journey for me, too. I have gone from skeptical about small groups to being able to do them, then to being able to do them well and in ways I know will be better for my students' learning. I'm excited about it all."

"It looks like we are nearly out of time," I interject as the two K teachers start gathering their things to leave. "I'll be setting a schedule for me to come see your classrooms and start implementing some small groups in there!"

"Hold on a minute." It's Ms. Armstrong talking, as she steps in front of the door to block their exit. "Patrick and I are going to have a training for you next Monday after school to acquaint you with small groups before he starts coming to your classrooms. We'll see you there."

Hmm. We hadn't talked about doing a training. There's no plan for doing a training. Once the other K teachers are gone, I wait for Ms. Armstrong to say something.

"That went well enough, don't you think?" asks Ms. Peterson.

"Why the look, Patrick?" asks Ms. Armstrong.

"Training them?" I say. "Were you and I going to talk about that?"

"Oh, yeah, it just occurred to me at the end," she says. "We don't want you in their rooms without them having some idea of why you are there."

"Thanks then, I guess," I whine. "Do we know anything about training teachers? Or do we have to learn all that the hard way, too? You know we are running out of time for these kind of experiments. We have to finish our plan and present it to Central Office."

"That's where I can help you two," says Ms. Peterson. "I'm in a graduate program right now to become a principal someday, and we're studying adult learning theory and professional development for teachers. I'll take that on. It's a perfect project for my semester end."

"How handy," I say, still rattled by being put on the spot, but glad to have Ms. Peterson on the team and invested. "Shall we three meet again tomorrow then?"

Mahler's Second Symphony

Tuesday evening, March 22

To celebrate Eric's good news, Grace broke our budget to pieces and bought three tickets to hear a visiting international orchestra do Mahler's Second Symphony. She knows it's my favorite orchestral piece of all time, full of great music, great trombone parts, and an underpinning storyline of the search for meaning in life, the inevitability of death, and the fervent hope for resurrection and heavenly glory. No matter what orchestra is doing it, Grace knows I'll want to hear it. Eric was excited to celebrate in this way, too.

We take our seats inside Orchestra Hall – way over on the left side of the lower balcony, looking directly across the stage at the trumpets and trombones. Grace sits between we two men. As the lights dim, I see her take Eric's hand and then feel her take mine. "Thank you again, Grace, my love."

The first movement begins, with its hauntingly beautiful strings and powerful brass lines. Looking at the musicians on stage, and then panning the audience as the music swells, I'm thinking about all the times I've heard this music with either or both of Grace and Eric, all the concerts we've heard in this hall, and the possibility I might never be sitting here again with both of them. Suddenly I'm feeling nostalgic for this moment, which isn't even gone yet.

Tears form in my eyes. I didn't see that coming. I don't like crying in public. If Grace sees me, she'll make a fuss and that will make it worse.

I discreetly wipe the corners of my eyes, then try to distract myself with the brass section. The principal trombone is maybe 35 or so.

That's older than me but unusually young, I would think, for a prestigious international orchestra. Looking further, I see that several of the brass players are about that same age. The principal trumpet sounds great on his solos, and every time he plays one, the principal trombonist watches him expectantly and smiling beforehand, then he rubs his feet back and forth quietly afterward, a musician's way of saying "nice job" to another musician onstage. How refreshing, compared to the staid professionalism of the CSO brass, let alone the orchestras I'm playing in these days. Their excitement and passion reminds me of my best experiences in college. These guys sound great playing Mahler: loud, soft, fast, slow, majestic, or fragile and beautiful. Even from where we're sitting, it's clear they're loving it all.

The concert ends and Grace stays standing like most of the audience once the boisterous ovations and many bows have finally ended. I stay sitting, trying to will the musicians to play it all again. "They're not coming back out, Patrick," she says, then sits back down next to me.

"That is why I love music," I say quietly, savoring the sounds and feelings that have come from that stage. "I'd almost forgotten, after all the freelance gigs and kiddy concerts."

"I'm so glad that's still there for you, Patrick."

Planning The Training Of K Teachers

Wednesday, March 23 - Monday, March 28

I have to look at my calendar to remember all the commitments I have made. We decided to have a training for the other two kindergarten teachers on Monday. Then I will start going into their classrooms to "visit" on Tuesday. First, we're in a room to plan the training, Ms. Peterson, Ms. Armstrong and me.

Ms. Peterson starts with laying out some adult learning theory that provides an overarching structure on which we then hang activities and process for Monday's training. I would have probably just said, "Here's what we want you to do. Now that we've told you how to do it, go do it." But, according to a professor in her graduate program for aspiring principals, there is a process that works better for adults than just telling them something new. It's based on the work, initially, of Malcolm Knowles. Often called "the father of adult learning" according to Ms. Peterson, Knowles said that to succeed at teaching adults, you follow this cycle: let them experience something, then have them reflect on that experience and try to make sense of it themselves, then provide some outside expertise to help them conceptualize their experience, and finally have them go back to a similar situation and apply their learning by experiencing that situation again themselves. Thus, the cycle begins again.

For our training, we decide to give Ms. Orr and Ms. Gage chances to experience some of the small group and work areas activities we have been using in Ms. Armstrong's room, let them reflect on those activities themselves, answer their questions, and provide some big-picture thinking and research about small group techniques.

We can keep the cycle going when I visit each of their classrooms once a week. I'll see what they have been trying, then listen to them reflect on their experiences of leading small groups. Hopefully, I will be able to provide some conceptualizing -- or we can go together to Ms. Armstrong or Ms. Peterson, if it gets over my head and into educational theory. Then they will go back in their classroom and apply what we've talked about. The cycle begins again.

We decide that, in Monday's training, Ms. Armstrong should lay out some key beliefs she has from doing things differently in her classroom, such as, "Some students need more." She suggested doing this beliefs piece, saying she wants to at least start the conversation with the other two teachers rather than just assuming they all believe the same things. Ms. Armstrong says her own beliefs have evolved, so she wants to consider the possibility that something similar will happen for the others, too.

Ms. Armstrong and I show Ms. Peterson the Seven Pillars. She loves it and its one-page format, and insists we find a place to introduce it on Monday.

The plan is for the K teachers to go into Ms. Armstrong's classroom as a group and look at how she has organized everything to make small groups and work areas happen -- the schedule, the physical layout, what's in each work area at this point -- so they can set them up in their classrooms, too. Ms. Peterson promises to get Mr. Bevington to pay for any simple supplies they might need for this.

Ms. Peterson insists that I talk about what I will actually be doing in their classrooms, to set their expectations. It will ease their anxiety about being observed, she says. We all agree that I will not have time to run my own small groups. What am I going to be doing, then, if not working with students directly? "Coaxing," as Ms. Peterson named it, quickly evolves into "coaching," perhaps a friendlier term.

"But what is coaching?" I ask Ms. Armstrong and Ms. Peterson. "And how do I do that?"

"You'll figure it out," says Ms. Armstrong, sounding like

Veronique, "based on what you've been doing with me all along. Then you'll write it on one page and we'll have it forever!"

So, with that idea firmly in play, we do the training on Monday. It goes longer than planned. Too much content. Nobody dies in the process. Nobody bails, either. So, we call it a success and look ahead to implementing small groups in K classrooms two and three. I will be their coach, learning as I go.

Creating Arts-based Lessons

Tuesday, March 29

At breakfast the morning after the successful teacher training, I suddenly realize Grace and Joey are staring at me intently, and I've been holding a spoonful of steaming oatmeal near my lips for a little too long.

"What's going on in that head of yours, Patrick?" Grace asks, placing her warm hand quietly over my free hand as I put the oatmeal spoon back in the bowl in front of me. Joey heads to the living room to play with his toys.

"Sorry, Grace. I was just thinking about something," I answer, feeling a little sheepish.

"About Eric and his new job?" she asks.

"No, but I could add that to the list. Maybe I should be doing more about auditions."

"About the school?" she asks, gently. I nod. "What's going on?"

"You really want to hear?"

"Yes, I do," she says clearly. "I always want to be involved with what you're thinking. So, Professor Einstein, what great thought is preventing you from getting that spoon in your mouth?"

"Well, then, the principal wants me to work with all three kindergarten rooms, to spread what's working in Ms. Armstrong's room, the room you saw on parent night," I say.

"It's great that he likes what you're doing. Have you got time for that?"

"I can make the time work," I answer. "It won't be as intense for me as going to Ms. Armstrong's room was at first."

"So, what's got you staring at your oatmeal like a zombie?"

"Well, Ms. Peterson, who pretty much runs the school, suggested I build trust with the other kindergarten teachers by teaching some whole group lessons in each of the other rooms. It's just that I had a pretty embarrassing experience teaching a whole group lesson in one room already two weeks ago and I don't want to repeat that."

"I remember. We talked afterward," says Grace, giving my hand an affectionate squeeze.

"Ever have one of those anxiety dreams," I continue, "where you're walking across a college campus and suddenly realize you are on your way to a test in a class that you haven't been to all semester? It felt like that."

"So what are you gonna do?" Grace asks.

"I was just asking my spoon of oatmeal that same question," I say with a half-smile. "The best my oatmeal could tell me was to call my guru for this stuff, this woman Veronique who was a professor of mine in college. You might remember her - she gave that great dance and barbecue party at the end of sophomore year. Maybe you remember the trombone and conga duet I played with her?"

"Oh," Grace's eyes suddenly flash, "I remember that party! I'm surprised you remember any of it, though. You dipped into the 'world music punchbowl' a little too much that evening, as I recall. It took three of us to get you home safely."

"I don't remember that part, I guess," I say, sheepishly. "Anyway, that's Veronique, who has become an expert at putting reading and the arts together."

"Well, call her!" says Grace, emphatically. "When you do, can I listen in?"

"Isn't that a little weird, introducing you as the quiet listener?"

"It doesn't have to be weird, if you do it right. You're very charming when you want to be," she answers.

I sit and think about this. Of course Grace is right. She has a lot of experience in schools. I know from the many discussions we've had throughout the years that her instincts and knowledge are very good. She wants to be involved now in this school. It's a great idea.

I pull my cell phone out and call Veronique. She picks up, sounding like she's next door instead of halfway around the globe. I explain my situation and my desire to teach a music-based whole group lesson in each of the three kindergarten classrooms. I'm waiting for the chance to introduce Grace into the discussion, too.

"So, you want to get all artsy on me, eh?" Veronique asks, with a lilt in her voice.

"Well, music is what I know best, not education," I respond. "Is there something wrong with using music or other arts to help teach reading?"

"Nothing wrong with that," she replies. "In fact, I think it's a great idea. Many students find the arts to be interesting ways to engage with content. The arts use different parts of the brain and students' different talents or 'intelligences.' But it's often done poorly, when it's tried."

"Can you give me some tools for planning music based lessons?" I ask. "I tried having students act out a story. It was pretty lame."

"At this moment, I'm finishing editing a video for a client," she says, reminding me that this is her profession, not something she does for only me. "If you come to my place in two hours, though, I can fit you in before my next thing."

"Can't we just do this by phone, as usual?" I ask.

"This is idea-generating work, Patrick. It's better to do it in person, with big paper and colored markers."

I quickly look at Grace as I write "Available in two hours to meet with V?" on a piece of scratch paper. Grace nods. "Okay, I'll come there. Before I ask where you are, I want to ask you if my wife can come, too. She's a dancer and visual artist who has worked in schools a lot. I'd love to get her involved in this."

"The more the merrier," Veronique responds. "Let me give you my address."

It turns out Veronique's place is only 20 minutes away, south down Western Avenue, then a left turn and across some railroad tracks, in an old industrial area now known for artist lofts and a few small storefronts.

Grace and I finish a few loose ends at home for the next 90 minutes, then get in the car, drop Joey at pre-school and head to Veronique's.

When we get there, we find a 1930's era building, looking like a two-story factory from the front. "Park in back," Veronique said on the phone. We do, then find an entrance and get ourselves buzzed inside through the large metal door. Inside, we make our way up the steel stairs to the second floor and find an old wooden slab of a door. Before we can knock, the door opens and there stands Veronique in a black Kimono, now sporting jet-black hair, with a white streak starting in front at the part and flowing down one side of her face. "Welcome, travelers," she says excitedly. "You must be Grace. Are you ready?"

"Ready for what?" asks Grace with a giggle.

"Ready for anything! We are here to create curriculum. We must be ready and open," says Veronique as she puts her arm around Grace and ushers us both into her space. It is huge, with large factory-style windows on one side, and floors made of ancient-looking wide wooden planks. In the center of the room is a large table with a large slab of golden brown wood on top, like it came from a fallen tree, sliced horizontally to create a foot-thick flat surface.

"We can do our work here today," Veronique says.

"What was this building before you got here?" Grace asks as she takes off her coat.

"It was a piano factory," says Veronique. "Doesn't that seem like a good place to create music-based reading curricula?"

"It does," says Grace, as Veronique turns over a fresh sheet of flipchart paper on the nearby stand and pulls the whole stand closer to the table. Veronique grabs a marker pen and sits with us.

"Let me ask you some questions, then we'll see where we are," she says, going back to her usual technique of never straight-out telling me anything.

"We need a whole-group lesson plan that's going to be successful this time, not bomb like last time."

"Then here's my first question: what outcome or outcomes are you trying to produce with the students?" She writes that question onto the flipchart.

"Do you want us to answer, or just write your questions to answer later?" I ask.

"Let's try answering them one at a time, at least initially, so you can then go back and talk to your teachers to finish answering them, if you want."

"Okay, then let's see," I start. "Well, I only have one lesson with them, so it can't be much of an outcome, can it?"

"Stop right there. Why just one lesson? Are students not in classrooms in your school for five days per week, 40 weeks per year?" she asks.

"Yes, of course they are," I answer. "But I'm just trying to build a little trust with these teachers, so they'll let me watch them begin to teach in small groups."

"Then reconsider your assumptions. You are thinking like a gigging musician who gets called to go into a school one time and entertain students and teachers. This must be more than that, something that produces an outcome. Otherwise, you are just wasting your time and students' time." Grace gives me a quick glance out of the corner of her eye.

"Well, I'll see if teachers will give me more time."

"Then you can ask the teachers for all the reading outcomes. But I know one thing kindergartners should be working on by this point in the school year is being able to hear the individual sounds in spoken words, then say those sounds individually back to you."

"You mean," asks Grace, catching me by surprise, "like the teacher says BAT and the student should be able to say buh, a, tuh?"

"Exactement!" exclaims Veronique in French, high-fiving Grace. "And being able to hear individual spoken sounds and put them together into a spoken word. So, buh, a, tuh gets put back together as

BAT. All of that leads to understanding that letters represent those sounds and can be joined together to write whole words."

"That is super-cool!" I say. "It's been so long since I was that age, and I'm sure I wasn't thinking about this when I was that age."

"Think you can do something with those multiple outcomes?" Veronique asks.

"I bet we can. What's the next question?" I ask.

"The next question is this: how much time do you have available for teaching the outcome or outcomes?"

"Trick question, right? As of a minute ago, I had one class period."

"But I talked you out of that, right?"

"Well, sure, I guess so," I answer. "Let's say I can talk the teachers into three sessions per week for three weeks. How's that?"

"That's a lot of your time, I'm sure," she begins, "but it's not much for a child who needs to develop a new skill. I'd usually recommend six or seven weeks of practice every day, depending on the skill."

"These teachers are already doing small group lessons each day of the week," I respond. "If I do whole group three days a week on the same skills, that makes for a little more dose of that new skill. That could work, if the students like my activities."

"We'll deal with creating activities that are engaging in a minute," Veronique adds. "If you were creating a whole curriculum, with multiple outcomes that occur during a whole year, the next question would be 'what's the scope and sequence, which outcomes get tackled in what order?' But, for this, let's assume you have just the three weeks. The next question is, 'What activities can I do to engage students in this outcome?'"

"Actually, it sounded like there were two outcomes: hearing a word as individual sounds, for one. And then hearing individual sounds and making those individual sounds into a word. Right?"

"Sounds right to me," she says, as she writes both up on the flipchart in bold blue marker.

"Can you say them more-formally, to be sure they're clear?" she asks.

"How about this?" I ask, standing up and thrusting out my arm, like Lincoln giving the Gettysburg Address or something. "Students can hear individual spoken sounds and say the spoken word they create."

"Lose the attitude and I think you've got it," she says, scribbling my statement on the left side of a page. "Next, you create what I call an 'outcomes-to-activities chart.' On this chart, you list the outcomes down the left side and list activities you could use for teaching each down the right side next to each outcome." As she says this, she draws a line down the middle of the paper, creating two columns. Then she writes "Outcomes" at the top of the left side column, above where she wrote my statement, and "Activities" at the top of the right side column. She draws a line across the paper from left to right, underlining the two words at the top.

"Now list all the activities you know for teaching each outcome."

"But I don't know any activities to teach these," I say, a little exasperated. "Until ten minutes ago, I didn't even know these outcomes existed."

"Of course," she says, gently but with excitement. "Now we get to the fun part – creating activities. From the sound of it, you wanted activities that are music-based in this plan. Right?"

"So, I have to write songs?" I ask, knowing the last time I wrote music was in Jan Bach's music composition class in college. I got an A, but that was awhile ago and it was classical music, not what kindergartners want to sing.

"Well, maybe it's songs you need, or maybe it's something else," she says. "The question I like to ask is this: what music skill is similar to the reading skill you want students to practice? Answer that and you will know whether you need a song or something else."

"Hmm?" I'm feeling challenged by the idea of finding the parallels between music and the reading outcome we chose. I sit quietly, trying to think of ideas for this.

"I've got an idea," pipes in Grace, breaking the awkward quiet. "Can I think out loud for a minute and you tell me if I'm on the right track?"

"Go for it," Veronique responds.

"So, the reading skill is about hearing individual sounds and then joining them to form a whole word," Grace continues. "Maybe doing this slowly and then faster and faster? Okay?"

"So far, I agree with that, yes," Veronique says.

"And the reverse is another skill they need, hearing a word and breaking it apart into individual sounds. Right?" Grace asks.

"Yes. Have you got some ideas for where music has those same or similar skills?"

"Well, there are individual notes that become a melody," Grace says, riffing on the new possibilities. "Students should be able to hear the single notes, then put them together into the whole arch of the melody. The reverse is also true. They should be able to hear a melody as a thing, then break it into its smaller parts that we call individual notes."

"So, the reading skill and the music skill are both about hearing, first of all," Veronique says, starting to summarize Grace's thinking. "They are also both about being able to hear individual sounds and groups of sounds, and about putting those sounds together or pulling them apart. Right?"

"You said it clearer than I did, but yes," Grace answers.

"That's a great start. Does that give you enough, so we can move on to further steps?"

"Sure, that seems like plenty for now," Grace says, looking again at me. She doesn't look as overwhelmed as I feel right now.

"Once you have a list of possible activities to consider, you've got to design a whole lesson for each day you are teaching these classrooms," Veronique says. "That's nine lessons. And each lesson has to hold the students' attention. Remember the highest levels of instructional time?"

"You mean 'engaged instruction?'" I ask, remembering our instructional time discussion.

"Yes. Engaged. Not what happened in that classroom you taught last time," she reminds me. "To answer your earlier question, maybe some songs fit into this. You have to structure the lesson for each day. And you have to vary your nine lessons, so the students get some things that are familiar each day, and help them learn through repetition, but also something new so they don't get bored."

"They got bored in one little lesson last time I tried this," I say.

"Did you ask any of these questions last time?" Veronique asks, curtly.

"No, I just thought it sounded like fun to write a little story and have them act it out," I answer. "I remember talking to Grace afterward and realizing that I should have managed the class differently."

"Don't be too hard on yourself, Patrick," Grace says.

"She's right," says Veronique. "A great activity can be structured poorly and bore the heck out of students. With more thought, your activity that failed could be pretty exciting for students that age and older."

"Really? How do we create and structure our activities and then our lessons so my teaching won't be boring?"

"Well, start by deciding exactly what you're trying to accomplish with students," she says. "Think about what skill or concept you want them to have. What practice do they need, or what accomplishment do you want to celebrate with them in this specific activity, to motivate them? What assessing of particular students' skill levels do you need to do? There are many possibilities, and you need to be clear which thing you are trying to accomplish in each lesson and then in each activity within the lesson."

"That makes sense," I respond. "Then what, once we decide whether they're practicing a skill, or performing and celebrating, or we're assessing?"

"Then you generate ideas for activities that could help accomplish those things," Veronique continues. "Once you have some activities in mind, as you did in Ms. Orr's room, a few questions or guidelines for structuring activities will help you. Reading and acting out a story is an activity, as is singing a song. Those are fine activities, for the right purpose and if structured well. Use these questions to structure activities for student engagement:

How often does each student have an opportunity to respond? Your goal is two responses per student in a 20 minute whole group.

What group sizes are used? Pairs are easier than trios, variety is better than same all the time, and having the whole group waiting while one student responds gets old.

Do students have the opportunity to share what they are learning? Do students perform, discuss, show visuals? Are students celebrated, and do they learn from each other's choices?

Are directions clear, simple to understand, and concise?

"These look great," I say. "They would have been useful for my Ms. Orr activities."

"I dare say they would have been," she says, smiling slightly. "Just the first of them - two responses per student in 20 minutes -- would have led you to doing your Ms. Orr activity differently. Right?"

"Yes, I should have written my little drama script as a two-part thing," I say, still feeling the sting of that experience. "I could've paired strong readers with strugglers, too, so the strugglers could have gotten help with the harder words. Then each student would have been busy the whole time and gotten a lot more turns to read."

"As far as putting activities together into a whole lesson, let me give you an overall structure to consider, to help make each lesson engaging," she offers.

"That would be super-useful," I gush.

"Simple structure: start with a warm-up, then skills through songs or music-based activities, and close with sharing a book together," she says. "The warm-up is practice with skills and processes previously taught. You can carefully add new skills, too, in very small doses – such as two or three new letters at a time. Skills through songs can be about introducing key concepts and skills, practicing them to build accuracy and rate, celebrating successes, or assessing skill level. It all depends on where you are in your overall plan and what you are trying to accomplish. Sharing a book is about hooking students' interest in reading, and focusing them so they're ready to go back to the rest of their day."

"Funny, that's the same as a lot of band rehearsals," I say. "Warm-up, introduce or practice a specific skill to improve it, finish by playing a whole piece, as a reward. This makes sense to me, as a musician."

"Same here, as a dancer," says Grace. A buzzer goes off, startling Grace and me.

"That's my five minute warning," Veronique says, getting up. "Are you ready?"

"Hey, wait!" I quickly respond. "Aren't we going to finish answering these questions?"

"You have good questions and guidelines to use," she says. "Grace is a wonderful addition, also. Go use them, together. I'll be interested to hear about what the two of you create."

Arts-based Lesson Success

Monday-Friday, April 4 - 8

After our brainstorming session with Veronique, I went back to the teachers the next day and asked for three whole-class sessions a week for three weeks, starting the next week. Some were more willing than others, but they all agreed to it. They had already said they'd do small groups, and we had trained them on the basics of doing them. So this was really just "sweetening the pot," adding more prize to get them all to stay in the game.

With that stronger "agreement" in place, I scheduled my teaching all on the same three days of the week so I wouldn't have to be at the school every day for three weeks. My schedule started with Ms. Armstrong's room each morning, to pilot the lesson, then a 30 minute break to make any adjustments, then the other two rooms. If something failed at first, I had time to fix it.

Before week one began, Grace and I went through the process Veronique gave us to create the actual lessons. Collaborating with Grace like this was a brand new experience. Our work in the arts and in schools had always been separated. This time, we were creating lessons together. It felt good.

On my first day in the classrooms, I started with a warm-up, something to get students' brains and bodies focused on reading. Grace and I had created an activity we called Rhythm Echo to use for this. That led right into a song I asked Eric to write, which he called "If It's a Match," to help students this young get clear about what "same" and "different" mean. Ms. Armstrong said learning those two concepts would be crucial before we did anything else.

Thank goodness for Eric. I explained what I needed these songs to do and he said, "Wait here." He went in the other room and came back 15 minutes later with two songs he'd just written. Both were perfect from the first time he performed them for me. Then he recorded them on his digital set-up, burned a CD of the finished product to use in classrooms, and sent me on my way. Amazing!

The students in the other two classrooms were not sure what to do when I started class. They didn't know me, and their teachers didn't usually let them sing songs and move around in class. I did Rhythm Echo with them first. I clapped a very simple four-beat rhythm, then they clapped the same rhythm. Listening to sound is important in learning to read. First try, about four students clapped my rhythm while the others either tried unsuccessfully or just stood there looking confused. I did the same rhythm again and maybe half the class could repeat it, while almost all tried to clap something. I did the exact same rhythm one more time and almost every student clapped my rhythm correctly this time. Okay, lesson number one for me about this activity is it's fine to repeat until they can all do it well. I went on from there, clapping new rhythms for the whole class to echo back to me. Good, their minds were now off of math and focused on what I was doing. In the days to come, this simple activity morphed from just echoing my rhythms to clapping the number of syllables in lists of words I called out - peas gets one clap, onions gets two, broccoli, cauliflower, teapot, sink, and on and on.

After a few minutes of Rhythm Echo, I went right into Eric's If It's a Match. I first taught students two hand movements that go with the song, one where students each bring their two hands together to match, palm to palm and finger to finger, and one where they essentially make an "X" with their two hands, showing they now do not match. This movement component was Grace's idea, giving students something physical to do to keep them busy and to help them learn the concept through their bodies and visually. The research says the more senses you can engage, the better they'll learn. With Eric's CD playing in a boombox I had brought, I then taught the students the song's simple and rhythmic words. "If it's the same, it's a match. If it's different, it's not." Finally, we put the hand movements and the word chanting together to do the song. I heard one little girl say to the girl next to her, "This is fun!" Magic!

After the two warm-ups, I gave a quick explanation of the key skill we'd be tackling during the coming weeks. I've learned this skill is called "segmenting" -- hearing a spoken word and being able to say the sounds in it. Lots of puzzled looks from students on that one. I was prepared for them to practice this skill via the other song I got Eric to write, called Segmenting Speed Challenge. I love this song, and the students were immediately taken with it also. It's got a catchy, rhythmic feel to it, bouncy, like we're all going to sing gospel music to it or something. I broke it down for the students that first day, spending time learning each part of the song, then immediately practicing it with Eric's recorded keyboard accompaniment on my old-school boombox.

After the whole class learned the song and got to sing it several times that first day, we were all pretty exhausted from the good work we had done. We had also taken more time than I had expected. So, I decided to save one part of the lesson for days two and three, giving individual students the chance to practice segmenting by themselves. I did the lesson this way in all three K rooms that first day.

We ended the lesson in all three rooms with a cool down, another chant-like tune to practice another skill I know the teachers have been working on in the second half of the year. To get more "dance" into this, Grace had added what she laughingly called "in-place choreography," a few arm and hand gestures to be done while standing in a circle. This also gave students a chance to watch their classmates for cues, as they all learned the movements. As she predicted, kindergartners loved that physical part, too.

The whole first lesson was a big success, I have to say, especially compared to my earlier failure in Ms. Orr's room. All through my lesson this time in her room, which I scheduled as last of the three rooms, I could see Ms. Orr on the sidelines, smiling. I believe I even saw her tapping her foot at one point.

Afterward, I stood next to the students as they lined up to go to lunch. Two girls with matching ribbons in their hair nonchalantly took my hands in theirs, as though they wanted me to be their partner in the lunch line. I had to tell them I was not going to lunch with them. "Will you be back tomorrow?" they asked, with inquisitive looks on their faces.

"Not tomorrow," I said, seeing their looks quickly turn to sad.

"Will you come back the day after that?" they pleaded.

"Yes, I'll be back in two days," I said, glad not to disappoint them again.

"Oh, yay!" they said in unison, with a small hop together.

Ms. Orr came over to me and said, "Well, I think that went pretty well, Mr. Patrick. See you in two days for whatever's next."

"You sure will," I said. "Actually, I just remembered, you'll see me tomorrow, too, so I can see what you've been doing with your new small groups."

"Were we supposed to start those already?" she responded, deflating my good vibe from the morning's lesson. "I'm so sorry, I must have gotten that confused. Can you come to see my small groups on Thursday, instead, just to give me a couple of days. I promise to get them started. I promise."

"Okay, but be sure you do then, and I'll come see you on Thursday."

"But you'll still come teach again on Wednesday, right?" she asks, a little bit sheepishly.

"Yes, I'll be here Wednesday with more music and reading fun."

So, I returned on Wednesday and Friday to do my whole group lessons, and on Thursday I expected to see what we trained her to do, finally. But she begged off again and promised it for next week. I have a solid plan for what to do the following two weeks, to teach her students and the other two classrooms, in whole group lessons. I'll go to all three rooms the other days all three weeks, also, to see small groups.

I was worried about the students getting bored with the same thing for nine sessions in my whole group lessons. So I varied my plan over the nine sessions by moving from lots of echoing me in the songs to more of students generating the correct responses. I also had Eric write some additional songs that would help everyone go from slower tempos to faster tempos, so students will be doing the same skills with accuracy at first and with increasing rate as the nine sessions progress.

Veronique told Grace and me variety, repetition, and increasing speed are all crucial to setting the skill firmly in those young minds. As we get better at each activity, we also will have time for more "solo turns" after some activities: that is, chances for individual students to "show their stuff." This gives me a chance to focus on students who need more practice and feedback loops.

Grace had another good idea for the warm-ups. After the first week,while listening on the CD to a rhythm track Eric created, I will have students stand in a big circle on the rug and do physical gestures or actions for each vocabulary word I say, in rhythm. Ms. Armstrong gave Grace some words her students needed to know: bounce, bend, jump, hop, and more, all of which can be acted out. Grace's activity plan ties this to our overall goal of teaching segmenting by having me say the first sound of the word, then the whole word: b-bounce, j-jump, and so on, and having students echo both while they do the appropriate action.

Nobody should get bored. I have learned that kindergartners love repetition and the chance to do a favorite activity over and over across days and weeks. I have also learned that kindergartners love singing. The couple of times I've seen Ms. Armstrong lead songs with her students, their eyes have lit up with glee. I hope doing something faster adds a new level of challenge and interest for students. I've seen students love getting a "solo turn," doing an activity all by themselves for a moment. That doesn't seem to feel at all like being "called out," even to the shyest student in the class. It feels like making a debut at Carnegie Hall from the proud looks on some of those shy children's faces after they perform.

"Fluency Isn't Important"

Friday, April 8

I'm looking forward to the candlelight dinner Grace promised to celebrate the end of week one.

I see two adults coming toward me from the other end of the hallway. As they get closer, I see one of them is Mr. Johnson, the sleeping 1st grade teacher, who I have not seen since the day I did a trombone demo in his class, months ago.

"Mr. Patrick, got a minute?" asks Mr. Johnson. This guy makes me uncomfortable.

"I'm heading out," I start, hoping to signal to keep it short, "but what can I do for you?"

"One of the kindergarten teachers told us about your Seven Pillars document," Mr. Johnson begins. "We're concerned about a few things in the 1st grade part."

"Well, okay, what parts are you concerned about?" I ask.

"The fluency parts," says the other teacher, a stout woman with dyed red hair that is thinning noticeably on top. I try to remember what we put on that part of the document.

"The district is testing comprehension, not fluency," says Mr. Johnson. "We need to focus on the skills we get evaluated on. Reading fast isn't important, comprehending is."

"Comprehension is on the Seven Pillars, too," I say, "and fluency is not just about reading fast. The research I've seen says it's also about reading with accuracy and expression."

"The discussion we had was only about fluency," says the other teacher, looking somewhat uncomfortable. "In my experience, having good fluency doesn't mean that students can comprehend. I have a student in my classroom right now who can read the words plenty quickly, but can't tell me a thing about what he just read. His fluency scores on DIBELS are fine, but his TRC scores are low. As Mr. Johnson said, we need help with TRC."

"I'm sorry, what is TRC?"

"TRC is the name of the test the district gives us to use," says Mr. Johnson, looking at me as though I'm a complete idiot. "Don't ask me what it stands for. Our point is, some students do fine on fluency, but they do poorly on comprehension. The two have nothing to do with each other. We can't be wasting our time on emphasizing fluency."

"That's not what I recall from the research," I respond. "I'll look at it again and get back to you."

"Listen, you don't have to get back to us," says Mr. Johnson. "We just came to tell you we won't be using your Seven What-evers, because it doesn't line up with what our students get measured on. So, we won't be teaching fluency."

With that, they turn and depart in the other direction, leaving me standing there wondering. I already knew Mr. Johnson would be a problem. His 1st grade colleague was unknown to me, though, until a minute ago. It's not a good sign that she came to me with Mr. Johnson, agreeing with whatever he said. But I'll withhold judgment long enough to talk with others, maybe meet with her without Mr. Johnson and then make a plan.

This encounter is a splash of ice water. It will not be so easy just to move everything up and be successful in 1st grade next year. It is also a call to get our act together to counter challenges from new teachers. Whether 1st grade teachers ever want to hear it or not, I can look up any supporting research and have it ready.

All the way home, their point keeps bugging me: fluency doesn't matter when students are being measured on comprehension. If that's true, then we should remove the Pillar for fluency and make it the Six

Pillars. On the other hand, if fluency does help with comprehension, we need supporting evidence to convince teachers of that.

I walk in the door, holler, "I'm home!" and throw my coat over a nearby chair in the living room. Silence tells me nobody else is home yet, so I head to the kitchen table and open my laptop computer. It's just 4 o'clock, so I'm early, but hungry, as usual. I get some milk out of the fridge and pour myself a big glass, then pop some bread in the toaster for an easy snack. Sitting at my laptop, I quickly find one of the research documents I used to create the Seven Pillars, which sounds like it directly addresses this question: <u>"Oral Reading Fluency as an Indicator of Reading Competence: A Theoretical, Empirical, and Historical Analysis"</u> by Lynn S. Fuchs, Douglas Fuchs, and Michelle K. Hosp, 2001.

As I peruse it, I pull these three specific points:

Efficient low-level word recognition frees up capacity for higher level, integrative comprehension processing of text.

Ms. Peterson said this means that being able to read the words efficiently gives a student more brain-power to use for comprehending what they are reading. That sounds like one good argument for fluency, and for why fluency is important for the real goal, comprehension.

There is a correlation between oral reading fluency and performance on the Reading Comprehension subtest of the Stanford Achievement Tests of .91… for middle school and junior high students with reading disabilities.

That .91 is really a strong correlation, meaning the two things being compared are practically the same thing. At a minimum, this means that you could measure fluency and predict what a student's comprehension level would be.

The high correlation for oral reading fluency, however, does corroborate theoretically driven hypotheses about the potential of oral reading fluency as an indicator of overall reading competence.

Though it's in research-speak, I think this supports the idea that fluency is an indicator of comprehension, too. Does this mean we can expect that teaching fluency and improving those skills will also improve comprehension skills and scores? Or is it just saying that measuring fluency will also tell you something about comprehension?

I'm pretty sure I had another document that showed the connection of teaching fluency and improving students' reading comprehension. After a few minutes of searching my laptop folder of studies, I find it: the National Reading Panel's 2001 report. The National Reading Panel reviewed studies where some students received fluency instruction and others did not. They found a very consistent pattern: fluency instruction led to clear improvements in reading comprehension, both for students who were targeted for instruction because they were low in fluency and for just run of the mill students in grades 1-4. So, yes, fluency is correlated with comprehension but more importantly fluency instruction leads to improvement in reading comprehension. Neat.

Thinking about the two 1st grade teachers' contentions that some students can read fluently, then can't tell you anything about what they've read, I find an older article that is both entertaining and useful. It's called Cool Studies: Word Callers by Lou Ferroli, published in The Illinois Reading Council Communicator, August, 2008. It looks at a 1985 study by Shankweiler, et al. That study says that students who read the words well but are pretty clueless when it comes to understanding what they've read are known as "word-callers." The study reaches the conclusion that "word callers" are more myth than reality.

In fact, the Shankweiler study found that just 6% of students were "word callers." My two 1st grade teachers said they had these students, though, and implied there were lots of them. If they have 6% who are "word callers," like the study found, here's the math - 30 students in their room times 6% equals two students per room. Does it feel like they have lots of them because such students are so frustrating? Knowing what to do to help every child is part of teachers' DNA, I sense. I need to know more about this from someone I trust. I call Veronique.

"Of course I know something about how fluency assists comprehension," she answers. "The best way for you to learn about this is for me to come and look at some student data with you and one of the teachers there. Can we do that?"

"Those 1st grade teachers said they didn't want to talk any more about this. They are not willing to do fluency work with their students. They just want to concentrate on comprehension."

"Ridiculous!" she responds. "Then tell them we want to look at their comprehension data to see if we can help them get better TRC scores. You probably want to start with the sidekick, not that one who sleeps in his classroom. The only day I can be there in my crazy consulting schedule is next Friday."

"I'll set it up," I respond, before she can change her mind. This will be interesting.

Dinner With Grace

Friday evening, April 8

Grace comes home with all the ingredients for Chicken Marbella, one of my favorite dishes. Once the chicken is in the oven, I prepare ingredients for the one dessert I know how to make - creme caramel from Julia Child. It looks as though Grace also has ingredients for fresh green beans, roasted potatoes and a lovely tossed salad. Add a few candles and we'll have that candlelight dinner we've both been looking forward to all week.

"Where's Joey?" I ask, as soon as the chicken's in and I've mixed my custard.

"Dropped him next door at Graciela's for an overnighter with her little guy, Carlos. They've gotten together several times since that parent night, so we thought this could work. We'll reciprocate next month. This could be a fantastic little arrangement for both families."

"Great. Tell me more about your week," I say.

"Sure. Wanna play some cards while we talk, just for fun?"

"Cards? Not very romantic, but if you want. I liked that one we played with your dad."

"I think you mean gin, my dad's favorite," she says, pulling out some cards.

"Waiting for chicken to cook is never very romantic, I guess. I'll deal." I start dealing cards. "Ten cards each, right? Remind me of the rules?"

"You make runs of three or more cards in the same suit, 7, 8, 9 of clubs for example, or sets of the same number, like three tens," Grace says. She picks up a card from the deck and discards one to the pile. "My week was great, especially hearing each day how the lessons were going in your classrooms. It took me right back to that first project we ever did together."

"Now that's romantic," I say, remembering our college project that brought us together. "Night at the circus, getting to know each other, first kiss."

"I remember our first finished piece was fun to perform, snappy trombone and accordion music, gymnastic dancing. Didn't we try to make some political point, too?"

"Doesn't every college piece have to make some political point? Anti-this or pro-that. Deep meaning, for sure," I say, picking up and discarding.

"Weren't we trying to say that poor people getting choice through food stamps and Medicaid might predict how choice from school vouchers will work out? Of course college kids know how to fix all that, right?" Grace laughs.

"I think it's fine to be that way when you're 19. You want to make the world a better place, and you have the naivete to think you can do it. If young folks didn't have that type of clueless idealism and energy, nothing would ever change," I say.

"Gin," she says, laying down a run of three hearts, a trio of queens and a trio of twos. I look at my cards. It's like she's been playing while I've just been talking.

"How'd you do that? I've got nothing," I say. She makes me show her my cards.

"You need my father's one rule of gin," she says, teasingly.

"That's one more rule than I have now. What was Roy's rule?" I ask, fondly remembering Grace's dad.

"He said, 'Never pick up a card that doesn't make a set.' He said it's a useful rule in the rest of life, too. Don't add something to what you're doing unless it makes a winning combination.

Hmm. Am I putting together winning sets these days? Music concerts in schools. Using the arts for teaching reading. Shouldn't I be doing orchestra auditions, like Eric?

We play a few more hands, then Grace gets up to check on the chicken, opening the oven and poking the crispy skin to see if the juices run clear.

"Why'd you become a dancer, Grace? I've known you how long and I don't think I ever asked you that."

"You've been thinking, haven't you?" she asks, moving her chair closer to mine. "Well, dancing and music were always a part of our house when I was little. I didn't get serious about it until I was 13 or 14. I was getting selected to perform with adult companies and in plays. In high school I was asked to work at a ballet studio teaching the little kids in return for free classes for me. I liked learning how to teach, and I also really liked creating choreography."

"I decided to study modern dance in college, along with visual art. I got hooked on the connections to experimental music and visual art. I liked thinking about the elements of each art form and how to experiment with them to create new pieces with other interesting people. I went into Chicago for classes and to see performances, and I also auditioned into the Jacobs Pillow Dance festival. Lots of crazy ideas being explored there. All through college I danced with the university's modern company.

"In addition to creating and performing, I did lots of work in schools. I still really like working with students and helping them to create. It always amazes me when teachers comment on how 'bad' students did so well during dance. I do classes in housing projects and never have any trouble with students. If you do a good job hooking students' interest, breaking skills down for them, then having fun with them as they practice, success is attainable. I've gotten as interested in teaching as performing."

"Was there a physical high from dance, like runners often say they experience?" I ask.

"Yes, definitely," she continues, putting one foot onto my lap, a cue to give her a foot massage. "It feels really amazing to train your muscles to work in certain ways and defy gravity. Dance can be an adrenaline rush, but it can also be calming and comforting. When I don't dance, I feel incomplete. When music plays or I hear a rhythm, I just feel compelled to move. Do you feel that way – incomplete – when you're not playing music?"

"I guess so. Sometimes, but not always," I answer, searching for the truth. "What things are you happy to miss, now that you are not part of a group of dancers?"

"There are some types of dancers I don't miss. I call them exquisite copiers. They aren't creative. They just do what they're told, mostly from my ballet days. They just weren't very interesting people and didn't seem to have much conviction about what they were doing."

"How much of a role did being good at it, or being competitive yourself, play in your dancing life? I've been wondering this for myself. Ever since high school, there has always been the competition to be first chair. And I always won."

"I was always competitive in class. I wanted to be the student who does things better than anyone else. I find it satisfying to push myself to perform at a high level. But, in dance at least, you want the company as a whole to be successful so you all can keep dancing."

"Teachers should feel that way -- successful as a team," I say quietly.

She stops and just looks at me for a moment. "Is this helpful for you, Patrick?"

"I can't believe we never talked about this before, Grace. It's very thought provoking."

"I'm glad. I guess the only thing I'd add, since you mentioned teachers, is that dance gave me a solid definition of good teaching. The elements of the art form are practiced with discipline and then used to perform. Lots of repetition and tons of modeling and feedback."

"Nice. For sure the same is true in music."

"I think that's what interests me so much about what we created with Veronique for your kindergarten lessons, Patrick. We applied the same principals from studying our art forms at a high level. I think it can happen with any type of learning."

"Do you miss dancing with other dancers, in a company?"

"I still love to move and dance. It's funny, but I get my team fix these days from serving meals to the homeless every Friday.

Those volunteers are my people for that now." She pauses and we're both quiet together. "I loved creating our lessons, you and me and Veronique."

Grace now moves to sitting on my lap.

"Tell me more about what you said earlier, Grace -- that my work in the schools reminds you of our early collaboration."

"You jump right in, fearless. You don't know anything about educational theory, but you see a need and you're willing to try something. Happily, you are charming and hard-working enough to bring along a few followers at the school. Now you're seeing some changes in the classroom, and it encourages you to keep at it. What you don't know about the theory or the business end of things, you're willing to learn on your own or seek interested mentors.

"I saw that in you in college, Patrick, when you wanted to mix music and dance and politics in one zany piece. I think it's doing the wacky and wonderful that makes you happy. It's one of the things that made me fall in love with you. I know that. Now you've found another need -- getting poor children to read -- to channel that energy, that idealism, that creativity. I think that's kind of marvelous."

"Some wise person at our wedding said marriage is one long conversation. Remember?"

"It was your dad," Grace says, touching my cheek gently. "Another said it is being a witness to the life of another. It's pretty fun reflecting things back to you just now, Patrick."

We embrace deliciously. I then move her gently off my lap, stand and switch off the oven. "This chicken is done. I hear Marbella is even better once it has time to cool to room temp."

Some Students Need More

Monday, April 11

As I enter the school Monday morning to start week number two of my three week plan, I am feeling less than energetic. I had a very busy weekend: driving around with Grace and Joey, brass quintet gig on Sunday all day. Tiring.

I go to Ms. Gage's room first to check on her small groups. I enter her classroom and sit to watch, as I have done several times since the training. She has been what I'd call "complying" with her promise to do small groups. She stops teaching and is coming over to talk to me.

"Giving more to some and less to others is too much to expect from teachers," she says loudly, as if we had been discussing something for the past half hour. "If I give more time to Sheena because her mother doesn't do anything with her at home, then what am I doing for Owen, whose mother is reading with him all the time so he's ready?"

"You seem upset, Ms. Gage," I say, trying to soothe her. "What's this all about?"

"I need time to challenge Owen," she continues. "It's not fair if I only see him a little, so I can see Sheena a lot. Where is parent responsibility in that equation?"

"Not fair to who?"

"Not fair to Owen and his mom," says Ms. Gage. "I need to be able to give Owen great things to be an even better reader. But I'm over there with Sheena, giving her extra material just to bring her up to level. All because her mother is not doing her job at home. Who gets blamed for doing a bad job with Sheena? Me, the teacher. It's not fair to me, either."

245

Now we are getting to the real issue. Maybe she's afraid she'll lose her job. That's nearly impossible, so maybe she just resents being blamed day in and day out by her principal, and by stories in the news. She learned a certain way to teach, mostly the same way as she, herself, was taught. Now she's being blamed because that way – give every student the same stuff in the same amounts – is not getting every child up to grade level.

"So, can you do anything to improve both Sheena and Owen?"

"Not really. There are too many Sheena's and too many Owens in my room," she says. "The best thing is just to give them all the same thing. That way, they all have the same chance. If their parents are not doing anything, that's on them, not me. Teachers can't be expected to do it all for these students."

"Is that fair to Sheena then, if her mother doesn't do anything at home with her to help her learn to read?"

"As far as I'm concerned," she answers, "that's as fair as we can get, given all the Sheenas I've got."

"What if you could help the Owens and the Sheenas?" I ask. "Would that be fair then?"

"It's impossible," she says, starting to sound angry. "There are just too many of them. The Sheenas are draining all my time."

"We showed you some things Ms. Armstrong has been doing that have been working for her," I say. "And you've been trying some of them. Aren't they working?"

"I respect Ms. Armstrong," she says back to me. "But I still say it won't be fair to the Owens in my classroom." With that statement, she is done trying to make me any smarter. She turns back to the students, leaving me to learn some other way.

Twenty Minutes Of Small Group Equals Weeks Of Whole Group

(same day, April 11)

Last week Ms. Orr promised Thursday small groups. That didn't happen.

So I bring up small groups this morning. She says, "I can't spend 20 minutes with just four students. I could be spending that same 20 minutes with the whole class, and they could all be learning something in that 20 minutes."

"But those four students will get greater help from your 20 minutes with them in a small group," I respond.

"I hope so," Ms. Orr says. "But nobody else gets anything in the time I'm spending with those four. I can't afford to let everyone else do nothing for those 20 minutes."

"Let's watch your whole group lesson," I suggest. "I'll count the number of times any student gives an answer and gets feedback from you about it being right or wrong. Since we agree that the loop of response and feedback is where learning really happens, we want to know how many of those loops happen in whole group lessons and in a small group."

"Seems like silly work, counting all of that," she responds. "You go ahead. I've got to teach."

I watch her regular whole group lesson, something from her core reading program. In fact, I watch several of her whole group lessons, including one for math and another for science, just to get an average and to rule out any weird one-time differences between her lessons.

The number of practice and feedback loops each student gets in her lessons averages 2 per 20 minute lesson (about the longest her kindergartners could handle for one big group lesson). That translates into 300 loops possible per week, if she did only whole group lessons all week (2 loops per student x 30 students x 5 days = 300 loops per week.) When you compare that to the number of loops I saw in Ms. Armstrong's small groups lately, you get 1,200 per week (60 loops per student in a small group session x 4 students x 5 days per week = 1,200 loops). So, on paper at least, small groups are providing four times as many learning opportunities.

Here's the problem: how those opportunities are distributed. Is it fair? If each student in a small group gets 60 loops from that 20-minute lesson, and those struggling students get small group five times per week, that means those students are each getting 300 loops, which is great for those four students' learning. The part that seems unfair to some teachers is that all the other students in the classroom are getting zero loops during that same time. Teachers might rather give every child two loops from that same 20 minutes in whole group times five days per week, meaning every child gets something; ten loops, to be exact. So it's 300 loops each for four students versus 10 loops each for every student.

To help deal with this, I pose another idea to Ms. Orr: "What if we could figure out how to make sure the other students were getting valuable opportunities during the time that only four students are getting small group instruction?" She seems agreeable to looking at this question, as a way to make the situation more equitable for all.

While her students are at lunch, Ms. Orr and I do a little brainstorming around this question. After a certain amount of "But they would never let us do that, would they?" (who are "they"?), we come up with these possible answers:

> *Find an additional adult to be in the room at the same time, to lead a second small group at the same time as the teacher, thus doubling the number of students getting valuable practice and feedback loops in every 20-minute chunk, by doubling the total number of loops. "Mrs. Pierce, a parent volunteer, comes to my room every day for an hour. Can we train her to lead a small group?" she asks. Yes.*

Create valuable things for the other students to be doing independently during the time that the teacher is working with her small group. Ms. Armstrong has been doing this with her "work areas" concept.

Spread the small group sessions amongst more than four students. If four students could get small group sessions for two days per week, instead of five days, that would be 120 loops for those four. Then distribute the other days per week to students who just need a little boost, say four students one day, another four students each of the other days. That's then 16 students who are getting the advantages of small groups, in the doses that should be right for them.

These are three really smart ideas. Ms. Orr looks pleased.

"Will you try small groups now?"

"I'll think about it," she says.

"If I do them first, to get the students started," I offer, "will you promise to then do some yourself?" I'm not averse to bargaining. Maybe she needs to see it again to be comfortable.

"Well, I suppose if you did it first," she concedes, "to show me what it should look like." She pauses, then adds, "And if you train Mrs. Pierce to do a small group, and we get some better books for the higher students." I guess I'm not the only one willing to bargain.

As I am about to leave Ms. Orr's classroom, her students are returning from their lunch break. One little boy grabs my hand and pulls me over to his desk. "I made you a picture," he says on our way across the room. From his jumble of papers inside his desk, he pulls one piece of heavy tan paper. "For you," he announces as he hands it to me. I kneel to look at it with him. I see he has drawn a simple picture of someone's smiling face and written some words below the image. "Can you read it to me?" I ask, though the words are written perfectly clearly and spelled correctly. I just seem to have some something in my eyes suddenly, making them watery. "Patrick," he has written, perhaps with some spelling help from his teacher, "a good guy."

COMPASS Draft #2

Tuesday morning, April 12

COMPASS

Teacher Radar & Student Response to Corrections	Instructional Time	Engaging Methods	Right Content	Assessment	Differentiated Instruction
❑ 1. Teacher addresses 90% of misbehavior quickly and efficiently.	❑ 1. Every student is receiving 80" per day of reading instruction.	❑ 1. Students are led with materials that are well-prepared in advance.	❑ 1. Focus skill of the lesson is from CCSS including foundational skills.	❑ 1. Students who are not at benchmarks are regularly assessed by their own teacher, so teacher has a solid knowledge of each student's level.	❑ 1. Students are learning in teacher-led small groups of no more than 4 others of similar skill, grouped via data.
❑ 2. Student bounces back quickly after their behavior is corrected. Minimal "pushback" after a correction.	❑ 2. Students who are a half year behind are receiving 20" more in a small group 2 times per week in K, and 4 times per week in 1st grade.	❑ 2. 90% of students are consistently on task throughout the lesson and in independent work areas.	❑ 2. Students can name the skill on which and why it is important.	❑ 2. Students are familiar with how each assessment works, and are given the opportunity to perform at highest level of ability.	❑ 2. Dosage of instruction for each small group is varied based on DIBELS or other data.
❑ 3. The rest of the class maintains their effort/focus in misbehavior situations.	❑ 3. Students who are one year behind are receiving 40" more in a small group daily in K and 1st grade.	❑ 3. Students can say or demonstrate what success looks like on each task.	❑ 3. Students are given sufficient opportunities to practice the skill and receive feedback from the teacher, in order to master the skill.	❑ 3. Students receive continued instruction and authentic practice to build their skills during assessment periods of the year.	❑ 3. Students receive increased or decreased challenge levels of instruction within the time allotted, based on data and individual responses to instruction.
❑ 4. Students know what the appropriate behavior is for the particular activity of the moment.	❑ 4. Non-instructional actions (bathroom breaks, transitions, etc...) are kept to minimum time required.	❑ 4. Each Student receives 50-60 Practice and Feedback loops per 20" small group and 1-2 per whole group lesson.	❑ 4. The skill is the one these students need next in order to progress.		
		❑ 5. Feedback given is useful for helping students make progress (right feedback for right student).			
		❑ 6. Students smile, laugh, and express joy during lesson time.			

"You never showed us this!" says Ms. Orr, responding to what I just put in front of her, Ms. Armstrong, Ms. Peterson and Ms. Gage at the morning meeting I called. It's a new draft of what I'm calling the "Compass," ever since Ms. Armstrong first called it that. It lists what Ms. Armstrong and I think we might all want to see teachers doing in classrooms. My agenda today is to share the draft with the other two teachers. Ms. Orr sounds irritated. Ms. Gage, meanwhile, is just sitting there, glowering at me. It's been a few days since I last saw her. Maybe she's upset about our discussion of fairness. Or maybe she hates this new tool, even as a draft.

I showed an early draft to Ms. Armstrong back in mid-March, but the other two teachers have seen nothing up until now. This more-complete draft has six columns, which is two more than it had when Ms. Armstrong first saw it. Each column is filled with specifics of things we'd want to see in a good classroom. Some are behaviors we'd see the teacher doing, such as leading a small group lesson.

Others are things we'd see on the walls or in some other form that tells us something important about that teacher's work.

I wasn't really ready to share this with all of them yet. I'd wanted to share it with them one on one, starting with Ms. Armstrong and Ms. Peterson. That way, I would get helpful feedback before showing it to my two more unpredictable teachers. But Mr. Bevington mentioned something to Ms. Orr, and that forced my hand, so we're making the best of it.

"I can see this being very useful," says Ms. Peterson, finally breaking the silence. "What do you think, Betty?"

"This is a lot of new information to take in," begins Ms. Orr, looking a bit overwhelmed by trying to process a bunch of new information. "Will we be evaluated formally on this criteria?"

"Patrick, this has nothing to do with formal 'observations' by Mr. Bevington, does it?" asks Ms. Armstrong.

"Not at all," I quickly respond, happy to be led away from that onerous word. "I created this draft as a tool for us to discuss. Hopefully, it can be a document we all agree on, that represents what we all want to see in our classrooms. That way, we can all be having conversations about our teaching, including mine, from time to time, and sharing how to get more and more of what we want to see in our classrooms. If we get visitors from central office, we have something to give them to look for, too.

Lots of head nodding. I look over at Ms. Gage. She's still glowering. Her cheeks are a shade of light crimson. Her eyebrows are drawn-in, nearly touching in the middle.

"It's just too much!" she suddenly blurts out. "I never asked for any of this so-called 'help' in my classroom!" With that, she jerks up to a standing position and, in the same motion, steps away from the group and heads toward the door. "I'm not letting you in my classroom anymore," she practically shouts, and she is gone.

Resistant Teacher

After school on Tuesday, April 12

The meeting broke up shortly after Ms. Gage left abruptly. Ms. Peterson and Ms. Armstrong encouraged me to go see her alone, not in a group. Geez! This is not music school.

I'm at her classroom after school. The door is open and I can hear sounds of someone inside. I knock before entering, then peek inside.

"Hello, Patrick," says Ms. Gage. "I figured I might be seeing you." She is sitting at her desk, holding a pencil and looking at several pieces of paper in front of her. As she speaks, she slides the pieces of paper together, creating a small pile.

"Hello, Ms. Gage," I begin, taking one more small step into her classroom, not sure how to proceed. "Have you got a minute to talk?"

"I have time," she says, still sitting, "but I'm not sure I have anything to say."

I walk slowly into her room, then sit uneasily on the corner of one of the student desks near her larger teacher desk.

"You seemed upset this morning when you left our meeting."

"I was upset," she says, matter of factly. "I had to get out of there."

"I'm sorry what we were doing upset you." I'm trying to find somewhere to begin. "Do you want to share with me what upset you?"

"As I said in the meeting," she answers, "I never asked for any of this so-called help. Nobody asked me if I wanted to participate. I just suddenly was in this group. Then you come into my classroom to watch me. Now we're looking at lists of what teaching should look like. What next?"

"I understand what you are saying," I say. "I do. Our 'save the school' committee got pushed to figure out what changes could appease Central Office. Then kindergarten enrollments for next year were way down, so we focused first on what to do in kindergarten. That quickly meant you got pulled-in, as one of the kindergarten teachers. We should have stopped to ask you and Ms. Orr if you even wanted to be involved and, if so, how."

"That would have been nice," she replies, straightening the papers on her desk.

"I apologize for that," I say. "I blew it."

"Yes, you did," she responds, dropping her shoulders just a little and sitting back in her chair. "Or somebody did."

"I'll take responsibility for that one," I say. I'm so far out in the deep water of my inexperience here, trying to figure out a way to get back to shore. "I'm sorry."

"There's a right way and a wrong way to do most things," she says, matter-of-factly. "If you want people to go with you somewhere, it usually helps to ask them first. Ask, don't tell."

"You get a lot of people telling instead of asking?"

"Are you kidding? Not just me -- that's every teacher," she answers. "Central Office. Our principal. Parents, sometimes. Even outsiders, like you. I just get tired of it. It's disrespectful."

"How about this?" I continue, slowly, after a moment of quiet between us. "How about we start over. You and me. Help me do it the right way." She looks at me over her glasses for a moment, then looks back down. For some reason, it's enough for me to feel encouraged. "How about I ask you if you would be willing to participate in this crazy-eyed, cockamamie group we've got that is trying to make a plan for kindergarten and for saving the school from the fanatics at Central Office who are trying to shut us down?"

"Is that your group's official description?" she asks, quietly. After another moment, she looks up at me. "I don't want to do anything just because Central Office is making us do it."

"Me neither," I say. "Let's do it because we want to, you and me."

"Ralph Bevington, principal of this formerly-fine school, put you up to this," she says quietly. "He's the one who hired certain teachers here and hasn't the guts to do anything to fire them, even if everyone knows they sleep in their classrooms. He just wants to save his retirement and pension. That doesn't inspire me, either."

"What does inspire you, then, Ms. Gage, enough to join our group of volunteer troublemakers?" I ask. "We've got a musician, a science teacher and two kindergarten teachers, so far. We're all doing this for no pay and numerous extra hours, and not because anybody told us to do it. In fact, my wife told me not to get involved. But that's a whole other story."

"Troublemakers, eh?" she says almost inaudibly, brightening a little and looking up again. "I like that moniker. I protested a couple of wars, back in the day. I make a pretty good chicken casserole, if someone gets thrown in jail and their family needs to eat."

"Those all sound good, for starters," I say. "I could use a good chicken casserole right about now." We sit in silence. Eventually, she pulls one sheet from the pile of papers.

"I looked at your so-called 'Compass' for a few minutes after the meeting," she adds, quietly again, looking down at the page she pulled out. I can see it has a few notes on it in pencil. I stay silent. "It wasn't fair that I hadn't even looked at it. You know, students here have changed greatly in the years I've been teaching. They have no control, no self-control, anyway."

After another pause, she points at the sheet. "I see 'Students know what the appropriate behavior is' on here," she says.

"That's right. It's under 'Teacher Radar & Student Response to Corrections,' as I recall."

"Maybe that's something we can work with in my room somehow." It's a statement, but it sounds almost like a question she's asking me.

"I'd love to work on that with you, Ms. Gage," I say, encouraged by the opening, but cautious not to overwhelm her with my eagerness. "Can I invite you to meet with me again tomorrow, to plan how we might work on this in your classroom the rest of this week and next? I don't know everything, but I've learned a lot from working in Ms. Armstrong's room."

"Thank you for the invitation," she responds. "I accept."

Fluency Again

Friday, April 15

With the help of Dorothy in the school office, I got a meeting scheduled with Veronique and the other 1st grade teacher, the one who came with Mr. Johnson to tell me they wouldn't be doing any fluency work next year with their students. Dorothy said the teacher sounded almost eager to meet, once she told her TRC and comprehension were the reasons.

That other 1st grade teacher's name is Ms. Becker. She's been with the district for 20 years, but at our school just since the fall. Something happened at her prior school, according to Dorothy, who thinks it lost enrollment and they closed her position. So, since she had union seniority in the district, she got put on a list to be reassigned. She came here mid-September, bumping some brand new teacher whom everyone (except Mr. Johnson) thought was terrific. Amazing what Dorothy knows and what I can learn standing in the main office.

Veronique is in the office when I arrive, chatting with Dorothy, who is laughing loudly as I walk in. "They usually wear that for funerals," says Dorothy, "but it looks good on you. No funeral here, yet." Veronique is smiling, dressed in an African Adinkra cloth top. "Mr. Patrick, I'm so glad to meet your friend here," Dorothy says.

"Thank you for helping get this scheduled, Dorothy," I say. "I'm sorry to pull you two apart, but let's get to Ms. Becker's room. She's expecting us any minute."

We head out of the office and down the hall to the 1st grade wing. Ms. Becker is sitting at her desk, no students in the room, just as planned. We make our introductions. Ms. Becker looks apprehensive,

257

but not as uncomfortable as when I first met her in the hallway with Mr. Johnson. "I have 20 minutes before the students come back," she lets us know.

"Let's get to it then. You told me you had some students in your room whose fluency was good, but whose comprehension was not good. Is that right?"

"Yes, that's it," she says. "We get measured on comprehension, so I was interested when Dorothy said you wanted to meet about that."

"Let me turn it over to Veronique here, who has deep expertise in this," I say. "She's a private consultant to schools and districts all over the world. She has graciously offered to meet with us today. I'm a former student of hers."

"Thanks, Patrick, and thank you for making time to share today, Ms. Becker. Since you mentioned being measured, what measurements are you looking at that show you that some students are fine on fluency but not fine on comprehension?" asks Veronique.

"We are told to use DIBELS for decoding and fluency, and TRC for comprehension," answers Ms. Becker. "It all shows up on one report we get."

"Great, let's dive deeper into your students' scores for those tests," says Veronique. "Can you pull up that report on the computer for us to look at?"

"I don't know how to look them up on the computer. I always get Dorothy to print the report for me," she says, handing us each a one-page print out, in color. "This is last month's report. Dorothy screamed about the color ink!"

I like that she prepared a little for this meeting. This issue must be important to her.

Grade 1	DIBELS Next						Reading 3D	
	MOY	NWF CLS	NWF WWR	DORF Flu	DORF Acc.	DORF Retell	TRC	WR
Name	Comp Score	Goal 43	Goal 8	Goal 23	Goal 78%	Score	Goal F	List Score
Xena A.		68	20	30	91	36	F	
Itzonil A.		35	0	1	11	0	PC	
Isaac B.		57	12	21	84	13	E	C13
Uriel C.		##	32	##	##	22	M	

Looking at the report, it seems to be showing each student's scores on several different tests and skills, according to titles across the top on each of the columns. Down the left side of the page, the students in her classroom are listed alphabetically from top to bottom. Individual scores for each student are listed in each row, corresponding to "MOY Composite Score" on the left to "TRC Goal F" and "WR List Score" on the right, eight scores in all.

"I need help just knowing what's being tested, with all these abbreviations," I say, dumbfounded by all these secret-looking codes.

"Sure, Patrick," says Veronique. "TRC stands for Text Reading Comprehension. DIBELS stands for Dynamic Indicators of Basic Early Literacy Skills. MOY is short for Middle Of Year, which is the test we give in the middle of the year, around late January or early February."

"What's 'composite score' mean?" I ask.

"That's kind of an overall score for that student as a reader, based on several DIBELS tests," Veronique continues explaining. "Like, in math, if you tested a student's ability to add and subtract and multiply and divide, then gave that student an overall math score to tell you how far along he was as a math learner. The composite score just gives you the overall picture."

"That's usually all principals look at, in my experience," adds Ms. Becker.

"Thanks," I say. "What about TRC Goal F, at the top of that column?"

"That tells us that the TRC score we want 1st graders to reach by MOY is Level F," says Veronique. "TRC has little books that go from easy to harder, and they give each level a letter. So, level A is easier and level Z is harder. Level F is where students should be at the middle of the year in 1st grade when this test was given."

"I don't know what WR List Score is," Ms. Becker chimes in. "I ignore it, mostly."

"WR stands for Word Recognition," says Veronique. "It tests students' knowledge of words they'll see a lot in text they read, like 'the, but, with, is' and others like that. Looks like you only tested one of these students on that. Okay, that's the column headings, each representing one test. Now let's look at a specific student, to get into how useful this can all be to you, Ms. Becker, when you have students you are trying to help. How about Isaac B, for starters?"

"That's exactly the student I had in mind, or at least one of them," says Ms. Becker, suddenly seeming very interested. "His composite score is green, showing he's fine, according to DIBELS. But his TRC score is yellow, saying he's not on track. Wouldn't you know, that yellow TRC score is the one thing my principal and the district office look at."

"Yes, his TRC score should be Level F by this time of year, but his is just below that at Level E," says Veronique. "So, we have to look at his other scores to see what else might be indicating skills holding him back, not quite developed enough for him to be reading and comprehending at Level F."

"Nobody at the district or my principal here at school ever looks at those other scores, as far as I can tell," says Ms. Becker. "So neither do I. Should I?"

"Well," begins Veronique, "for Isaac and students like him, there's rich information there that could possibly help you teach Isaac what he needs next. Are any of his columns yellow, other than his TRC column?"

"Let's see," Ms. Becker begins again, now squinting at the colored sheet in front of her. "Yes, his 'DORF Flu' score is yellow. What's DORF Flu?"

"DORF is DIBELS-speak for Dynamic Oral Reading Fluency. The 'Flu' part means how many words he reads in a minute."

"The column header says 'DORF Flu' should be 23. His is 21," says Ms. Becker. "Does that mean he didn't miss by much?"

"Right, not by much," says Veronique. "Look at his DORF Retell score. It's just 13. Other students that are green on TRC are in the 20's and 30's on retell. That tells us something, too. He's less able to retell the story, which may be affecting his TRC and comprehension."

Ms. Becker is looking closely at the sheet of scores now, studying them intently, as if they may hold some magic solution.

"So, to summarize, one of the reasons why Isaac is yellow on TRC, which measures comprehension, basically, could be because he is not a fluent reader," Veronique continues. "We see that in his oral reading fluency score, for one. The difference between 21 and 23 isn't much, but it would be better if he was reading 23 or higher. We can look more closely at his other DIBELS results, too, to see more specifics of his skill development. We won't do this right now, but you can go back and look at the actual words he missed on the DIBELS passage. There might be a pattern. Did he miss all the high frequency words, the multi-syllable words, or words with certain vowel patterns, like 'ou' or 'ea'? Bottom line, we need to find out how to help him increase his rate of words correct per minute.

Children with higher fluency rates tend to read more and remember more of what they read because they spend less cognitive energy on decoding individual words and integrating new information from texts into their knowledge banks. We can see in his data that this isn't happening for Isaac yet.

"His 'DORF Retell' score is also low. This may indicate he is not reading enough words per minute to be able to tell what the story is about, and then retell it to someone else. This is what is likely affecting his TRC score. Reading slowly causes comprehension issues."

"Nobody ever showed me this before," says Ms. Becker, looking a little overwhelmed. "It's a little much to take in all at once. But I see that going deeper into a child's scores gives me clues."

"Yes, clues to help you solve this child's case, I'd say," says Veronique. "So, back to the question, why are some students' DIBELS scores ok and TRC not so great? The answer is in this report. The teacher has to first rule out if there is a low foundational skill that may be affecting the comprehension score. Knowing this, you can then adjust the dosage and content for Isaac. Give him more decoding or fluency instruction and practice, but still some comprehension. If the student does not have any low foundational scores, then the teacher can work mostly on comprehension skills."

Ms. Becker seems energized by this, not discouraged. "This all seems great. I wish someone had explained this to me, as you just did, a long time ago," she says. "Tell me this - how to do this with more than just Isaac? I've got 30 students in my room. Not all of them are like Isaac, but several more might be."

"Good question," says Veronique. "Each student's report will show you different clues. I'm glad you want to go there now."

Frankly, so am I, now that Ms. Becker has raised this further issue. I am eager to get Veronique's answers.

"First, to do this with your whole classroom of students, you sort the students on this data sheet into six groups." Veronique proceeds methodically to draw boxes around six groups of students on the page, writing the numbers one through six next to the six boxes. "The first group have a green composite score and a yellow

DORF Accuracy score - DORF Accuracy measures how many words they read accurately versus the total words they tried to read. They need additional instruction with phonics because they are not decoding words accurately. They will probably need more time with vowel sounds and pairs of vowels.

"The students that are in the second box," Veronique continues, pointing to the box with students who have green composite scores and yellow DORF Fluency, "are just like Isaac. They need to increase their rate and words correct per minute, their accuracy. They can work on this through repeated readings of the same text until it sounds like fluent spoken English. They will also probably need help with expression, what experts call prosody and phrasing, which affects fluency. Basically, you are trying to help their reading out loud sound like they are speaking naturally, not word-by-word reading like a robot. Drama activities are terrific for that.

"The students in this third box have green composite scores and yellow Nonsense Words Read scores. They will need additional time with blending and vowel sounds. When we have more time, I can give you several easy ways to help them.

"The students in the fourth box," Veronique says, pointing to a group with no yellow scores in DIBELS but a yellow in TRC, "are strong in foundational reading skills, but need more support in comprehension. This is where your core curriculum is key and your guided reading groups will be of assistance. I can also show you a few extra activities for them."

"This is a lot of different groups to keep track of," says Ms. Becker, looking a bit bewildered.

"Just two more groups to mention," says Veronique. "I know it feels like a lot right now. Once you have them defined in your classroom, you'll be surprised how easy it is to keep track, though. It's just a new way of thinking, for you and many other teachers. Most teachers adjust to it all in a week, once they get it set up and they try it for a few days."

"If you say so," says Ms. Becker, warming to Veronique's gentle yet expert approach.

"The students in this fifth box," Veronique says and points to the group with no yellow in DIBELS and blue/green in TRC, "are solid all the way, they are strong in early literacy skills for their grade level and comprehension skills. These students will need enrichment.

Your core reading curriculum will meet the needs of these students, plus a guided reading group at their instructional level to challenge them. However, these students would benefit from my special TRC Acceleration packet and increasing the rigor in whatever independent learning centers you are doing. You are doing centers, aren't you?"

"Well, uh, not really at the moment," stammers Ms. Becker.

"Okay, another item for the list of changes for next year then," says Veronique. "The rest of the students, in this sixth group with all scores in yellow and red, need more intensive small group instruction on basic foundational skills of phonics. They've got a long way to go and a lot of catching up to do. But you can make all the difference for them, as their teacher."

"There are eight of those students in that group," says Ms. Becker, suddenly sounding not very happy. "That's too many!"

"If you mean it's too many to let fail, I agree. Even one is too many to let fail, like they just can't be spared that," says Veronique, looking a little concerned about where Ms. Becker might be thinking. "If you mean it's too many for one teacher to handle, I disagree and can show you how to do what needs doing with these eight and all the rest in your room. Or Patrick can. Have you seen what he and the kindergarten are doing with these same ideas?"

"I have not seen the kindergarten," responds Ms. Becker, sheepishly. "I have talked to several of the K teachers. They seem to have mixed feelings about all of the change there."

"Go see for yourself. Better yet, Patrick and Dorothy can work to schedule someone to cover your classroom soon so you can go watch his favorite K class and then talk with Patrick and the K teacher. If that teacher can handle all of her yellow and red students successfully, so can you," says Veronique, enthusiastically.

We hear sounds at the classroom door, followed quickly by 30 1st graders pouring into the room. It's striking to me how old and mature these students look, after spending all my time with kindergartners these past few months. These students move in orderly fashion, mostly, to their seats, seeing adult guests in the room with their teacher.

"I must be going now," says Ms. Becker. "Thanks for all of this. I think it will be very helpful, once my head stops spinning."

Veronique and I stand and move to the door and out into the hallway. After about ten steps, she stops and turns to address me.

"That's an important piece of the puzzle, Patrick," she says. "You heard her -- she doesn't usually look at the data. That's a clue for us. Nobody has taught her how to use it. She's not doing small groups nor learning centers, what you call 'work areas'. You now have the tools to help her from day one next year. I can give you several more tools that I mentioned to her, when you need them next year. Best thing is, she seems willing to try. She'll be fine."

"Thank you so much for coming out today to show me that," I say, still only beginning to digest all I just saw and heard. "I learned a lot."

"That's life -- one big learning opportunity, if you are awake and open to it," Veronique responds. "College seems to teach us we need to be something, right now. Lock it in right away, or we're failures. That's partly why I had to get out of that scene, go out on my own."

"Yeah, I can relate," I say. "I thought trombone was all there was. College taught me anything else would be failure. I'm beginning to see how many other things are worth doing and worth being good at."

"Then you'll be fine, too. Good luck, whatever comes next." With that, Veronique takes a step forward and kisses me on the cheek. Surprised, I stand there motionless while she then kisses me on the other cheek and gives a little giggle. As she turns and takes a few steps in the opposite direction, she says over her shoulder, "I just got back from France. That's called 'une bise.'"

Adults Need Support To Try New Things

Monday morning, April 18

"Our teachers don't do what we tell them to do," says Mr. Bevington, responding to a comment I just made. "They are resistant to anything new. Or they do it for a little bit, then they stop once I am not watching closely anymore."

I shouldn't have mentioned to him that I was having any pushback from his teachers. Who knows what he'll do next -- he can't fire me, I'm a volunteer. Tell me to stop going to classrooms? Or, the reverse, yell at his teachers to cooperate with me more? That would be bad, right when I'm gaining some trust and making some progress with all three K teachers.

"What kind of support have you given them?" I ask him.

"Well, we had the rep from the publisher come out when the new books got here and walk teachers through them. If it was me, that would have been enough," he answers. "When the district tells us to roll-out some new science program or math textbook or whatever they throw at us, sometimes they just ship the materials. More and more they are sending someone from Central Office to train and coach our teachers. But the teachers do it while someone is looking, then they go back to the way they were doing things before that. Teachers just don't like to change."

This reminds me of a story Frank Crisafulli told me about his experience playing in the Chicago Symphony for 50 years. "When we don't like the guest conductor," he said, "we meet him halfway. We play it his way in the rehearsal and our way in the concert."

"All teachers, or just at this school?" I ask him.

"Most of them everywhere," he responds, eyeing me, "but especially at this school."

I am thinking of my own issues with learning new computer programs, but the ease with which I learn new music. "Maybe they are resistant to some things and open to others. How do you and your teachers discuss change and new ideas and mandates that come from Central Office?" I ask him.

"Discuss?" he responds. He's been looking out the window, but he turns and looks directly at me. "It's a mandate from Central Office. There's no discussion."

"Have you ever had success at getting your teachers to do something you want them to do?" I ask him.

"Well, yes, I got all the 1st through 8th grade teachers - except Mr. Johnson - to do a new math curriculum two years ago. They're still doing it." He stands and steps to the file cabinet.

"Not kindergarten?" I ask, wondering why the whole school did it, but not my K teachers.

"No, they didn't want to do it," he says, matter of factly.

"Ok! I'm wondering what was different about that time that made the 1st - 8th grade teachers change and use the new instead of their old math curriculum?"

"Well, for starters, they convinced me to budget for an expert in that math curriculum from the local university to come every other week that first year and meet with them to answer their questions and model some lessons," he says, seeming to reflect on a long-ago pleasant experience, like the memory of a delicious meal he once tasted.

"So, why not do more of that if it worked -- provide expert support while they do it the first time?"

"Too hard! There was an expert at the local university, who was looking for a school to work with. That doesn't usually happen. Then there's never time," he says, frustrated, like I am asking him such an obvious question he can hardly believe how naive I am.

"What's the result if you don't provide support?" I ask. He is eyeing me, like I stepped over some line of polite chit-chat and into something less friendly, challenging his authority.

"Then some ideas don't get implemented. Teachers don't change. The school doesn't improve," he says. I can't tell if he's angry at me, or at the teachers, or on the verge of some new insight.

Coaching Cycle

Wednesday, April 20

I did meet with Ms. Gage again, as we agreed to do. We did make a plan, and we've started working in her classroom on the topic she picked from the Compass - "students know what the appropriate behavior is." She's right, her students have behavior and self-control issues. But their issues are typical of kindergarteners, from my experience with Ms. Armstrong's students and in Ms. Orr's room. A couple things I have seen Ms. Armstrong use have proven useful to Ms. Gage, too, once I demonstrated them with her students. "Johnny, that's one, two, three" for cueing misbehavers is one. Another is telling students what to do, rather than what not to do. These have helped Ms. Gage see me as an ally rather than an enemy in her classroom.

Both Ms. Armstrong and Ms. Peterson have approached me privately since the blow-up to ask how things are going with Ms. Gage. I've let them know, without breaking Ms. Gage's confidence, that we met and things are better.

The final piece, I hope, for presenting a coherent argument to Central Office is that one-page document Ms. Armstrong said I would be able to create once I could answer my own question: "what is coaching?" After all, our basic argument is that we can fix our own school, by knowing what we are looking for in classrooms (the Compass and the Seven Pillars) and using coaching to help spread what works from classroom to classroom. That one-pager should define what good coaching looks like, so I can do it, for starters, and so others here have a guide to do it.

I take my ideas to Ms. Peterson to help me understand them. After all, she's in grad school, studying adult learning. I find her and blab away about my experiences in the K rooms.

"It's a process," she says.

"What do you mean by process?" I respond.

"What is your coaching process, so we can teach it to others later and repeat all this?"

"It's everything I just told you," I say.

"How do we put it on one page for others to use?" she asks me, a little impatiently. "We can't tell everyone half a dozen stories."

I think about this for more than a moment. I love pictures of ideas. I especially like models that show something that repeats, like the water cycle in nature, or what my 90 year old barber is always saying, "We come from dust and to dust we will return," summing up the entire cycle of human life from birth to death in one sentence.

"How about a circle?" I say to Ms. Peterson. "I'm thinking about how coaching repeats, over and over, with each teacher. Coaching starts with creating a relationship, without which you have nothing. In hindsight, I was just lucky that Ms. Armstrong was so willing."

"You still had to actually do something," says Ms. Peterson, pushing my example further.

"Yes, and we had to talk about what I was doing. That got us to know each other a little," I continue. "Eventually, she started sharing more with me and both of us tried some new things."

"So far, it sounds mostly like "Establish positive relationship."

"That wasn't so easy with Ms. Gage, or even with Ms. Orr," I add.

"So there's lots of rich detail we could add behind that first stage," she adds, as she draws a box at the top of the sheet of paper in front of her. She sees me looking intently at what she is drawing, and she pulls it away. "What's next in this process?"

"Well, thinking about Ms. Gage," I say, "once we started over, we looked at the Compass and talked about what skill she wanted to improve. That generated a bit of trust, because I finally listened to her. Then she invited me into her room to help her."

"That was a huge step for her, wasn't it?"

"Absolutely," I say. "I went into her room and just watched at first. I could see what she called her students' self-control issues. We talked afterward and I had a few ideas, from watching Ms. Armstrong's room. Then we were off and running, or at least walking."

"Are you and Ms. Gage still working on her initial 'student self-control' thing?"

"No, we moved on from there. After a few days last week and a few more this week, her students were getting better at self-control and she was getting better at managing them differently. We've been working on something else she wanted to do after that, from the Compass."

"How's that going?"

"We've had our ups and downs, but it's much better overall," I say. "She even asks me to model what I'm telling her now. I always send her an email between visits, to remind her what we agreed she'd be trying when I'm not there. She says that really helps her stay focused. I find it useful as a reminder of what I'll be looking at when I'm there again. A lot is going on in my life, so I need that reminder, too."

"So, is that it?" she asks. "Do you have a picture of the coaching cycle?"

"No, I've just been blabbing away. Do you have one?"

"How's this?" she says, showing me what she's been drawing while we talked. It's a circle, pretty much, and looks like this:

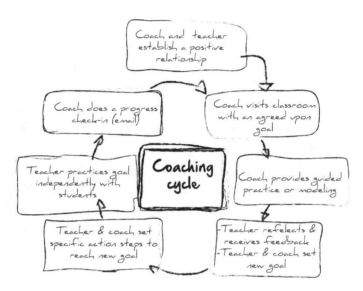

"I like it," I shout, relieved finally to have something so clear.

"Here you go. You just got your Masters in Education the old fashioned way -- on the street," she says, handing her picture to me and slapping me on the back.

Assessment And The Playground

Thursday evening, April 21

I wrote a note just now about something that I didn't know I was thinking until I wrote the note. Ms. Armstrong today said she was testing, so could I skip today? "How about if I just visit later today, once you are done testing?" I asked her. "All you'll see later is more testing," she said. "I'll take my chances, if that's ok with you," I told her. She had no problem with my doing that. I went later and she was still doing testing. So, I watched as she tested one child at a time. The 28 other students in her classroom were a mess while she tested one student at a time, and she had to keep stopping her testing to reprimand them. Her testing took lots longer than it should, and the other students were getting very little. In fact, they were probably just learning bad habits that she'll have to correct for weeks after testing ends.

What I realized when I reread my note was that I need something on the Compass that is specifically about what should be happening during these crazy testing periods, where a month might slip away with very little teaching. How do we keep students learning something valuable while their teacher is in the corner testing one child at a time? We can't write off the whole month, if we value instructional time. No wonder responsible teachers despise testing -- it saps their teaching time.

* * *

Ms. Orr caught me in the teachers' lounge today. She's finally been doing small groups, as agreed. So I trained her parent volunteer, Mrs.

Pierce, to do them too. Mrs. Pierce is quite talented, and she's eager to do small groups every time she's in the classroom, which puts healthy pressure on Ms. Orr to do them regularly. I wasn't sure how Ms. Orr was feeling about that pressure.

In a somewhat conspiratorial voice, Ms. Orr said to me, "Do you know what students are doing on the playground, because of you?"

"No, what?" I asked, taking her bait.

"They are singing your songs," she responded, like she was revealing state secrets or something. "A parent told me they are singing your songs at home, too. She asked me to get her an MP3 file to download. Do you even know what that is?"

"That's terrific," I said, relieved. "Now they are learning day and night. Let's all retire."

"Who you calling old enough to retire?" teased Ms. Orr. "But, really, what's an MP3?"

No STEM Without Reading Skills

Friday, April 22

Mr. Bevington wants Ms. Armstrong and me to show off her classroom to some folks from some big corporate foundation he is sure is going to give the school money. "Their money will save the school from closing," he said with great confidence. "Having their money tells the folks downtown that somebody important believes in us. It also gives us some money to play around with to improve the school." I can practically see him drooling.

"What are they interested in funding?" I ask, not being familiar with the funding world, generally, nor this foundation in particular.

"They make their money in the technology and aviation business," he says, "so they are big on projects that develop students' STEM skills, mainly. They especially want to observe really young students and what STEM work they might fund there. That's why I'm asking you."

"STEM?" I ask him blankly.

"STEM," he says again but louder, like I speak a foreign language and saying an English word louder will make the meaning clear. "Science, technology, something with an E, and math. STEM. It's the future. And we're falling behind, as a nation, in all those things. The Japanese are beating us. Or is it the Chinese? Or India? Anyway, they want to fund it, and they're coming here today."

"We don't do any of those things in kindergarten, Mr. Bevington," I say. "Why don't you send them to the 8th grade science room? I'll bet Ms. Peterson has something they'd be more interested in seeing."

"They asked to see the youngest students," he responds, somewhat annoyed, as though I was not being a good team player. "Just try to emphasize the science or something. Have the students read books about computers or airplanes while these folks are in the room."

"We'll do our best."

"Good, because here they come," he says, looking over my shoulder and down the hall. As he brushes past me, I turn and see two men in suits and a smartly-dressed woman coming toward Mr. Bevington's outstretched hand. "Welcome to our school!"

After some initial introductions and pleasantries, Mr. Bevington hands them over to me to usher up to Ms. Armstrong's classroom for a visit.

"We don't have any special demonstration or anything like that to show you," I say as we walk, trying to set their expectations, "just a normal morning in one classroom of 30 kindergartners learning to read."

"That's exactly what we were hoping to see," says one of the men. "We have been funding a middle school near here and learning a lot there. So, we wanted to see what happens at the younger grades, especially kindergarten, where it all starts."

"What have you seen in middle school, just so I know what you are used to seeing."

"It's a charter school," says the woman. "We helped get it started three years ago, to focus on science, technology, engineering and math -- STEM. Our company is in the aviation and technology business all around the globe, so we naturally gravitated toward that issue in schools."

"Why are you so interested in seeing kindergarten?" I ask, increasingly concerned. "We don't do much with any of those four subjects in kindergarten. What you'll see this morning is kindergartners learning to read. I hope we're not wasting your time."

"That's perfect, actually," says one of the other men. "We have been studying our middle schoolers for the past three years. We figured it would take several years to show real results. But we did figure that we'd then see 8th graders who had much higher science literacy and math skills and could build creative machines and such."

"And have you seen that?" I ask, still puzzled.

"Frankly, no we have not," says the woman. "That's why we're here today. We need to know more about what happens in the earlier grades."

"Our students come from the same neighborhoods as your students," the third man chimes in. "We set our school up to show that the same kinds of students could do better on STEM if given that focus in their schoolwork."

"But we are seeing actually lower scores in 8th grade" says the woman, with discouragement in her voice. "On every subject - math, science, language arts, computers. Everything."

"Ouch!" I say. I'm surprised that she is being so candid with me, a stranger. On the other hand, she's an engineer or something, with a good day job, not a teacher whose livelihood depends on these results with students.

"Right?" she continues. "We went into those classrooms, talked to teachers and students and looked at their test scores and grades. You want to know the real barrier for our students?"

"Sure I do," I say. The visitors look at each other, a quick glance, before speaking again.

"Our students can't read," says one of the other guys, quietly, as though he doesn't want the world to know. "Not at an 8th grade level, at least. And many of them aren't even reading at a 4th grade level."

All are silent for a moment as we walk toward Ms. Armstrong's classroom door. Finally, the woman breaks the silence. "That's when we decided we needed to look at reading lessons in kindergarten and 1st grade and on up. Our 6th-8th graders can't read the math textbook, which is about 80 percent words and word problems. Too many can't read the science textbook nor any other book in their STEM classes. Our school will never succeed until the students have a solid foundation in reading and writing skills. It all starts with reading."

"And that all starts in kindergarten," says the first guy, "which is why we're here today to see how that works."

"Glad you explained all of that to me," I say, sure that we do have something they'll want to see. "Welcome to Ms. Armstrong's kindergarten reading laboratory."

School Committee Meets More

Tuesday, May 17

Once I had implemented my whole group lesson plan relatively successfully, the teachers and I moved on to me just coaching in the three K classrooms. Now, in the fourth week of that, all three K teachers are implementing small groups. I come to see them just once every other week.

The visit from the corporate foundation folks went well. They saw good things going on in Ms. Armstrong's room. They asked lots of questions afterward. Mr. Bevington can barely contain his optimism that there will be a big check in the mail soon, which will be our salvation. He has not, however, said what that money would be spent on. Which grades? Benefitting which students?

This morning we are back in the library for a meeting of the "committee to raise reading scores and save the school," or whatever title you want to give our group. Since Ms. Peterson told me she'd be in charge of the committee, there have been fewer meetings.

"We haven't met for awhile," begins Ms. Peterson. "We got a notice yesterday from Central Office that we're going to have a surprise inspection in the next two weeks, leading to a meeting with the school closure panel."

"How can it be a surprise if they're telling us ahead of time?" I ask.

"They're not telling us what day it will be," she answers, giving me a wink. "So, that's the surprise part. We need to be prepared."

"How can we be prepared?" asks Ms. Armstrong, who was not on the original committee. "Should we do something special every day, or

just be ready to do something when they show up and say 'surprise?'"
Others snicker.

"We can only do what we know how to do," says Mr. Bevington.

"We can all be ready to point them in the right directions when they're in the building," Ms. Peterson quickly adds, "and prepare things to say to them when they're poking around."

"Such as…?" asks Ms. Armstrong.

"Well, point them to kindergarten rooms," Ms. Peterson says.

"Our plan starts in K, then moves up, grade by grade, building on that strong foundation."

"Is that true?" asks Ms. Armstrong. "I don't see the other grades and what goes on there."

"It's true in kindergarten," says Ms. Peterson, "so we will show them K when they visit and tell them the rest of our plan. For the other grades, we need to catalog any good things there and be able to talk about them if the inspectors ask."

"Now's a fine time for some good news then," says a now-excited Ms. Armstrong. She stands and walks to the whiteboard nearby, then writes "62%" on it. How can 62% be good news? "I collected all the end-of-year student reading scores yesterday from the three kindergarten rooms. Last year we had 62% of our kindergartners reading at grade level at the end of the year. Remember that?" Out of the corner of my eye I see Mr. Bevington nod slowly and look at Ms. Peterson for confirmation of an unpleasant memory.

"Aren't you testing a little early?" asks Ms. Peterson. "The testing window just opened on Monday. Shouldn't we be giving students every day of instruction possible before testing them for year end scores?"

"Well, they were ready, in my professional opinion," Ms. Armstrong continues, "so I went ahead. So did the other two K teachers. I stayed up late last night looking at all the final scores and checking them over and over, just to be sure I had them."

"Come on, Ms. Armstrong," says Mr. Bevington, "how'd we do?"

"Well, since you asked, this year we have 76% of our kindergartners reading at grade level!" She writes 76% on the whiteboard next to the 62%.

"That's terrific news!" Mr. Bevington nearly shouts. "How could you hold it in?"

"It wasn't easy," says Ms. Armstrong, beaming. She sits and Ms. Peterson slaps her gently on the back in congratulations. "I just didn't want to brag too much first thing out this morning."

"Wow, that's a 14 percentage point difference -- very positive," exclaims Ms. Peterson.

"We'll do better next year," Ms. Armstrong continues, proudly. "All three K rooms were at that 62% last year, pretty much. Not much variation between us. This year, one of us went up to 91% and the other two improved less, but still into the low-70% area. They hadn't done anything different until March or so. We'll all start right away in the fall next year with small groups and all, and I bet we'll all be at 90% or higher by next May."

"Should I guess who that 91% teacher is?" asks Ms. Peterson. Ms. Armstrong gives her a little wink and I see Ms. Armstrong's face is blushing slightly.

"Patrick, maybe we're ready for that 90% goal school-wide now," says Mr. Bevington, reminding me of a long-ago discussion we had about special ed percentages.

"Our 8th graders are not reading better, just because you have something good in kindergarten," says Ms. Zara. I don't remember her as a sour-puss, but she sounds like one now.

"That's true," says Ms. Peterson. "If Central Office wants to see that we fixed everything, in the few months since they put us on notice, we're sunk. But if they want to see that we fixed kindergarten reading, and that responsible, smart, hard working adults are running this school and working here, and that we have a plan for how to move kindergarten's success to 1st and then 2nd and then 3rd grades over the next several years, then we have a really good chance to get a positive decision from the panel."

"Just like from the parents," I find myself mumbling, without intending to say it out loud.

"What did you say, Patrick?" asks Ms. Peterson.

"Just like the parents," I repeat, a little more confidently. "The kindergarten parents gave us a huge vote of confidence by enrolling their students here next year, based on what we could show them at the open house. Those parents didn't see test score results yet. If the panel members are reasonable folks, they'll give us a positive decision, too."

"That panel may or may not be reasonable," says Ms. Peterson. "But let's go with that for now. These K results are great. That'll make it harder for anyone not to be impressed with what's going on here."

"I met with the 1st grade team last week." I look around to see who's speaking and see it was Ms. Gage, slipping into a chair behind me. "Bottom line, the group agreed to expand your ideas to their grade. They will create their own Compass - or use ours once they get a longer look at it. They also want to use the Seven Pillars."

"Well, that's exciting," I say. "That's where we should focus our report - on what has been working well in kindergarten, and how we'll expand it to teachers in the next level of grades. That makes it something that is systematic, rather than a hodgepodge of programs."

"We'll need something more systematic for the upper grades in the years to come, too," says Ms. Gage.

"Right," I respond. "For this report, we can focus our plan on getting the big ideas applied to 1st grade next year, and then to higher and higher grades in later years. You know - do time audits to see where they are on instructional time. Help them build their own Seven Pillars document to define the skills their students need. Start using the Compass to rally around the effective teaching practices that everyone agrees to use. Launch small group instruction. Get the conversation going across all grades, while actually building capacity through coaching in the entire K-1st team for next year."

"That makes it sound like we actually have a plan," says Ms. Armstrong.

"We do now," says Ms. Gage, "because he just said it!" We all sit there for a moment, looking back and forth at each other in semi-stunned silence, silly grins on our faces. Then we burst into spontaneous laughter and applause.

"We can put some final touches on it before we present it, whenever that ends up happening in the next few weeks," I say, once the gaiety has subsided. "Hearing myself say it makes me realize we are not that far away from having a decent plan to present."

"It wasn't always easy or fun," says Ms. Armstrong, "but it was sure a lot easier and more enjoyable than some things in my life right now."

"That goes double for me, too," says Ms. Gage, and they both give each other knowing looks. Everyone's life is complicated.

Inspectors Come To School

Friday, May 27

As I get to the school this morning, something is different. I notice it right away. There's a black Mercedes sedan parked in the spot marked "Principal" in the parking lot. Mr. Bevington's grey Toyota is parked next to it. Once I'm inside the building, I see Dorothy sitting in the main office with her back to any visitors, talking in low tones into the telephone. Mr. Bevington's door is closed, but I can see through the frosted glass that the light is on inside. Ms. Peterson is running down the hallway outside the office.

I head to Ms. Armstrong's room. "Didn't you hear?" she immediately says, as she scurries around her room straightening piles of materials here and there. "There are several people here from Central Office. It's our 'surprise inspection.' Surprise!"

"That was quick. Mr. B just got the notice last week. Are we ready?"

"As ready as we've ever been, but not as ready as we could ever be," she says. "I can tell them whatever they want to know about kindergarten, but I haven't had time yet to get all the other grades' good stuff catalogued. I'll do the best I can at this point."

"You'll do very well." I wish we had more time. "Your students will make you proud. Can you do small groups until the inspectors leave?"

"I don't want to freak out my students by changing our schedule," she responds. "These are just kindergartners, after all. I'm going to pretend nothing unusual is happening this morning, run my normal schedule. Those inspectors will see small groups for reading, and maybe a music-based whole group lesson. I'll hand them a copy of the Compass when they walk into my room. It's what we said we'd do."

"We did?" I ask, trying to recall.

"Sure we did," she says, rather emphatically. "We said the Compass was our way to say to visitors, 'Here's what we think good teaching looks like. You tell us if you see this going on as you watch.' Well, today's that day."

*   *   *

The inspectors eventually come out of Mr. Bevington's office and do their "inspection" -- or was it just a tour? Whatever it was, it took about an hour. Can you tell if a school is any good in an hour? I'm not sure, considering it's a K-8 building with two or three classrooms at each grade level and three floors to "inspect." But that's how long they stayed in the building.

"I gave them the Compass," says Ms. Peterson afterward. I'm in the teacher's lounge with her and others, pacing back and forth in the already-cramped space. Mr. Bevington has told a group of us to meet together in the teachers' lounge so he can debrief us while students are at lunch. He's not here yet, probably delayed by walking our visitors out to their car. Ms. Peterson is still talking, but I haven't been listening. "I told them to use the Compass to judge whether good teaching was going on in our classrooms," I hear her say.

"What did they do with it?" asks Ms. Armstrong.

"They looked at it for a minute and then filed it, from what I could see," says Ms. Peterson, a bit sour-faced. "I don't know what they were looking for, but I tried."

"In my room they spent all of three minutes," says Ms. Gage. "They looked at stuff on the walls, and they knelt to talk to students once or twice."

"What did your students do?" I ask.

"Their usual stuff, like nobody was there," says Ms. Gage. "No one threw up. None of them sat there staring at visitors like they were from outer space."

"I gave them our list of good things that are going on here," says Ms. Armstrong, "such as it is. I hadn't had time to finish it. The big thing I gave them was a page with our kindergarten reading results on it, showing 62% last year and 76% this year. That ought to impress them."

At that moment, Mr. Bevington enters the room. All eyes turn to him. His face never looks happy, so that's nothing new. But now the look is different. Is this his worried face?

"Well...?" says Ms. Peterson after two seconds have passed and he has said nothing.

"Well, they're gone," he starts, "and I'd say they seemed confused."

"Confused?" asks Ms. Gage. "We hustle our bustle all morning, and they're confused?"

"It was just an hour here, not all morning. Of course they're confused," says Ms. Peterson. "They popped into some classrooms but not others. They took our Compass but put it in their files. Now we can all be confused. How does a school win this little game they're playing?"

"I have no idea," says Mr. Bevington. "I just know, out by their car, they gave us one week to create something clear and concise about how we are going to improve our school, especially our reading scores, and then present it to them Friday at 4 o'clock. Then they decide."

"Decide what?" asks Ms. Gage.

"They decide whether we stay open or get closed down," says Mr. Bevington. "A whole career and it comes down to this: one week."

"We don't know what criteria they are using, and what the rules are," says Ms.Peterson. "Look, they don't want to close all the schools on that list. Where would all those students go then? I say we make our best case and assume positive intent from those Central Office folks. They didn't stay long enough to be looking for every good or bad detail of this school. They must be looking at some bigger picture. Are the adults energized and working at it, or have we given up? Is there a plan and does it make any sense, or is there no plan?"

"If only Central Office were so rational," says Ms. Gage. "Maybe they are just checking to see how much it will cost to put new windows in and bring the physical plant up to code."

"What else have we got to go on?" asks Ms. Armstrong. "I say we finish the assignments we gave ourselves, put together an honest presentation, and wow them with our best shot."

"By 'honest' do you mean tell them we started with K," I ask, "learned a lot, got incredible reading results, and now have tools for developing teaching and results in all grades?"

"Yes, absolutely," says Ms. Armstrong. "I'd go on to present to them our plan to do this same thing in 1st grade next. We'll share our knowledge of the gaps in our programming in all those other grades and our plans for filling those gaps."

"We've done great work here during the past five months," says Ms. Peterson. "We know we've improved in many ways. I know I feel more invested and focused. Our students' parents know it because they see it in their children. We see it in kindergarten reading scores. Our community sees it, and they've enrolled their children in our kindergarten for next year in record numbers. If someone can't see that, then shame on us for not being able to present it clearly, or shame on them for not wanting to see it."

The Simple Model

Monday, May 30

"I hear we have a plan to present. Right?" asks Ms. Peterson to the group of Ms. Armstrong and Ms. Gage from kindergarten, Joan Grabowski from 3rd grade, Lizzy Zara from 8th grade, Mr. Bevington, and me. We're assembled for one final time to finish creating the presentation for Friday at Central Office.

"That's right," says Ms. Armstrong. "Or at least Patrick has a plan, as of our last meeting. Right, Patrick?"

"We have a process to present," I respond, "which came out of my mouth at that meeting. We can use it to show the panel we know how to grow the good work the K team has done."

"Show it to them, Patrick," says Ms. Gage.

"I wrote it up from memory because you all were so happy after I said it in our meeting," I say, pulling out copies of my handwritten list. It's five items for next year, starting with 1st grade:

1. Do time audits to see where each teacher is on instructional time.

2. Help them build their own Seven Pillars document to define the skills their students need.

3. Start using the Compass to rally around the teaching practices that everyone agrees to use.

4. Launch small group instruction.

5. Build teacher ability through coaching in the entire K-1st team.

"This is great, as a multi-step plan for next year," says Ms. Peterson. "It seems to me that we need to give the Central Office folks some idea of the thinking behind all of this, from kindergarten, before we can say, 'Our plan is to expand this to all grades.'"

"Let's acknowledge, too, that nobody could have just handed us the answers to our school's problems and had us implement them," says Ms. Armstrong. "We had to find the answers ourselves, difficult as that process sometimes was. So, if anybody comes around looking for all our answers, don't tell them!"

"Is that a joke?" asks Ms. Grabowski, the 3rd grade teacher.

"I'm serious. Well, kind of serious," Ms. Armstrong replies with a snort.

"So let's give them the questions that helped us," I say. "Such as, 'What's stopping this school from being great?' That's what started all this for me." I stand and go to the flipchart and write "Questions To Use" at the top. Then I write the first one below it: "What's stopping this school from being great?"

"We never asked that question before," says Mr. Bevington. "You're just making that up."

"No, he's not," says Ms. Peterson. "I remember him asking me that after one of the frustrating early meetings of this committee. I hated just getting questions, at that point, when we really needed some answers."

"I remember your frustration," I say.

"I was arguing for 8th grade comprehension being what's stopping greatness at this school," Ms. Peterson continues.

"So, as I asked five months ago, what's keeping 8th grade reading from being great here?"

"Eighth grade reading relies on 7th grade reading, which relies on 6th grade reading," Ms. Armstrong chimes in, "all the way down to K and 1st grade reading. It's all about building the strong foundation by the end of 1st grade or we're sunk, as a school."

"That's pretty much exactly what I eventually realized," says Ms. Peterson, smiling while fist-bumping Ms. Armstrong. "The research supports that, too."

"So, our 1st question leads quickly to a second: 'What's keeping us from having great readers in K and 1st grades?' Right?" asks Ms. Armstrong.

"That became our goal. Answer that so we can figure out all the other grades from there," I respond.

"That led us to the 1,200 hours rule," says Ms. Armstrong.

"What the heck is that?" asks Ms. Zara.

"Maybe it's not really a rule, but it's a very useful guideline," responds Ms. Armstrong. "What's keeping us from having great readers in K-1st is that students aren't getting at least 1,200 hours of reading experience and instruction by the end of 1st grade. I can do the math for you, Ms. Grabowski and Ms. Zara…"

"Please don't, not again," says Ms. Peterson. "I can send you the PDF."

"So, take my word for it on the math," Ms. Armstrong continues, looking amused by Ms. Peterson's outburst. "We have to be sure every student has 1,200 hours by the end of 1st grade, or pay the price for seven more years through 8th grade."

"We and others have to keep it going, too, so students have 10,000 hours of reading by the end of 12th grade and are expert level readers," adds Ms. Peterson.

"Doesn't it matter what's being taught in those 1,200 and 10,000 hours, or what the teacher's doing in the classroom?" asks Ms. Zara again.

"Great question," says Ms. Peterson. "That led to us creating the Seven Pillars and the Compass, which we should put into our presentation, right?"

"Absolutely," says Ms. Armstrong. "The Seven Pillars and the Compass show our thinking behind how we want to fix this school. They are tools we've created and will use to train teachers in other grades."

"You're all so excited about those tools," says Mr. Bevington, "but I have to say I don't get it, how they fit together and all. Why do you need the Seven-thing and the Compass-thing?"

"Can I tell him?" asks Ms. Armstrong, with a tone of disdain in her voice.

"Please do," says Ms. Peterson.

"No, can I try?" asks Ms. Gage, speaking for the first time. "I've been studying those documents. They're rich with information. I'd like to know if I'm understanding the connections between them."

"Great," says Ms. Armstrong, looking happily surprised.

"The Seven Pillars tells us what we want students to be able to do by the end of Kindergarten and 1st grade. It is our goals for students," says Ms. Gage.

"Right on it, so far," says Ms. Armstrong.

"Good," says Ms. Gage, straightening up a little in her chair. "If we know what we want students to be able to do, then we have strong clues for what we need to teach them."

"You've really been reading that thing, haven't you?" asks Ms. Armstrong.

"Sure I have," says Ms. Gage. "Seven Pillars tells us what to teach. Then the Compass tells us how to teach -- what people should see us doing if they walk into our classrooms."

"What to teach and how to teach. Hmm," says Mr. Bevington, caught up in this idea.

"That's right," says Ms. Gage. "The Compass is mostly behaviors we agree anyone should see us doing when they visit our classroom. For example, spending 80 minutes per day teaching reading to every student, and spending additional time with struggling students in small groups."

"You've got it," says Ms. Armstrong. "Our Seven Pillars and Compass are huge accomplishments -- what to teach and how to teach it."

"Some teachers aren't going to like being told what to teach or how to teach," says Ms. Grabowski. She's been quiet until now.

"That's why we have steps in future years' plan for each grade to create their own Seven Pillars. That way, they can come to agreement on the goals for students in their grade level," says Ms. Peterson in response. "In addition, the Compass will prompt a discussion at each grade level. You're right, some teachers won't be happy about anything that tells them how to teach. I think once we have those discussions, and teachers really look at the Compass, most teachers will be willing to try a few of the behaviors on there. Then, as they experience success, they'll continue to try other ideas there."

"That can be helped by having coaching all year," says Ms. Gage. "That made all the difference for me, once I was willing to try one thing off the Compass and let my coach help me."

"We learned that teachers need support in order to change," says Ms. Armstrong.

"We also learned that small groups for instruction are great for engaging students. Right?" asks Mr. Bevington. "And that music and drama are good ways to engage students."

"What would have happened if you hadn't been a musician, Patrick," asks Ms. Armstrong, "and you hadn't brought that sensibility, that way of looking at everything, into our classrooms? I know I would never have thought about putting music and reading together, or theater and reading. That was brilliant."

"If Ms. Orr were here, she would remind us that it wasn't so brilliant at first," I say.

"Right. You learned the hard way, as usual," says Ms. Armstrong, laughing. "Everyone fails on his or her way to success."

"I learned that I can't just do anything in a lesson and think because it's some arts and some reading it will be great," I continue. "We needed a process for inserting the arts into our lessons, which I got from Veronique."

"Who's Veronique," asks Ms. Zara. "Sounds foreign."

"She's my former college professor," I answer, remembering that most people in this group have not met her. "She's been a mentor to me."

"So, what were our key questions, which we can tell others to ask themselves if they come wanting our answers?" asks Ms. Peterson, going back to the start of this discussion.

"We've got three," and I write them as I say them.

What is keeping this school from being great? (Goal)

What skills must students be able to do by the end of each grade? (What to teach)

What do we agree we want to see teachers doing in classrooms? (How to teach)

"Those are good," says Ms. Armstrong. "I just want to say that I notice we are saying, 'we learned this' or 'we learned that.' What all of this is making me think is we also have a set of things we 'believe' now that may be different from what we believed before we started working on this school plan. A list of those could be really useful for any conversations we have with other schools."

"I love that idea,' says Ms. Peterson. "It would also be a good way to show our thinking behind all this to the Central Office folks. Let's do it now."

"What if somebody wants to do what we've done, but doesn't believe what we believe?" asks Ms. Gage.

"Then our list could help those folks have a rich conversation," says Ms. Armstrong. "The main point is to get any group to make their own beliefs visible and clear. That way, they can discuss them and disagreements can be clarified as a group. That conversation about education beliefs would be good for parents and community members and politicians, too."

"Okay. Let's do it," says an unusually enthusiastic Ms. Gage.

Ten Beliefs

"Start with *Every minute counts*," says Ms. Armstrong. "We have to use every minute for instruction, get efficient with potty breaks and the million other things that come up. That's the only way we're going to make sure our students get their 1,200 hours."

"That's the truth," says Ms. Gage. Several heads nod, so I write it on the flipchart. The group is quiet for a minute, reading our first core belief and thinking about more beliefs we share.

"It took me a long while to agree with this next one, but I want it way up high on that list," says Ms. Gage. "I now believe that *Some students need more than other students*, especially when we first get them in kindergarten. I'm sure it's true into 1st grade and beyond, too. These youngsters didn't get everything they need at home. So it's up to us to provide what's missing."

"That's a huge change for you, Ms. Gage," I say. "Do others agree?" More head nods, including Ms. Gage's, so I write it on the list.

"Add *Nearly every student can learn to read at grade level*," suggests Ms. Armstrong. "Giving some students more instruction only makes sense if we really believe that nearly every child can actually succeed."

I write it up on the list, then look at Mr. Bevington and see no objection from him. It is quiet again, as folks think and reflect on our experiences during these past months.

"Right at the top, we have to put this one," starts Ms. Armstrong, and she kind of puffs up her chest and clears her throat. "*Reading in kindergarten is the foundation for a successful life*," she says finally. I see her 3rd grade and 8th grade colleagues tense their shoulders and raise their eyebrows just a touch.

"Amen to that," says Ms. Peterson. "Strictly speaking, we need to add 1st grade to that one. Students who are reading at grade level at the end of 1st grade, are going to be reading well for the rest of their lives, 88 times out of 100."

"I'm fine with letting 1st grade into our beliefs," says Ms. Armstrong, "especially since that's who we need to convince next to do things differently. Third grade and 8th grade, don't worry, you have important roles to play in students' reading skills once we build a great foundation in K-1st."

"I'm okay with that idea," says Ms. Grabowski. "If you can send us better readers for 3rd grade, we'll be glad to give you lots of credit for making our lives and students' lives easier."

"That reminds me of something," says Mr. Bevington, who has been sitting quietly.

"Do tell, kind sir," says Ms. Peterson, slightly mocking, and him not seeming to care.

"I learned that teachers need support in order to feel comfortable trying new things," says Mr. Bevington, somewhat sheepishly. "I can't just buy the latest textbook or publisher's reading program and expect teachers to unpack the boxes and use it well."

"Or expect us even to unpack the boxes," says Ms. Gage.

"That means providing a coach who knows how to do the new things," he continues. "That might be someone such as Patrick here. Or maybe it's another teacher. Maybe we can get one of the K teachers to do that for 1st grade teachers next year, for instance."

I write Teachers need support to try new things on the flipchart.

"That's a good addition. But could we say 'adults' instead of just teachers?" I ask. "We all need support when confronting something new."

"That would include principals then, too, right?" asks Mr. Bevington.

"That's right," Ms. Peterson answers. "Even principals. Especially principals, maybe."

So I write Adults need support to try new things.

"We had that big issue with comprehension," says Ms. Peterson, with a quick look toward Mr. Bevington. "We better say something about these other skills being important and relating them to comprehension. Otherwise, someone is going to say the skills they teach down there in K-1ˢᵗ are not important."

"How about Foundational skills are important, as our statement?" I ask, ready to add it.

"How about Foundational skills enable comprehension, to make the tie-in more explicit, for some in our audience?" says Ms. Peterson, looking right at Mr. Bevington.

"All right, I surrender," he exclaims, looking only a little hurt. "I get it. I think even my boss downtown will get it now."

"It's in the National Standards, you know," says Ms. Gage. "Central Office better understand that and how important what we do is in achieving their precious later goals for reading comprehension in 3ʳᵈ and 6ᵗʰ and 8ᵗʰ grades. If they don't get it, then their jobs are on the line."

That quiets the group for a minute, as they appear to be deep in thought.

"Can we say learning should be fun?" I ask to break the silence. Ms. Armstrong gives me a wink. I wonder if she'll say anything about "joy" being part of learning?

"How about we say it in words others will accept more readily?" asks Ms. Armstrong. "How about we say Learning should be engaging? Maybe the word 'fun' would make critics think we're not serious enough."

"That's right," chimes in Ms. Gage. "Don't give anybody a reason to say we're not on top of our game. We should add something about where the learning really happens. How's this: Practice and Feedback = Powerful, just to keep it short and sweet."

"Just like you - short and sweet," says Ms. Armstrong, teasing Ms. Gage for maybe the first time ever.

"And powerful," replies Ms. Gage, mockingly serious. "We saw how powerful those practice and feedback loops can be. I'm working every day now, as a result, to increase how many loops my students get in each small group."

"I can't believe we haven't even mentioned small groups yet," says Ms. Armstrong. "They are what gives my classroom and my students all those powerful practice and feedback opportunities. I'd say 20 minutes of small groups is equal to weeks' worth of whole group instruction, in fact. I'm working on using small groups in other subjects now, too."

I write 20 minutes of small group = weeks of whole group on the big flipchart list.

"That's nine," says Ms. Gage, after a minute of quiet from the group. "Nice list. Wish we'd had it when we started."

"But we wouldn't have believed these unless we had taken the journey we did," says Ms. Armstrong. "We had to learn these beliefs. Anyone else's list would have been bogus for us."

"You're probably right," responds Ms. Gage. "Let's keep that in mind when we are introducing them to new teachers. We want to make it a discussion, not a mandate."

"Good point," says Ms. Armstrong. "It's still a good list. Very helpful." All are quiet again.

"I want to add one more," I say. "Tests get such a bad rap these days, mainly because there is too much time spent on them. Can we have one final statement in our beliefs about tests and data?"

"I now believe -- learned it the hard way with you, Patrick -- that individual Student data is crucial," says Ms. Armstrong. "If it's high-quality and I can get it immediately, then I can use it to alter my teaching. The complaint with testing is the data goes away to Central Office. It feels like a threat, not a tool for teaching."

"Because you don't even see it, while someone could be getting ready to use it against you?" asks Mr. Bevington.

"Exactly," says Ms. Armstrong. "That and it takes away so much time that we could be teaching. I see that data can be super useful to my teaching."

"Should that belief say something about all the other students in a classroom learning something while the teacher is doing the testing?" asks Ms. Grabowski.

"That's in the Compass now for heavy-testing times of year, under the assessment column," I explain. "We don't have to put every detail into these beliefs."

"Well said," says Ms. Peterson. "I'm putting ten into our presentation. Here's the list:

Our Beliefs

Reading in K-1st is the foundation for a successful life.

Adults need support to try new things.

Nearly every student can learn to read at grade level.

Some students need more.

Foundational skills enable comprehension.

Every minute counts.

Learning should be engaging.

Practice and Feedback are powerful.

20 minutes of small group equals weeks of whole group.

Student data is crucial.

"We need a slide for the six-step process we use in each new grade, too, from the start of this meeting," says Ms. Armstrong. Before anyone says anything, she goes to the flipchart and writes this list:

Do instructional time audits, to see if teachers are doing enough instruction.

Build a Seven Pillars for each grade level to define the content.

Use the Compass to rally around the teaching practices everyone agrees to use.

Use the arts and anything else to make the instruction engaging for students.

Launch small group instruction, at least for reading instruction.

Start the conversation across all grades, while actually building capacity through coaching in the K-1st team for next year.

"You added that fourth step yourself, didn't you?" I ask.

"You forgot the arts, and I added them. I wanted it represented in our plan."

"Okay, here's our presentation," says Ms. Peterson. "First, we introduce our team and give some overall data about our school. We follow with the questions we used and our answers, then our strategy, our ten beliefs, the Seven Pillars and the Compass, and close with the 6-step process we'll use for expanding into 1st grade and beyond. That's enough. Get me your final pieces. I'm finalizing our presentation on Wednesday, so we can practice it Thursday and present it on Friday."

Final Presentation To Central Office

Friday, June 3

We all traipse down to Central Office on Friday - Mr. Bevington, Ms. Peterson, Ms. Armstrong and Ms. Gage from kindergarten, Joan Grabowski from 3rd grade and after-school, Ms. Zara the 8th grade teacher, and me. It's an eclectic team, a "coalition of the willing." After sitting in the hall outside a windowless-door for 30 minutes, the door opens and a woman we all recognize from the inspection team comes out, all business-like, no smile.

"Tell me your names and roles in the school," she says, closing the door behind her and keeping us in the hallway until she has, one-by-one, written down that information.

When it's my turn, I say, "Community member." She says, "Nope. Only school personnel, no parents or others from the community." I consider causing a scuffle. I sense that others in our group are ready to support my insurrection. My gut says, "Let it go." So the group goes in and I stay in the hallway and wait, like an expectant father. It's their show now.

After about 45 minutes, the whole group comes out, accompanied by the "inspection lady." "Thank you for coming," she says with nothing in her voice to reveal what happened in the room. "Please exit quietly through those doors," she says, pointing. Charming.

No one is smiling. No one is crying, either, if that means anything. I am dying to know how it went, what questions they were asked and... well, everything.

They make me wait until the parking lot before anyone says anything. I'm about to burst.

"We have no idea how it went," says an exasperated Ms. Peterson. "They listened to our presentation. We got through everything, we did all our slides, including the two you were supposed to do, Patrick. We even gave them copies of everything, just as we'd planned."

"Sounds good, so far," I say, still waiting for some punch line, positive or negative.

"They didn't ask any questions," says Ms. Armstrong. "None, nada, zero."

"They just said thank you and you'll be hearing from us very soon," says Mr. Bevington.

"Is this good news or bad?" I ask. "What can we tell others on Monday?"

"Heck with Monday," says Ms. Peterson. "I've already gotten three texts from other teachers asking how it went and what we know. We know nothing."

"I wonder when 'very soon' is," says Mr. Bevington, sounding dejected.

*   *   *

Friday evening and Saturday morning are hard, wondering and waiting. Grace and I are doers. We like to make a list and then knock things off that list. This waiting around stuff is going to be hard if the district folks don't tell us for weeks. The school year will be done soon. Where will Joey go to kindergarten if they close our school? Lots of questions. No answers.

The sky looked very threatening all morning, as it often looks in late spring in the Midwest. By Saturday mid-afternoon, Grace and I can't stand being cooped up anymore, so we decide to go for a drive. We put Joey in the car and head south, for no particular reason. After about 15 minutes of quiet, except for Joey singing pleasantly in the backseat, Grace suddenly says, "Turn left here." With no other direction in mind, I turn left. After a set of bumpy railroad tracks, we are soon driving right past Veronique's building, with its distinctive 1950's warehouse look.

"I thought we were near here. Go around back," says Grace. "Let's see if Veronique is home."

"Then what?" I ask, wondering how much of a plan Grace has and why.

"I don't know," she answers. "I just have a good feeling about this."

So, I turn down the side street and head for the back, where we parked when we came here to create curriculum with Veronique. As we round the corner, I see a large and brightly colored tent over the parking area behind the building, and I hear recorded music.

"Pull over here and park," says Grace, now dancing in her car seat to the music that is getting louder as we park. "It's a party!"

We get out and Joey runs ahead, excited by the music and the colorful tent. It sounds like a party, but I can see the tent is empty, save for three or four people milling about inside, setting up chairs and tables around the edges. The music stops as we approach, just as Grace says loudly to me, "There's Veronique!"

Indeed, there she is, decked out in full dance party regalia, a sudden flashback from college days. Flowing fabric, purple feather boa, baseball cap with "Give Peas A Dance" printed on it, covering her still-black hair, with the white streak down the side.

"Hey, kids, you're too early for the party," she says to us. Then looking down, she says excitedly, "This must be Joey." He suddenly turns shy and comes back to Grace and tries to hide in her skirt.

"We were just trying to forget our troubles for a minute, and we ended up in your neighborhood," I say, realizing how lame it must sound. "What's all this tent and music about?"

"Don't you remember? It's 'One World Dance Party and BBQ' season," she says, sounding incredulous I would even need to ask.

"Just like in college?"

"You were in college then," she answers, "but I was an adult. I still am. This is a lifestyle choice, not something college kids do to pretend they're cool. The arts are part of my life, all the time. Come back in a couple of hours. Bring your trombone and we can do another duet, if it's all right with your wife. Or a trio this time."

"We could use a little fun," I say. "It's been crazy since we last talked. We presented our school's case to the Central Office folks and they just said, 'Thanks, we'll let you know.' So, now we're just waiting around. It will drive me crazy if it goes on for long."

"Did you do the lessons we were creating last time we talked, here at my place?" she asks. I realize, in the rush to do everything, I never got back to her about that.

"I'm sorry, I meant to circle back with you."

"The lessons were great," says Grace, saving me, and starting to help Veronique unbundle plastic knives and forks and place them in containers for use. "The students and the teachers loved them. All three K teachers are on-board to use them next year and have asked us to create more, for the rest of the year, if the school stays open."

"Whoa. I'm happy to hear the lessons went well," Veronique says. "But what's this about the school staying open or not?"

"We told the district our plans," I say. "That was just yesterday, in fact. Now we're waiting to hear if the school stays open or if they want to close us down."

"What? It's almost the end of the school year and you don't know?" she asks, getting revved up. "What do you do if they say you're closed? What do parents do? That sounds nuts."

"It feels nuts," I say. Veronique keeps looking first at Grace and then to me.

"Here's what you do," Veronique says finally, with a wild look glowing in her eyes. "If they say you're closed, you come here and we'll start our own school, just like in the 60's, a Freedom School or whatever you want to call it. The whole first floor here is open. You get your neighbors together and we'll create a school from scratch, starting with your kindergartner there," she says, pointing at Joey who has found his way over to the door of one of those inflatable bouncing "moon rooms" people can rent.

"That'd be a heap of work, wouldn't it?" Grace asks, looking scared and excited. There's a look in her eyes I haven't seen in years.

"Life is work," Veronique says, lovingly. "Doing the right thing is work. High quality anything is a lot of work. Doing nothing is easier. Doing things poorly is boring and can be just as hard, especially when you lie in bed at night and realize this is your only life and you're wasting it on doing things badly."

"We've got Joey and a house and jobs," Grace says, looking at Joey who is headed back to us, probably to ask us to bounce on the inflatable thing with him. "We can't do everything."

"You can't do everything," Veronique responds. "But you can do any one thing you decide is most important. Pick the thing that is most worth doing. It's got to be something that also brings you joy. Then do it as well as it can be done. Create a school. Fix a school. Have a dance party!"

With that, as if on cue from Veronique, the dance music starts again. Veronique grabs Grace by the hand and they both begin dancing, alone under the giant tent. Joey, seeing this fun and wanting some for himself, reaches out and grabs my hand. Dancing now, he drags me toward the other dancing pair, where he grabs his mother's hand and I grab Veronique's. We all are, for a moment, dancing together as one happy world family.

*   *   *

Sunday was excruciating, even after the joy of being with Veronique and Grace and Joey and two hundred of Veronique's other dancing artist friends on Saturday night. We ended up staying to help finish the set-up for the BBQ. Joey fell asleep right on the inflatable moon room after a long while of jumping on it, oblivious to the music and frivolity around him. So we stayed for the dancing. Maybe my Sunday headache was from all that dancing, or maybe from the stress of more waiting. It certainly was not from the One World punchbowl, which I avoided.

As I enter the school by the main office on Monday morning, headache still pulsing under a Tylenol blanket, I hear loud adult voices coming from somewhere nearby. Suddenly a small group of people comes bursting out of the main office doorway. I see Mr. Bevington and Ms. Peterson first.

"We won!" cries Mr. Bevington, grabbing me and giving me an uncharacteristic hug. "I just got the call from downtown. We're open another year. We're still on their list of schools to keep an eye on. Publicly they'll be announcing some schools that will be closing, but we're one that's staying open! We won!"

Suddenly, we love this game, for which we still don't know the rules nor how we won.

Lots of back slapping and loud carrying-on ensues, as more teachers come into the hall from their open classrooms and hear the good news.

"Tell Patrick the best part, Mr. Bevington," shouts Dorothy, the school clerk, who is still standing inside the office.

"Well, Patrick," he begins, relishing the moment, and its effect on his retirement plans, perhaps, "the caller said they were very impressed we'd chosen to start with kindergarten and build from there over time. They were also impressed with the energy and visible commitment of the team we have here, with how well we know our school's strengths and weaknesses, and with the tools we have created for developing the rest of our grades as we did for kindergarten."

"Come on, Mr. Bevington," insists Dorothy again, having come out to stand in the hallway with us. "Tell him the best part!"

"Yes, yes, Dorothy," he begins again. "Patrick, they want us to be a behind-the-scenes model for other schools in our area, a place where other schools that survived the purge can come to learn how to do some of what we have done here. The panel said they were particularly encouraged by the large rise in the percentage of kindergartners reading at grade level this year. Other schools can learn with us as we move those best practices up into 1st grade and beyond. Of course, I'll be retired by then, but I'm sure Ms. Peterson or someone else can run this place after I'm gone." Ms. Peterson looks at him, then me and smiles broadly.

Well, what do you know about that?

Lots more excited gabbing about how great this is, how great our school is, how great every one of us is. The bell rings and students flood indoors from outside where they have been waiting. Hundreds of little and big feet trudge up the solid stone steps, grinding another day's worth of undetectable dips into each stair.

"Come on, students, move it along," says Ms. Armstrong, quickly turning from the group of adults to face her students. "Time's-a-wasting. Every minute counts, you know!"

As the hallway clears, and I turn to leave and go home to tell Grace the good news, Ms. Armstrong suddenly comes out of her classroom and stands facing me again.

"We would never have done this without you guiding us, Patrick," she says. "I just want you to know that, and know that someone noticed. Here we are, all congratulating ourselves. That's fine, because we did some really good work. But it wouldn't have happened if you hadn't been here, Mr. Trombone Player from Oregon."

"Thanks for that, even though I didn't know what I was doing most of the time," I say, feeling humbled. I fell into this helping schools, partnering with teachers, not-trombone-playing thing. Whatever this thing is that I've been doing these last five months. "You and the other teachers taught me so much."

"I understand what you are saying. And I agree that you didn't know what you were doing most of the time," she responds, teasingly. "Most of us feel like that in some part of our life or another. But you stayed and figured it out. Now you do know what you're doing. You could do this in lots more classrooms, maybe even in whole new schools. I think you should, starting right here next year. Even the district seems to think you should, though at the presentation they wanted to deny you even exist. Lord knows there are plenty of other classrooms and schools that could use your help. Maybe you've found your calling. If that trumpet thing doesn't work out."

"It's trombone, not trum…," I begin to respond. She smiles, then turns back toward her open classroom and her waiting students. "But you knew that," I say, almost as an afterthought.

Maybe she has something there. Even if I could make the trombone thing work out, there's a world of need, and good work to be done, in schools. The arts are particularly well-equipped to add a boost of real effectiveness and different thinking to a problem that has vexed schools across our country for decades. "That trombone thing," starting in music school, was all about creativity, being truly excellent at something, and expressing myself as a unique presence in the world, if you want to get all high-minded about it. When I stop and think about it, I've gradually found all of that and more in this schoolwork these past months. Maybe there is enough here to keep it interesting and rewarding for a while. Then, if this "school thing" doesn't work out, I'll find some other worthy goal that brings me joy.

Goodbye Lunch With Eric

Thursday, June 9

"I can't believe you are moving next week," I say as Eric and I slide into our favorite booth at Bill's Diner. It's been three months since Eric got the orchestra gig in Canada. They want him for their summer season, so he's moving his stuff now - six trumpets, three boxes of trumpet music, eight trumpet mutes, a metronome, two music stands, a really nice stereo for listening to trumpet music, and a bowl and spoon for eating cereal. Oh, and a chair and folding table, for sitting to eat that bowl of cereal every morning. He's leaving the mattress here, lying on the floor where it's been ever since college.

Eric and I have played plenty of gigs together since I heard his news, and we've discussed the pros and cons of the opportunity to play music every day. It feels like I've come to terms with my mixed emotions about Eric's new life. I used my credit card to rent the small truck he'll be driving next week, loaded with all his stuff. He'll pay me back from his first paycheck. He and I thought about making it a big road trip, just Eric and me and 2,000 miles of America, one last time. Reality intervened for me -- Grace, Joey, my work -- and he's driving solo instead now, which he says is fine.

"Next week, all right," Eric responds. "I'm ready. I'd love to be driving tomorrow, but there's no truck until next week. After dinner with you, my calendar is empty." He's always been a guy who liked to get on with it. His future is in Canada, and his mind is already there, too.

Parts of Eric -- little bits of the rational, organized Eric -- have become part me. I wish it was more. Together, we've been a good combination of ration and passion, organizer and idea generator, tenacity and… tenacity. We'll each have to find more of the things that the other brought to the relationship.

"Seems like all we've talked about lately is my new thing," he says, moving on. "How's your school thing going?"

"It's been good," I say. "I feel as though I've made real progress with all three kindergarten teachers. Now 76% of their students are reading at level. That's a jump from 62% last year, just for context. The teacher I worked with the most got 91%. The principal, who's a bit of a goof, wants me to expand my work into 1st grade next year, then 2nd and 3rd. He even says he can find some money to pay me for it next year. That gives us a basic plan to keep the school open and improve it over time. Oh, big news. They won't be closing the school."

"Wow, really?" Eric seems surprised. "When did they decide and tell the school what's going to happen? School's about done for this year, right?"

"Last day is next Friday," I say. "Central Office told us on Monday. Screwy, right?"

"Really screwy, I'd say, to be doing all this with just two weeks left in the school year," he says, getting as worked up as Eric ever gets about something. "Where's that leave you in all this?"

"You mean me, the freelance musician? Or me the guy with a future kindergartner at home?"

"Both."

"Well, the guy with the future kindergartner at home is upset but relieved," I answer. "This is no way to run a railroad, but I'm glad my train is still going."

"That's for sure."

"The freelance musician in me is okay with this new gig, too. Schools are such interesting puzzles, and teachers are responding positively to a couple of things I've figured out, with a lot of help," I begin. "It's invigorating, even for a guy who hated everything about music ed majors." Eric is watching me intently. I've seen that look on his face before, like when I told him I was staying in Chicago after senior year, and Grace and I had decided to get married. He asked me lots of questions. Then he showed me the brass quintet arrangements he'd been secretly creating, hoping I'd be staying.

"I do worry about the constant turmoil for all schools," I continue. "More could close next year. That's a drag. Just when I find something interesting to do, other than playing the trombone, they decide to mess with it and make it harder."

"Are you all right with that kind of constant uncertainty?"

"I don't know, I guess the upside for me is greater than the downside. I feel as though I've found something that really interests me, other than music. I want to follow it, see where it leads, explore this some more," I respond. "Hey, why all the questions?"

Eric sits silently for a moment.

"I just wanted to see where your head is at these days," he begins, a small smile crossing his lips now.

"And…?" I ask, gesturing with both hands, as if to say, 'Give me what else you're hiding behind that silly grin.'

"Well," he begins again, "first, I'll say I see your excitement about what you are doing in that school these days. I have never, in all the years I've known you, heard you be so excited about anything other than playing trombone. Well, oh, yeah, and Grace." He laughs his little Eric laugh. "So, that's worth stopping to think about. It's really great for you to have found that thing."

"But…?" I ask, getting impatient with this slow reveal.

"Okay, I've said I heard you," Eric starts again, hesitantly. "Here's what else is on my mind. I just heard my new orchestra will be looking for a trombonist for next year. The current guy is leaving after the summer season, and nobody knows yet. I just called him to get acquainted, and he told me on the phone. So they'll need someone on short notice. Things in Canada are a little different, with the union and orchestras. So, I should be able to get you a private audition, once he gives notice and before they announce anything publicly. We could be playing together again, buddy, the way we always dreamed!"

Now my head is swimming. Eric has just told me my dream is within reach. This comes right after I told him how excited I am about schools and applying what I've been learning about solving the many complex puzzles in schools. I finally find something new, and he tells me I can have the original thing. This is cruel.

"Is this for real?" I blurt out finally, half over-excited and half angered he might be messing with me in some way, which would be very un-Eric-like.

"Well, it's probably for real," Eric says, quickly sounding less-sure than just a moment ago. "The guy might ask for a one-year leave from the orchestra, to go try the other orchestra that wants him. Apparently, that other orchestra has some 'issues' that he wants to see about, see if he likes it there, with the option to return if he doesn't."

"So, it's a temporary, one-year contract. Is that what you're saying?"

"Yes, but he hopes it will work out for him in the new orchestra. Then it would be an ongoing contract for you," Eric says, back to low-key pitching his idea and the dream to me. "Besides, if he comes back, you'll have gained real orchestra experience for your resume. That makes it easier to get the next orchestra to take you seriously for an audition."

"I've got a house here and family and Joey's schooling to consider," I say, slowly beginning to think this through. "Would I just up and move there, like you are doing next week?"

"I'd think so," he says, looking quizzically at me. "Hey, I thought you'd jump at this."

I have to say he's got a point. This is the dream, right? Play in an orchestra, Eric on first trumpet, me next to him on first trombone, just like in college. Mahler's Third Symphony, Pictures at an Exhibition, Mozart's Requiem. Get paid a full-time wage to play my trombone every day. Stop running around to little brass quintet gigs in smelly schools with cranky teachers.

Why am I hesitating? Is it the unknowns and the uncertainty of the specific situation that Eric has described? Maybe he can get me the inside track and the orchestra will hire me. Maybe the other guy won't come back, if I do get the job, and I can keep the job beyond one year. Maybe Grace and Joey will want to go on this adventure with me. Maybe I should have been practicing those orchestra excerpts. Six months ago I would have jumped.

Wait. Maybe I should listen to myself. I was, moments ago, telling him how interesting my work with our school is, and how excited I was about that work. Where'd that excitement come from? Did it evaporate, or was I just overwhelmed by the sudden excitement of Eric's plan?

I remember Psych class in college. We read that humans experience change as loss as well as gain -- emotional loss, destabilizing, loss of prestige, loss of competency. Right now, I'm at some kind of moment of change. I either go play in an orchestra and give up this interesting school thing plus our house and neighbors and friends in Chicago, or I commit more to doing this school stuff, which means giving up that orchestra dream and my identity as a musician.

This has been coming for a while, I realize. I love playing in orchestras, making that music happen. On the other hand, I've tried getting excited about practicing six bars of this and six bars of that orchestral trombone music. If that's what it takes to get into an orchestra, I'm going to have a really hard time. If somehow I got a job doing that all day, I know myself - having a guy waving his arms at me all day and telling me what to do would wear thin quickly.

On the other hand, sitting with a six year old and helping him or her make some leap in understanding that propels that child to suddenly "get it" and go from non-reader to reader in front of my eyes -- this is an honor to be part of and to witness. Standing with a tired and struggling teacher and helping her (or him) remember why she wanted to be a teacher in the first place, by offering some simple changes that help transform her, is amazing, too.

I realize there's been a long pause. Eric has always been patient with long silences.

"This is a great opportunity," I say finally. "I've always dreamed of playing in a professional orchestra with you, Eric, playing our horns every day for a living."

"But...?" he says, mimicking me from moments ago.

"But…I can't take the orchestra job," I say, feeling those words in my mouth. Eric sits silently, looking at me for a gentle period of time. Then he smiles.

"This is a big moment," he says. "This feels like the end of our college selves and the beginning of our adult lives… the ones where we're both doing what will make us happy as adults, not what made us happy as high school and college students."

"I don't know for sure what will make me happy as an adult, if it's not playing trombone full-time," I start. "But I'm willing now to try to find out. That's new for me. That's happened because of my work at this one school. I think there's something there for me. It makes me feel creative and successful and useful in the world. It gives me energy."

"I knew you'd say no, as soon as I heard your answers to my questions earlier," Eric says. "I also knew that was going to be okay, as soon as I saw the look on your face. You like this school thing. I can tell. You should stay right here and do that."

"Really, you're all right with that?" I ask him.

"I'm great with that. You're my friend. We'll always be friends. This move to Canada means I'm leaving town, not you. Good friends are hard to find. I don't plan to lose any."

"I'll miss you, Eric," I say, getting a little choked up. "In 30 years, we'll look back on this and see what great and happy things came from the decisions we are making right now."

"In 30 years, we can both write books about all of this, looking back to the days when we were very young, very poor, and very happy," Eric says.

"That's Hemingway, right?" I ask, recognizing the last lines of A Moveable Feast.

"Sort of, but he was writing about Paris, not Chicago."

"Well, then, I'll go to Paris and write the book about all of this."

"That's a deal," Eric says. "I'll be excited to read that book and see how it ends."

Author's Statement

This is a book about teaching young children to read, and making every school the place where this is done successfully. It is a primer on best practices, rich in specific information for teachers who want their classrooms to be fun and effective as places for all children to learn to read.

It is not really about how to get your school off some list of potential closings. I don't have the insider experience to answer that question. It is not a book about me, though it draws heavily from what I have seen over 35 years as head of Reading In Motion, a Chicago-based literacy organization. It condenses years of experience and learning into a few months. I once asked a lawyer if the TV legal dramas were true to life. His answer pertains to this book too. "They're often accurate but things take longer in real life."

While the book's characters are fictional, they draw life from some very real people I know, often mixing talents and attributes of several individuals into one character. Three of those real people with whom I have been honored to collaborate for over 25 years are Elizabeth Johnston, Reading In Motion's former Director of Programs and now our Curriculum Content Leader; Little Tom Jackson, a senior coach at Reading In Motion; and Avo Randruut, who wrote all the music for Reading In Motion's curriculum, and was the first person to ever teach our curriculum to students. Two others are my co-founders of Reading In Motion, Eric Murphy and Sally Braswell. I am grateful to each of these terrific human beings. I hope you each see yourself at points in this story. You are there.

I am also most grateful for early draft readers, whose comments helped shape the narrative. These include Debra Snider, who gave me spot-on advice from the start to finish about the process of writing a novel. Others readers were Peggy Clough, Nancy Vonau, Dale Rose, Jason Patenaude, Elizabeth Johnston, Annie Snider and Tim Shanahan.

Jean Clough, my dear wife, gets particular thanks. She was my first editor, assuring me I had a book here and then helping me refine ideas and fill-out characters. She did proofreading of the last draft, too. She made the writing clearer and deleted most of my exclamations points in the text, calling them a rookie writing crutch. Imagine! She also kept me going through the many drafts and publication doldrums.

Jean asked me several times why teachers in my story would let a musician with no teaching experience or education degree do anything in their classrooms, let alone offer ideas for improvements. In the 35 years since I first wandered into a classroom with my trombone, I have experienced many teachers who were most welcoming of new ideas and generous to one such musician.

I thank them all for their patience and for teaching me so much.

There are other folks I want to thank, who in some way encouraged this book and the work in schools that fed it: our sons Patrick and Joey, Sarah Donovan, John Maki, Lynn White, Grace Dawson (the first principal I ever worked with in Chicago), Greg Pierce, Susie Diers, Ed Crego (who gets a cameo in the book), Paul Baffico, Jane Pigott, Pana Campbell, Steve and Kathy McShane, Frank and Donna Marrese, Rick Andrew and the Andrew Family Foundation, David Kornhauser, Mark McKeown and the entire Reading In Motion Board of Directors, who granted me a year's sabbatical to finish the writing of this book.

About Reading In Motion

Reading In Motion believes a child's reading ability at the end of first grade is predictive of positive or negative outcomes for the rest of that child's life. The organization acts on this belief by creating world class arts-infused reading curricula that engage young readers without them even realizing they are learning. Then Reading In Motion trains teachers to use these music and drama-infused methods, supporting them with in-classroom coaching all year long. In 2018, the organization reached 3,875 students in Pre-K to first grade, in 38 schools in Chicago plus an additional 475 students in the nation's fifth largest school district, Clark County, Nevada (Las Vegas and area). Ten outside studies have been done of Reading In Motion's results with students and teachers, including four published in peer reviewed academic journals and two used by Harvard researchers in a meta-analysis of the arts' effects on other academic skills. Last year, 81% of students in all of Reading In Motion's classrooms were reading at grade level by year's end, compared to 57% of all K-1st students in Chicago. More at **www.ReadingInMotion.org**.

Appendices:

Our Beliefs

These key beliefs guide Reading In Motion's approach to any school's issues and how we might help them reach their goals.

Reading in K-1st is the foundation for a successful life

Reading is the skill that gives access to all other skills. Without the ability to read, a person's ability to realize their potential in the world is more-limited, as so many daily interactions rely on written language. Research says that a low reader at the end of first grade will, 88 times out of 100, remain a low reader for the rest of their life. This tells us the importance of each child achieving grade level reading skills by the end of first grade.

Adults need support to try new things

Most adults, including teachers and principals, need support as they try new things and consider changing their beliefs, behaviors and actions. It is the rare adult who can read a book and then successfully change something of any importance. Often, another caring and experienced adult is needed to provide expertise and encouragement.

Nearly every student can learn to read at grade level

For all but approximately 10% of the total student population in the United States, learning to read at grade level or above is possible, given enough instruction. That 10% often includes students with IEPs and other diagnosed learning issues.

Some students need more

By one calculation, every student needs 1,400 hours of language and literacy experiences (i.e. being read to, being taught to read, conversing with a caring adult, reading books) from birth to the end of first grade. Some students enter Kindergarten with fewer hours of literacy experiences, while others enter with more. Those with fewer hours will need more instruction during school, in order to get their 1,400 hours total and catch up and read at grade level. At the same time, those students with more literacy hours already will need to be challenged with higher-level texts and tasks, to push and motivate them.

Foundational skills enable comprehension

The Common Core State Standards identify a set of reading skills they call "foundational skills", which make later reading skills, especially reading comprehension, possible. We focus on these skills heavily in K-1st, with a much smaller focus on comprehension, in order to build a solid foundation for all that comes later.

Every minute counts

The more instruction students are given, the more progress they will make toward the goal of reading at or above grade level. The school day has only so many minutes in it, and it is easy for many of those precious minutes to slip away for non-instructional purposes including bathroom breaks, classroom disruptions, behavior problems and discipline, homework hand-in, and on and on. The teacher must make great efforts to use as many minutes as possible for instruction.

Learning should be engaging

When a student is looking at the teacher and the student's mind is thinking about what the teacher is saying, that student is engaged. This is when maximum learning occurs. Making music and drama central ingredients in classroom lessons is one way to make the learning engaging, so students learn more.

Practice and Feedback = powerful

When a teacher asks a question, a student answers, and the teacher then tells the student whether the answer was right or wrong, we call this a practice and feedback loop. Research shows these are the moments when new learning occurs or is solidified into retained knowledge. These are powerful moments. The more of them can happen per day, the faster students will learn.

20 minutes of small group = weeks of whole group

In a normal whole group lesson, an individual student might get two or three chances per hour to raise their hand, get called on to answer a question, and get a response from the teacher - a practice and feedback loop. In a 20-minute Reading In Motion small group session, a student can routinely get 50-80 such loops. Thus, it might take 20-30 hours of whole group instruction to give each student the same amount of learning as one 20-minute small group. Those 20-30 hours can easily take weeks to achieve, particularly if we are talking about just reading instruction, which is typically two hours per day.

Student data is crucial

When the teacher has high-quality, immediate data from a test the student has just taken, that teacher knows what the student needs to learn next, and can plan lessons to deliver that next skill or knowledge.

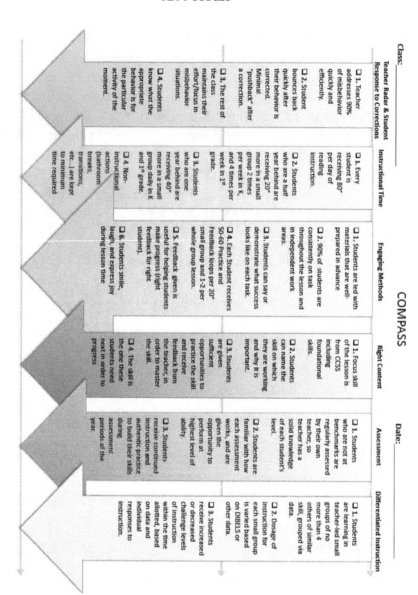

COMPASS

Class: _____

Date: _____

Teacher Radar & Student Response to Corrections

☐ 1. Teacher addresses 90% of misbehavior quickly and efficiently.

☐ 2. Student bounces back quickly after their behavior is corrected. Minimal "pushback" after a correction.

☐ 3. The rest of the class maintains their effort/focus in misbehavior situations.

☐ 4. Students know what the appropriate behavior is for the particular activity of the moment.

Instructional Time

☐ 1. Every student is receiving 80" per day of reading instruction.

☐ 2. Students who are a half year behind are receiving 20" more in a small group 2 times per week in K, and 4 times per week in 1ˢᵗ grade.

☐ 3. Students who are one year behind are receiving 40" more in a small group daily in K and 1ˢᵗ grade.

☐ 4. Non-instructional actions (bathroom breaks, transitions, etc.) are kept to minimum time required

Engaging Methods

☐ 1. Students are led with materials that are well-prepared in advance

☐ 2. 90% of students are consistently on task throughout the lesson and in independent work areas.

☐ 3. Students can say or demonstrate what success looks like on each task.

☐ 4. Each Student receives 50-60 Practice and Feedback loops per 20" small group and 1-2 per whole group lesson.

☐ 5. Feedback given is useful for helping students make progress (right feedback for right student).

☐ 6. Students smile, laugh, and express joy during lesson time

Right Content

☐ 1. Focus skill of the lesson is who are not at benchmarks are regularly assessed by their own teacher, so teacher has a solid knowledge of each student's level.

☐ 2. Students can name the skill on which they are working and why it is important.

☐ 3. Students are given sufficient opportunities to practice the skill and receive feedback from the teacher, in order to master the skill.

☐ 4. The skill is the one these students need next in order to progress

Assessment

☐ 1. Focus skill of the lesson is from CCSS including foundational skills.

☐ 2. Students are familiar with how each assessment works, and are given the opportunity to perform at highest level of ability.

☐ 3. Students receive continued instruction and authentic practice to build their skills during assessment periods of the year.

Differentiated Instruction

☐ 1. Students are learning in teacher-led small groups of no more than 4 others of similar skill, grouped via data.

☐ 2. Dosage of instruction for each small group is varied based on DIBELS or other data.

☐ 3. Students receive increased or decreased challenge levels of instruction within the time allotted, based on data and individual responses to instruction.

COMPASS Big Takeaway Strategies

Teacher Radar & Student Response	Instructional Time	Engaging Methods	Right Content	Assessment	Differentiated Instruction
•After introducing rules, post them with pictures for clarity. •Use school's management system consistently and with fidelity. •For students who push back, address misbehavior one on one •Have student practice the correct/expected behavior •Have an established place for time-out •Keep track of students misbehaving on a Post-it note during small group and simply call out to student, "John, that's one". If it happens again, "John, that's two". At the third infraction, student gets a the predetermined consequence. •Tell students what you want them to do. (example: John, sit down. *Not John, could you please sit down?*) •Ensure that students know the consequence for misbehavior, i.e. – time-outs or can't participate in "Free-Time Fridays" or choice time. •Though student's behavior improves, still give time-out as promised. •For BOY teacher says, "if you are misbehaving, I will come as quickly as I can, tap you on the shoulder and you will take a 5" time-out." •If you are instructing, simply write student's name on board and after you are done teaching, give those students a time-out.	•Teach the core daily. (core introduces appropriate skills on 7 Pillars of Reading Success) •K Students a half year behind should be seen 2/wk in small groups + core. 1st grade 4/wk in small groups + core. •Students full year behind should be seen for 40" in small groups daily. •Break up student's 40" into 2- 20" sess. – one in the one morning, one in afternoon. •If 40" not doable, try 2 - 15" sessions. •For first graders, always add some guided reading activities into the small group schedule. •Chart the time it takes for the class to take bathroom breaks in order to shorten the time.	•Look at the spectrum of Skill Development, Echo first, then generate, then generate with speed and accuracy. •Practice-feedback loops. •BOY = 10-20 •MOY = 30-40 •EOY = – 50-60 •Teacher says, "I want to see if you can tell me the 1st sound of the word. If I say bat, can you tell me that the 1st sound is /b/? Can you tell me the FIRST SOUND? (Let students finish the sentence). If correct, move on. •Feedback should not be a monologue, nor a mini-lesson. It is solely a response to student's real time performance, right or wrong. If correct, simply go to next student or say, "Good". If incorrect, teacher or another student gives the correct answer. •Either teacher or student leader preps daily materials.	•Make sure that activity/ lesson targets specific skill deficit, i.e. FSF. •Teacher should take notes after testing or progress monitoring to keep up with student progress until the next progress monitor. •Adjust content for in-between testing growth.	•Every student should be assessed for BOY, MOY, and EOY. •If students are scoring far above (or below) recommended measures, skip ahead to a more progressive measure (or go back to simpler measures). •The progress of every student should be assessed at least once a month. At BOY, intensive students don't usually make enough progress to test every week. Unless the teacher is building a portfolio on the students, stick to only one PM each month. •DIBELS is an indicator of student academic health. It gives a snapshot of whether or not the student is where s/he needs to be at a specific time in the year. It measures the foundational skills that support word usage, connected text reading, and comprehension.	•Using DIBELS data, take the red students and place them in groups starting with the lowest. Continue this process until you get to yellow students. Each of the groups that consist of red students and low yellow should be seen 2x week. Mid or high yellow, should be seen 1x week. •After grouping students by color, teacher can use anecdotal information to tweak the groups. • Use digital platform to assist in creating groups. •Teacher can use "Student Skill Acquisition Chart" to challenge students from the skill they are teaching to a subsequent skill or progressive level of the same skill. Focus should be on accuracy, then accuracy and rate.

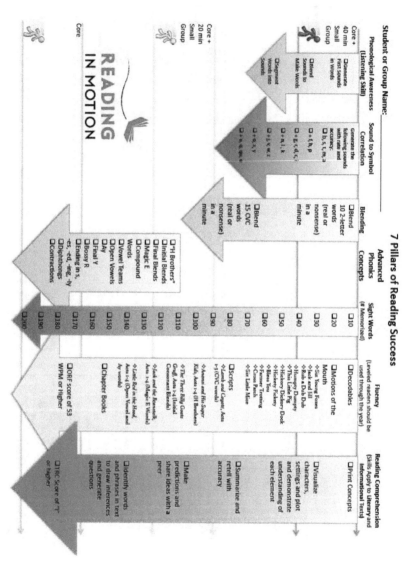

Instructional Time Audit
(see chapter "How To Observe A Classroom")

Karl Androes

Teacher:

Students: List names above each box at right, from left to right, from highest to lowest reading scores

Time	Activity Description/Notes	1	2	3	4	5	6	7	8	9	10	11	12	13	14	15	16	17	18	19	20	21	22	23	24	25	26	27	28	29	30
8:30																															
8:35																															
8:40																															
8:45																															
8:50																															
8:55																															
9:00																															
9:05																															
9:10																															
9:15																															
9:20																															
9:25																															
9:30																															
9:35																															
9:40																															
9:45																															
9:50																															
9:55																															
10:00																															
10:05																															
10:10																															
10:15																															
10:20																															
10:25																															
10:30																															
10:35																															
10:40																															
10:45																															
10:50																															
10:55																															
11:00																															
11:05																															
11:10																															
11:15																															
11:20																															
11:25																															
11:30																															
11:35																															
11:40																															
11:45																															
11:50																															
11:55																															
12:00																															
12:05																															

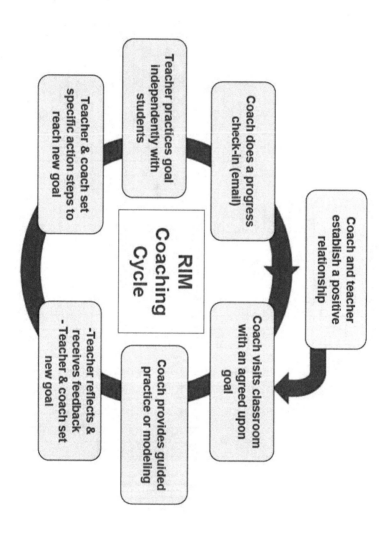

RIM Coaching Cycle

- Coach and teacher establish a positive relationship
- Coach visits classroom with an agreed upon goal
- Coach provides guided practice or modelling
- -Teacher reflects & receives feedback -Teacher & coach set new goal
- Teacher & coach set specific action steps to reach new goal
- Teacher practices goal independently with students
- Coach does a progress check-in (email)